The Open University

Environment: Sharing a Dynamic Planet

Carbon, Food, Consolidation

Environment: Sharing a Dynamic Planet

Carbon, Food, Consolidation

Edited by Parvati Raghuram, Nick Bingham, Jane Roberts, David Humphreys, Joe Smith, Sandy Smith and Philip O'Sullivan

This publication forms part of the Open University module DST206 Environment: sharing a dynamic planet. Details of this and other Open University modules can be obtained from the Student Registration and Enquiry Service, The Open University, PO Box 197, Milton Keynes MK7 6BJ, United Kingdom (tel. +44 (0)845 300 60 90; email general-enquiries@open.ac.uk).

Alternatively, you may visit the Open University website at www.open.ac.uk where you can learn more about the wide range of modules and packs offered at all levels by The Open University.

To purchase a selection of Open University materials visit www.ouw.co.uk, or contact Open University Worldwide, Walton Hall, Milton Keynes MK7 6AA, United Kingdom for a catalogue (tel. +44 (0)1908 858785; fax +44 (0)1908 858787; email ouw-customer-services@open.ac.uk).

The Open University, Walton Hall, Milton Keynes, MK7 6AA

First published 2013.

© 2013 The Open University

Edited and designed by The Open University

Typeset by the Open University

Printed in the United Kingdom by Bell & Bain Ltd, Glasgow

ISBN 9 781 7800 7327 9

1.1

Contents

DST206 module team

Claire Appleby, Consultant

Roshni Amin, Media Developer (Sound and Vision)

Mustafa Bektik, Media Developer

Dr Nick Bingham, Co-chair and Block 6 Leader

Prof. Andrew Blowers, Adviser

Avinash Boroowa, Media Project Manager

Dr Mark Brandon, Adviser

Clare Butler, Proofreader (freelance)

Wendy Chalmers, Learning and Teaching Librarian

Prof. Nigel Clark (Lancaster University), Block 1 Leader

Heather Clarke, Cartoonist

Matt Compton, Media Developer (Sound and Vision)

Prof. James Connelly (University of Hull), External Assessor

Sian Contell, Sound and Vision Assistant

Howard Davies, Media Developer (Interactive Media)

Ben Duncan-Jones, Production and Presentation Administrator

Jeff Edwards, Graphic Artist (freelance)

Dr Susan Fawssett, Consultant

Pam Furniss, Block 3 Leader

Richard Golden, Production and Presentation Administrator

Owen Horn, Media Developer (Sound and Vision)

Dr David Humphreys, Co-chair and Block 4 Leader

Jason Jarratt, Media Developer (Interactive Media)

Dr David King, Module team member

Dr Maggie King, Module team member

Dr Nick James, Consultant

Dr Petr Jehlička, Interim Co-chair and Block 5 Leader

Dr Victoria Johnson, Consultant

Jo Mack, Sound and Vision Producer

Dr Wendy Maples, Module team member

Isobel McLean, Indexer (freelance)

Margaret McManus, Rights Consultant (freelance)

Katie Meade, Rights Executive

Dr Dick Morris, Consultant

Lucy Morris, Curriculum Manager

Dr David Morse, Consultant

Dr Pat Murphy, Consultant

Greg Muttitt, Consultant

Dr Donal O'Donnell, Module team member

Celeste O'Neill, Media Developer (Editor)

Dr Philip O'Sullivan, Block 2 Leader

Mark Overton, Curriculum Manager

Neil Paterson, Media Assistant

Dr Stephen Peake, Consultant

Dr Parvati Raghuram, Academic coordinator (AV)

Will Rawes, Media Developer (Interactive Media)

Matthew Rigby-Burr, Media Developer (Graphic Designer)

Dr Jane Roberts, Learning Outcomes and Assessment Group Lead

Amber Ross, Media Developer (Editor)

Mat Schencks, Media Project Manager

Dr Joe Smith, Module team member

Dr Sandy Smith, Module team member

Prof. Robert Spicer, Adviser

Howie Twiner, Media Developer (Graphic Artist)

Dr James Warren, Consultant

Kelly Weekes, Curriculum Assistant

Chris Wooldridge, Editor (freelance)

Block 4   Carbon

Chapter 1   The carbon cycle

David Humphreys

Contents

1 Introduction

As the 1990–91 Gulf War drew to a close, Iraqi forces began
withdrawing from Kuwait. The Iraqis had invaded Kuwait in
August 1990 but after sustaining heavy losses from a US-led coalition
of forces they were forced to retreat. Before leaving, the Iraqi forces set
fire to over 600 Kuwaiti oil wells (Figure 1.1). While the fires burned
they contributed approximately 2 per cent of the world's daily carbon
dioxide emissions (Hobbs and Radke, 1992). The destruction of the
wells also led to the world's largest-ever oil spill. The fires and the spill
represented a massive anthropogenic (human-induced) movement of
carbon through the Earth's carbon cycle. The oil had been formed and
stored deep in the Earth over hundreds of millions of years but was
released into the Earth's atmosphere and seas in just weeks.

Figure 1.1 As Iraqi forces retreated from Kuwait at the end of the 1990–91
Gulf War they set fire to the oil wells, also generating the largest oil spill in
history

The fires were visually spectacular but represented just one small
example of anthropogenic influence within the carbon cycle. Most
greenhouse gas emissions are not the result of spectacular events such
as the Gulf War fires but are the consequence of mundane, routine and
everyday actions such as driving a car or switching on a light. Driving a
car uses fuel that has been formed and stored deep in the Earth over

hundreds of millions of years, but the simple act of driving releases that carbon into the Earth's atmosphere as carbon dioxide. The driver plays a part (albeit a small one) in moving carbon from inside the Earth into the air, and in so doing contributes to two of the biggest concerns that we have in the world today: energy supplies for the future, and human-induced climate change. Car-driving is part of a whole way of life which is dependent on carbon products such as oil and coal. Fossil fuel use has had a profound impact on the Earth's carbon cycle and its climate. The accumulation of carbon dioxide and other greenhouse gases in the atmosphere is leading to climate change, one of the most pressing global environmental issues of our age (Book 1, Chapters 1–4).

In this chapter you will learn about the Earth's carbon cycle and the main paths through which carbon moves through this cycle. In so doing you will understand how the problems posed by carbon, its combinations and its presence in the atmosphere as carbon dioxide are often difficult to respond to. Chapter 2 looks at the second half of the problem of carbon: concerns over dwindling oil supplies and what this means for our way of life. The following two chapters look at some of the responses to these two problems of carbon. Chapter 3 explores alternatives to carbon as a source of fuel, while Chapter 4 focuses on some of the technical fixes that can, or might, be taken to limit climate change.

As you work through this chapter you will see why an understanding of the carbon cycle is necessary in order to understand climate change. Exploring the interconnected subjects of climate change and the carbon cycle provides an opportunity to engage with the question for this block: *Why are environmental issues so difficult to resolve?* One lesson of this chapter is that much environmental change is shaped by biophysical processes that lie largely outside human control. Another is that different parts of the carbon cycle operate on vastly different timescales (ranging from hours to millions of years) and, as you will see, these different timescales have a direct bearing on how the Earth's climate has changed throughout its history.

2   Understanding climate change

Is contemporary climate change due to human actions, to natural biophysical processes or to a mixture of the two? This chapter will argue that while natural processes have been significant in climate change in the past, and will continue to be so in the future, scientific research shows that these natural processes alone cannot adequately explain contemporary climate change (Intergovernmental Panel on Climate Change, 2007). For this we need to look to human activity. To explain why this is so we now consider how and why the Earth's climate changes over time.

The Earth's temperature is determined primarily by the Earth's radiation balance. The Earth receives incoming electromagnetic radiation in the form of sunlight. Electromagnetic radiation is also re-radiated back into space. If the incoming and outgoing radiation is in balance over a given time period, the Earth will get neither warmer nor colder. But if energy-in exceeds energy-out, the Earth will warm. The relevant parts of the electromagnetic spectrum are shown in Figure 1.2. Incoming radiation is mostly in the form of visible light, with some shorter (ultraviolet) and longer (infrared) wavelengths as well. When this hits the Earth's surface, some is absorbed and some is reflected. The absorbed radiation warms the Earth's surface, which in turn leads to the emission of long-wave infrared radiation, or radiated heat. So, as shown in Figure 1.3, outgoing radiation is a mixture of reflected light and radiated heat.

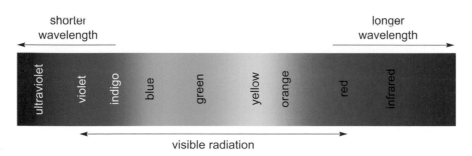

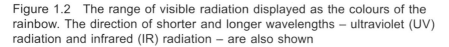

Figure 1.2   The range of visible radiation displayed as the colours of the rainbow. The direction of shorter and longer wavelengths – ultraviolet (UV) radiation and infrared (IR) radiation – are also shown

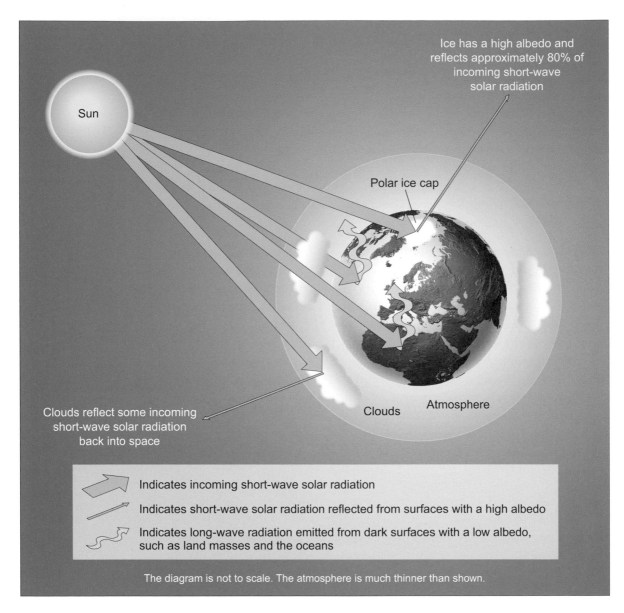

Figure 1.3   Diagram depicting radiation entering and leaving the Earth's atmosphere

Infrared active
A compound is
infrared active if it
absorbs long-wave
infrared radiation owing
to the way its molecules
vibrate.

Greenhouse gases have a type of molecular structure that enables them
to absorb infrared radiation that would otherwise travel through the
atmosphere back into outer space. Greenhouse gases are said to be
infrared active; they absorb particular wavelengths of long-wave
infrared radiation owing to the way that the bonds between the atoms
making up the molecules of the gas vibrate. To be infrared active, a

molecule must contain three or more atoms and vibrate in a way that will absorb a particular wavelength of infrared radiation (Warr, 2007).

By capturing a small proportion of outgoing radiation, greenhouse gases disrupt the energy balance between incoming and outgoing radiation, thus raising the temperature of the Earth (Figure 1.3). This is known as the greenhouse effect and it is important in determining the Earth's climate. If there were no greenhouse gases in its atmosphere, the Earth would be too cold for most forms of life. The greater the concentration of greenhouse gases, the greater the greenhouse effect. But also, the greater the proportion of long-wave (infrared) radiation in the outgoing radiation emitted from the Earth's surface, the greater the greenhouse effect.

This means that another important factor in the greenhouse effect is the albedo, or reflectivity, of the Earth's surface. Albedo is a numerical measure of the reflectivity of a surface. A perfect white surface has an albedo of 1. Such a surface reflects all solar radiation that strikes it without changing the wavelength of that radiation. A perfect black surface that absorbs all solar radiation that strikes it has an albedo of 0. The darker a surface is, the more solar radiation it will absorb and the more longer-wavelength infrared radiation it will emit, some of which will be absorbed by greenhouse gases. So, all other things being equal, the lower the Earth's albedo (the more dark surfaces it has), the greater the greenhouse effect.

Albedo
A numerical measure of the reflectivity of a surface.

The Earth's climate has fluctuated over timescales of millions of years between ice ages, when much of the planet is covered in thick layers of ice, and greenhouse conditions, when ice cover is scarce, even at high altitudes and high latitudes. At present the Earth is within an ice age (the Quaternary Ice Age) that began at the start of the Pleistocene Epoch some 2.6 million years ago (MacDougall, 2004). This might seem strange given current concerns over global warming. However, these concerns about anthropogenic climate change can only be understood in the context of much longer natural cycles. Within ice ages there are colder periods when glaciers advance towards the equator and warmer periods when they retreat to the poles.

We have seen that greenhouse gases and albedo can influence the greenhouse effect and therefore the amount of outgoing radiation leaving the Earth. However, an analysis of the radiation balance of the Earth also has to consider those factors which affect incoming solar radiation. This depends on two things. The first is solar activity. The

Solar flares
The sudden release of
intense energy from the
surface of the Sun.

amount of solar radiation emitted by the Sun fluctuates over cycles of
around 11 years. Within these cycles there are **solar flares**, the sudden
release of intense energy, usually lasting several minutes. When the Sun
is particularly active there may be several solar flares a day (compared
with one or two a week when the Sun is less active). However, changes
in solar cycles and flares are estimated to be in the order of 0.1 per cent
of total solar output and are unlikely to have much impact on the
amount of incoming radiation and therefore on global warming
(Schneider et al., 2010).

The second and much more significant factor is the astronomical cycles
which influence the amount of incoming radiation. The Scottish scientist
James Croll and the Serbian astronomer and meteorologist Milutin
Milanković identified three cycles relating to the tilt of the Earth and
its orbit around the Sun that affect the amount of solar radiation
striking the Earth. These three cycles play out over different periods of
time (Figure 1.4):

- *Orbital eccentricity.* The Earth does not move around the Sun in an
  identical orbit every year. Instead, the Earth's orbit changes very
  slightly every year, moving from an elliptical shape to a more
  circular one and then back again. This cycle takes about 400,000
  years. At present, the Earth's orbit around the Sun is close to
  circular. It will become more elliptical over the next few tens of
  thousand years (Archer, 2010, p. 136; Paillard, 2001).

- *Tilt of the Earth's axis.* The Earth's axis is not perpendicular to the
  plane of its orbit around the Sun. If it were, all parts of the Earth
  would receive the same amount of sunlight all year round. The tilt
  of the axis means that the amount of solar radiation striking the
  Earth varies as it orbits the Sun, leading to seasonal change.
  Milanković found that the angle of tilt varies between 22.1° and
  24.5° over a cycle of about 41,000 years. At present, the angle of tilt
  is approximately 23.5°, so the Earth is about halfway through this
  cycle.

- *Precession of the Earth's axis.* The Earth's axis wobbles slightly, a bit
  like a spinning top. This wobble, which is caused by the gravitational
  pull on the Earth of the Sun and the Moon, is known as precession.
  The precession cycle lasts about 23,000 years, during which the
  Earth's axis traces a conical shape. At present the northern part of
  the Earth's axis points to the 'North Star' or Polaris. But in the past

the axis has pointed to different points in the northern sky and it will do so again in the future (Marshak, 2008).

The Milanković–Croll cycles drive processes of glacial advance and retreat that contribute to climate change over cycles of several thousand years. Assuming all other things are equal, in particular the atmospheric concentration of greenhouse gases, these three cycles affect the Earth's ice cover. This may happen in two ways.

1   When the Earth is furthest away from the Sun on the orbital eccentricity cycle, less sunlight will strike the planet, leading to cooling and glacial advance. As the ice advances, the Earth's albedo will increase, leading to further global cooling which accelerates glacial formation. Similarly, as the Earth moves closer to the Sun on the orbital eccentricity cycle, the Earth warms, leading to glacial retreat. This will decrease the Earth's albedo by exposing more dark surfaces, leading to further warming.

2   The greater the tilt of the Earth's axis, the less sunlight the poles receive during their winters. This will lead to the formation of thick ice sheets, first at the poles, but extending over time to lower latitudes. During the last glacial period, much of what is now the north of the United Kingdom was covered in ice. Similarly, the less pronounced the Earth's tilt, the less pronounced the process of polar ice formation during winters. Finally, precession will affect the solar radiation striking different parts of the Earth, and this will influence when seasons begin and end, leading to relative warming on some parts of the precession cycle and relative cooling on others.

Might changes in the solar radiation striking the Earth be sufficient to explain climate change over the history of the Earth? Scientists have been able to track the temperature of the Earth over history through the analysis of ice cores (Figure 1.5). If incoming solar radiation was the sole driver of climate change, we would expect the historical changes to the Earth's temperature indicated from ice core data to be consistent with changes of solar radiation over time. However, what scientists have found is that while changes in solar activity and, in particular, the Milanković–Croll cycles are major factors in climate change, they are insufficient to fully explain all climate changes.

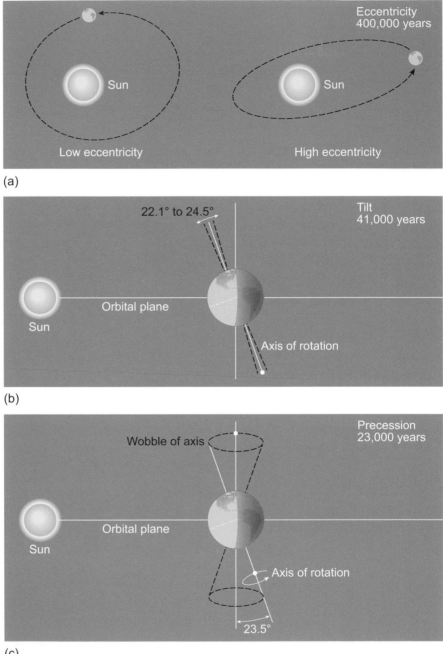

Figure 1.4   The Milanković–Croll cycles: (a) Orbital eccentricity;
(b) Tilt of Earth's axis; (c) Precession of Earth's axis (Source: based
on Marshak, 2008, p. 795)

Figure 1.5   Scientific analysis of ice cores has yielded data on past climates. By plotting carbon dioxide concentrations in the past, scientists have been able to reconstruct changes in the Earth's climate

As has been argued, understanding climatic variations requires an understanding not only of changes in solar radiation but also of changes in the magnitude of the greenhouse effect. As carbon dioxide is one of the major greenhouse gases, this, in turn, requires an understanding of the carbon cycle and the role of human activity in moving carbon around the Earth.

3   Introducing the carbon cycle

The carbon cycle is one of the Earth's biogeochemical cycles. A biogeochemical cycle involves the circulation of chemical elements through the Earth system using biological, geological and chemical processes. One example of a biogeochemical cycle is the hydrological cycle (see Book 1, Chapter 9, Section 4). The **carbon cycle** is the movement of carbon through the various constituent parts of the Earth system: the oceans, land, the atmosphere and life. Carbon can be found in many different forms. As an element its most common crystalline forms are diamond and graphite, and its most common non-crystalline form is coal. Carbon is also a component of a large number of compounds.

Carbon cycle
The movement of carbon through the various constituent parts of the Earth system, both living and non-living.

Carbon plays a vital role in the regulation of the Earth's climate. It does so primarily as carbon dioxide (CO_2), a major greenhouse gas, but it also combines with other elements to produce other greenhouse gases. An important natural greenhouse gas that contains carbon is methane (CH_4). Examples of human-manufactured greenhouse gases include chlorofluorocarbons (CFCs) and hydrofluorocarbons (HFCs) – both of which comprise various combinations of chlorine, fluorine, carbon and hydrogen – and perfluorocarbons (PFCs), comprising fluorine and carbon (Box 1.1).

Before we move on it is worth noting that not all greenhouse gases contain carbon. Water vapour (H_2O), nitrous oxide (N_2O) and ozone (O_3) also act as greenhouse gases. Although concentrations of water vapour may fluctuate regionally owing to human activity (for example, agriculture), the total atmospheric concentration of water vapour is affected only to a small extent by human activity, so although water vapour has the largest contribution to global warming of any greenhouse gas, it will not be discussed further here.

Box 1.1 Chemical elements: atoms, ions and molecules

An **element** is a substance that consists of only one type of **atom**. Scientists use symbols of one or two letters to denote elements. Table 1.1 shows the symbols of the elements that feature in this chapter:

Table 1.1 Element symbols in Chapter 1

Symbol	Element
C	carbon
Ca	calcium
F	fluorine
H	hydrogen
Mg	magnesium
N	nitrogen
O	oxygen
Si	silicon

An **atom** is the smallest unit of an element. Atoms have three main types of particle. Electrons have a negative electrical charge and orbit around the nucleus of an atom. The nucleus comprises protons (with a positive electrical charge) and neutrons (with no electrical charge). In an atom the number of electrons and protons are equal so that the atom has no overall electrical charge (Figure 1.6).

A **molecule** is formed when two or more atoms combine . A molecule may consist of atoms of a single chemical element, such as oxygen (O_2), or of different elements, such as water (H_2O) or carbon dioxide (CO_2). CO_2 denotes a molecule of carbon dioxide, which has one carbon atom and two oxygen atoms.

An **ion** is an atom or a molecule that has lost or gained some electrons, and which is thus positively or negatively charged. For example, a calcium ion has lost two electrons and will have a positive charge of 2, denoted Ca^{2+}.

Element
An element is a substance that consists of only one type of atom.

Atom
An atom is the smallest unit in which a chemical element is found.

Molecule
A molecule is formed when two or more atoms combine.

Ion
An ion is an atom or a molecule that has lost or gained an electron.

You have seen that carbon is present in some important greenhouse gases, namely methane, carbon dioxide, CFCs, PFCs and HFCs. Of these, carbon dioxide makes the greatest contribution to the greenhouse effect, as there is a higher atmospheric concentration of carbon dioxide relative to other greenhouse gases. The total warming effect of a greenhouse gas depends on a combination of:

- the quantity of the gas in the atmosphere
- how much infrared radiation a molecule of the gas can absorb
- how long the gas stays in the atmosphere (residence time).

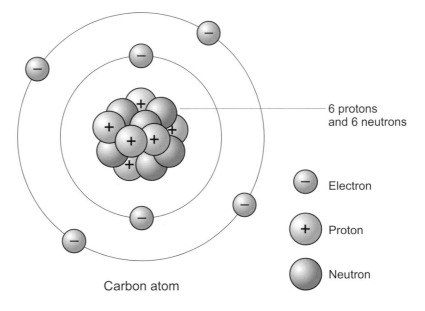

6 protons
and 6 neutrons

Electron

Proton

Neutron

Carbon atom

Figure 1.6   Carbon (atomic number 6) has six electrons, six protons and six neutrons

Global warming potential (GWP)
The relative contribution of a molecule of a greenhouse gas to atmospheric warming.

These last two factors are often expressed as global warming potential (GWP). The **global warming potential (GWP)** expresses the relative contribution of a molecule of a greenhouse gas to atmospheric warming. Because some greenhouse gases have longer residence times than others, GWP is calculated for a specific time period, usually between 20 and 500 years. CO_2 is given a GWP of 1; it is the reference point against which other greenhouse gases are compared. A molecule of methane (CH_4) has a GWP that is about 25 times greater than a molecule of carbon dioxide over a 100-year time horizon, and therefore has a GWP (100 years) of 25 (IPCC, 2007). However, because of carbon dioxide's much higher concentration in the atmosphere, it has a greater effect than methane on global warming, despite methane's higher GWP.

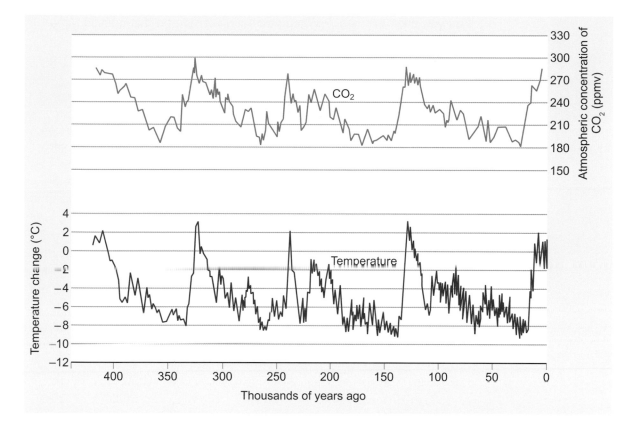

Figure 1.7   Data from ice cores and other sources provides evidence that the concentration of carbon dioxide in the Earth's atmosphere, and the Earth's average temperature, have naturally fluctuated in a cyclical pattern for the last 450,000 years. During that time frame, there have been alternating glacial periods and warmer interglacials (Source: based on IPCC, 2001)

Anthropogenic climate change is due in large part to the movement of carbon from other parts of the Earth system into the atmosphere as carbon dioxide; for example, through fossil fuel burning and deforestation. The atmospheric concentration of carbon dioxide at the dawn of the Industrial Revolution was about 285 parts per million by volume (ppmv). Since then it has risen to about 380 ppmv (IPCC, 2007). Ice core data has enabled scientists to estimate atmospheric concentrations of carbon dioxide (though not other greenhouse gases) for the last 600,000 years (Figure 1.7).

Activity 1.1   Carbon dioxide and changes in the Earth's temperature

Examine Figure 1.7 and note that changes in the Earth's temperature do not seem to exactly track changes in atmospheric carbon dioxide. Why do you think this is so? When you have considered this question, read on.

Comment

From your work so far in this chapter you may have noted two main reasons. First, carbon dioxide is not the only greenhouse gas. Other greenhouse gases also help determine the Earth's temperature. Second, some temperature changes are caused by changes to incoming solar radiation (Milanković–Croll cycles). We should also note that while scientists understand many of the causes of long-term climate change, scientific understanding is not complete. Uncertainties remain over some of the feedbacks and complexities of the Earth's climate.

The next section examines flows of carbon within the carbon cycle and the different time spans over which these flows take place. This will enable us to consider the relationship between the carbon cycle and climate change over long-term geological timescales, and whether, and to what extent, contemporary climate change may be considered a problem. You will see that different parts of the carbon cycle operate on vastly different timescales (ranging from hours to millions of years), and these different timescales have a direct bearing on how the Earth's climate has changed throughout its history.

4   The movement of carbon into the atmosphere

Activity 1.2   Carbon movements into the atmosphere

Have a look at Figure 1.8. It depicts the various movements within the carbon cycle. Can you identify the main movements of carbon into the atmosphere?

Comment

Carbon moves into the atmosphere from a variety of sources: from life forms, from the oceans, and from terrestrial (land-based) sources.

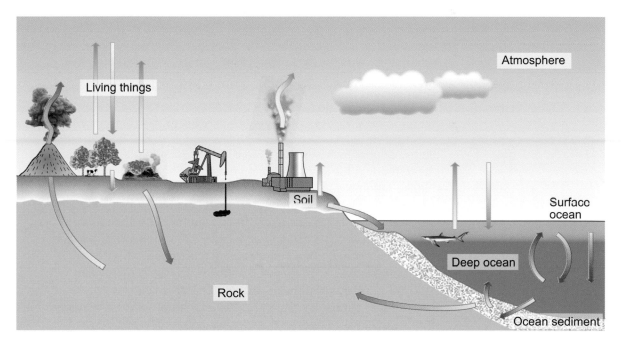

Figure 1.8   The carbon cycle

One terrestrial source of carbon dioxide is volcanic eruptions. In addition to carbon dioxide, volcanoes emit other matter that influences the climate, including other gases and particulate matter such as ash.

For example, the eruption of Mount Pinatubo in the Philippines in 1991 led to the emission of several million tonnes of sulphates. Atmospheric

Aerosol

Fine pieces of particulate matter suspended in the atmosphere that reflect some solar radiation back into space.

sulphates are an example of what climate scientists call an **aerosol**: fine particulate matter suspended in the atmosphere. Aerosols reflect back into space some solar radiation that would otherwise strike the surface of the Earth, increasing the planetary albedo and leading to a cooling effect on the global climate. The eruption of Mount Pinatubo increased the planetary albedo and led to a cooling effect on the planet that lasted about two years before the aerosols were washed from the atmosphere (Figure 1.9).

The eruption of Mount Pinatubo also led to the emission of millions of tonnes of carbon dioxide. While the aerosols emitted by Pinatubo disappeared from the atmosphere after a year or two, the carbon dioxide emitted from the eruption has a far longer residence time. The immediate short-term cooling effect of the Pinatubo eruption has now given way to a longer-term warming effect (Box 1.2).

Box 1.2   Supervolcanoes

Yellowstone was the first national park to be established in the USA. Today it is home to a diversity of wildlife, including bears, bison and elk, and some spectacular mountains, geysers and hot springs (Figure 1.10).

Yellowstone has changed enormously over geological time. The entire national park sits atop one of the most geologically powerful phenomena in the world, a supervolcano. Whereas most volcanoes release magma and volcanic ash through a single vent that connects the magma chamber to the atmosphere, a supervolcano has several vents (Figure 1.11). Yellowstone has erupted three times in the past: 2.1 million years ago, 1.3 million years ago and 640,000 years ago. This suggests that the Yellowstone supervolcano erupts every 6–800,000 years. Geologists have detected a large and growing magma chamber underneath Yellowstone, although they do not believe an eruption is due soon (Breining, 2010). However, the Yellowstone supervolcano will certainly erupt again at some time in the future.

Like other volcanoes, supervolcanoes emit aerosols, which have an immediate but relatively short-term planetary cooling effect, and carbon dioxide, which has a longer-term warming effect. Yellowstone's last eruption covered much of the western USA in ash and prompted a planetary cooling effect lasting decades.

Figure 1.9   The Mount Pinatubo eruption in the Philippines in 1991 had a short-term cooling effect on the world's climate lasting some two years. However, over the ensuing decades the eruption will have had a net warming effect

Figure 1.10   Yellowstone National Park is one of the most popular tourist attractions of North America. It sits atop what scientists believe to be the most powerful supervolcano on Earth

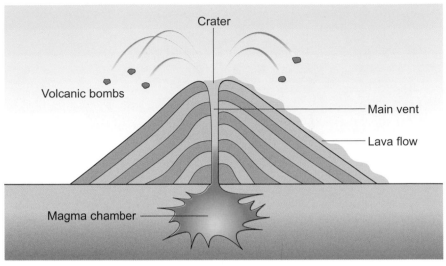

(a)

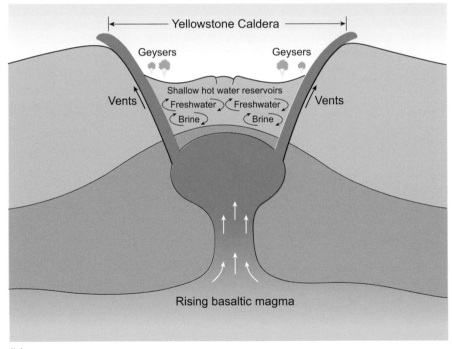

(b)

Figure 1.11   Cross-sections of: (a) a conical volcano with single main vent from magma chamber; (b) a supervolcano with more than one main vent

Another major source of carbon dioxide in the atmosphere is forest fires. Forests are major reservoirs of carbon, but forest fires result in the carbon stored in trees and other plants combining with oxygen to yield carbon dioxide, which is released into the atmosphere. Many fires start from natural forces; a lightning strike can trigger fire in forested areas that have suffered drought. In many tropical regions forest fires are started to clear land for cattle, agriculture or commercial forestry. Deforestation 'hotspots' where forests are particularly at risk of burning and conversion to other land uses include southern Mexico, Central America, south and east Brazilian Amazonia, eastern Nigeria, south-western Cameroon, eastern Malaysia and South Kalimantan in Indonesia.

While the natural causes of greenhouse gas emissions can be separated from the social causes to some extent, the causes are often a complex mix of social and natural processes. Take cattle agriculture for example. Digestive gas emissions from ruminant animals such as cows contain methane, and the generation of this greenhouse gas is the result of natural biological processes. But the number of cows on the planet is far in excess of what it would be were it not for human farming of cattle for milk and meat. Most analysts consider greenhouse gas emissions from livestock to be anthropogenic. A 2006 report for the UN Food and Agriculture Organization concluded that on a global scale the livestock sector is responsible for 27 per cent of anthropogenic methane and 65 per cent of anthropogenic nitrous oxide, most of it from manure, with livestock occupying 26 per cent of ice-free terrestrial land and 70 per cent of all agricultural land (Steinfeld et al., 2006). (The relationship between human diet and environmental change will be considered in Book 2, Chapters 5 and 6.)

Other greenhouse gas sources are unambiguously anthropogenic, such as carbon dioxide from manufacturing cement and from the use of coal, oil and gas.

5   The movement of carbon from the atmosphere

Once carbon dioxide enters the atmosphere it does not stay there indefinitely. There are several paths by which it can be removed. It is important to understand how this may happen because, all other things being equal, if carbon dioxide concentrations in the atmosphere fall over time the Earth's temperature will also fall. In this section we consider in turn three ways by which carbon may leave the atmosphere:

- short-term movement into life forms, both terrestrial and marine, by photosynthesis (see Box 5.1 in Chapter 5 of Book 1)

- intermediate-term movement into the oceans

- long-term locking of carbon into rocks by geological processes.

5.1   Photosynthesis

Carbon dioxide is removed from the atmosphere by green plants through photosynthesis whereby it reacts with water to form carbohydrates. One of the simplest forms of carbohydrate is glucose, a sugar, which is used by plants and animals in two ways: it is a good energy store and an excellent building block for more complex molecules, such as cellulose and starch, which make up much of the tissues of plants.

The generation of glucose ($C_6H_{12}O_6$) is represented by this chemical equation:

$$6CO_2 + 6H_2O \xrightarrow{\text{Light energy}} C_6H_{12}O_6 + 6O_2$$

Activity 1.3   The chemical equation for photosynthesis

This equation indicates that solar energy drives a chemical reaction between six carbon dioxide molecules and six water molecules to form one glucose molecule. Can you identify what else is produced by this chemical reaction?

Comment

Six oxygen molecules, each with two oxygen atoms, are also produced ($6O_2$). The oxygen molecule O_2 is the most commonly occurring atmospheric form of oxygen. Note that chemical equations must 'balance': if an atom appears on one side of an equation it must also appear on the other side. So, on both sides of the equation there are 6 carbon atoms, 12 hydrogen atoms and 18 oxygen atoms.

The opposite of photosynthesis is respiration or combustion (Box 1.3).

Box 1.3   Respiration and combustion

There are two ways that carbon dioxide may be released from living plants to the atmosphere: respiration and combustion (burning). In both cases the chemical equation is the opposite of that for photosynthesis, with oxygen taken from the environment and carbon dioxide emitted.

Respiration is how plants and animals extract the energy stored in carbohydrates, releasing some carbon dioxide and water in the process. The basic chemical equation for respiration is:

$$C_6H_{12}O_6 + 6O_2 \rightarrow 6CO_2 + 6H_2O$$

With respiration, small amounts of energy are emitted gradually over time, but the combustion of plant matter can lead to rapid emissions of intense heat at high temperature. In both reactions, carbohydrate and oxygen combine to produce carbon dioxide and water, releasing the energy originally captured by photosynthesis when the carbohydrate was formed.

As far as the carbon cycle is concerned, the main thing to note is that plant matter which respires or is burnt consumes the same amount of oxygen that was produced by photosynthesis, and releases the same amount of carbon dioxide that was absorbed by photosynthesis.

5.2   Ocean sequestration of carbon dioxide

The term 'ocean sequestration' refers to the process by which carbon dioxide is removed to the oceans from the atmosphere (Figure 1.8). At present approximately some 90 Gt (gigatonnes) of atmospheric CO_2 is dissolved in surface seawater annually (IPCC, 2007). However, this is a two-way process; almost as much carbon dioxide is released back into the atmosphere. Because the oceans store vast quantities of CO_2 they are often referred to as a carbon sink. Some of this dissolved CO_2 is taken up by marine plants called phytoplankton through photosynthesis (Figure 1.12).

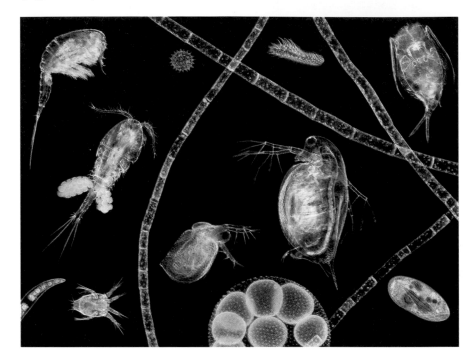

Figure 1.12   Highly magnified marine plankton, including green phytoplankton (plants) and zooplankton (animals) with calcium carbonate shells

Not all oceanic CO_2 is taken up by plants. Some reacts with water to form carbonic acid (H_2CO_3) as denoted by the chemical equation:

$$CO_2 + H_2O \rightarrow H_2CO_3$$

It is estimated that oceans have absorbed over 40 per cent of the carbon dioxide emitted by human activity since 1750. This has significantly slowed anthropogenic climate change. But the absorption by the oceans of carbon dioxide has come at a price, making the oceans more acidic (Box 1.4).

Box 1.4   Ocean acidification

Ocean acidification is an increase in the acidity of the world's oceans due to the creation of carbonic acid from dissolved carbon dioxide.

The pH scale (Figure 1.13) is a measure of the acidity or alkalinity of a water-based solution. Pure water is neutral, neither alkaline nor acidic, with a pH level of 7. Battery acid has a pH of just under 1, vinegar around 2, and baking soda 9. The average pH of the oceans has fallen by 0.1 pH units over the last 200 years, meaning that the oceans have become more acidic. The Royal Society (2005) has estimated that by 2100 the average pH of the oceans could be reduced by 0.5 pH units.

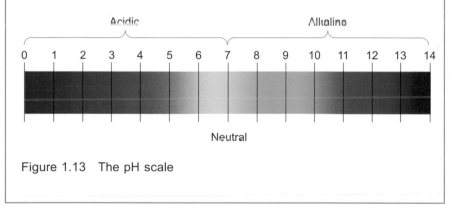

Figure 1.13   The pH scale

There is growing evidence that CO_2 induced changes in ocean chemistry are negatively affecting the marine biosphere (Riebesell, 2004). Marine crustacean species with a skeleton or shell, such as crabs and lobsters, are particularly threatened by acidification. They make their skeletons or shells from calcium carbonate ($CaCO_3$) through a process known as calcification. Increased levels of carbonic acid in the oceans inhibit the process of calcification by dissociating calcium carbonate. The term **dissociation** is the breaking up of an ionic compound (a compound that contains ions) into its component ions. The dissociation of calcium carbonate in acidic seawater makes it more difficult for crustaceous species to form or maintain their shells. This can be expressed by the chemical equation:

$$CaCO_3 + H_2CO_3 \rightarrow Ca^{2+} + 2HCO_3^-$$

Dissociation
The breaking up of an ionic compound into its component ions.

Note that the two ions are produced from this chemical reaction. Recall that the chemical symbol Ca^{2+} denotes a calcium atom that has lost two electrons, leaving a calcium ion with a positive charge of 2 (Box 1.1). This leaves two HCO_3^- ions, each of which has a negative charge of minus 1. This is denoted by the minus sign at the end of the chemical symbol HCO_3^-.

5.3   The rock cycle

When marine plants and animals die they fall to the seabed (sometimes being cycled by being eaten by other animals on the way). The calcium carbonate skeletons or shells accumulate on the ocean floor. After millions of years the calcium carbonate is buried up to several kilometres below the ocean floor. As this process continues the weight of the overlying deposits exerts enough pressure to compact the sediment, squeezing out any water and trapped gases. This is accompanied by chemical changes brought about by the heat emanating from the Earth's interior. As a result of compaction and chemical changes, the sediment is converted into rock. The type of rock formed depends on the initial composition of the sediment. Carbonate rocks store about 4×10^7 Gt of carbon, by far the largest reservoir of carbon on Earth (IPCC, 2007).

Figure 1.14   The White Cliffs of Dover in southeast England were formed millions of years ago from ocean sediment composed of the skeletal remains of marine life

You may think carbon buried underground in rock would remain there forever. However, on Earth nothing is permanent. Geological processes push deeply buried rocks to the surface over tens or hundreds of millions of years. The net effects can be spectacular. Carbonate rocks that long ago were ocean sediment today make up many mountains and chalky cliffs, such as the White Cliffs of Dover in England (Figure 1.14). The formation of new rock under the oceans and uplift of this to the land surface is part of the **rock cycle**, which can remove carbon from the Earth's atmosphere for millions of years.

Rock cycle
The cycle in which any rock may be converted into other rock types.

6   The formation of fossil fuels

The previous section outlined three paths by which carbon dioxide can be removed from the atmosphere. The removal of atmospheric carbon dioxide by photosynthesis is the first step in the creation of fossil fuels. Coal, natural gas and oil were all formed from the remains of life. Over geological time the formation of fossil fuels removes carbon from the biosphere, sequestering it in underground geological formations.

Coal is formed from prehistoric forests. During the Carboniferous Period, which lasted from approximately 360 to 300 million years ago, there was massive growth of fast-growing trees on swampland, which after they died sank deep into the swamps, eventually being buried by sediment, forming underground coal seams. The carbon sequestered in these trees was, in effect, removed from the atmosphere and biosphere on a long geological timescale and thus was unable to contribute to the greenhouse effect. It is thought that this resulted in a significant drop in the carbon dioxide levels in the atmosphere, eventually leading to a period of global cooling in the late Carboniferous Period.

Like the formation of coal, oil and natural gas formation has also led to the sequestration of carbon in geological formations. Oil and some gases have their origins in marine organisms that lived millions of years ago. As you have seen, when marine organisms die they fall to the ocean floor and, over time, are buried. For oil and gas to be formed, the organic matter needs to sink to a depth in the Earth's crust where the temperature is hot enough for the organic matter to 'cook'. Generally, for oil this starts at a depth of around 1.5 km at temperatures over 50 °C. Below this depth, the organic matter will, over millions of years, change into oil. At greater depths and higher temperatures, oil breaks down to natural gas. The formation of coal can also produce gas. And there must be certain geological structures in place to prevent the oil and gas seeping away, including an impermeable cap rock to prevent it escaping.

7   The carbon cycle and the regulation of the planetary temperature

By now you are familiar with the flows of carbon in the Earth system, and can describe how carbon flows into and out of the atmosphere. You have seen that carbon moves within the Earth system according to very different timescales, from sudden and (in human terms) catastrophic flows, such as volcanic eruptions and the 1991 Kuwaiti oilfield fires, to the very long-term and gradual processes of the rock cycle that play out over geological time.

The movement of carbon within the carbon cycle also depends on temperature. The warmer the atmosphere, the faster the overall movement of carbon within the carbon cycle. Furthermore, at different temperatures different paths of the carbon cycle will act in different ways, sometimes slowing the process of climate change and sometimes speeding it up.

For example, at present, the Earth's forests, soils and oceans have absorbed a significant proportion of anthropogenic carbon dioxide emissions. Without these increases in absorption, climate change since the Industrial Revolution would almost certainly be more pronounced than it is now. This is an example of a *negative feedback* in the Earth system, an interaction that moderates change within a system so that the output is less than it would have been without the feedback. (You may recall that negative feedback and positive feedback were introduced in Book 1 Chapter 8.)

However, as the planet warms, it is likely that some carbon sinks will become less effective and may indeed become sources of carbon dioxide. For example, soils retain carbon better in cold conditions, with soil carbon levels lowest in the warm tropical latitudes and highest in the colder high latitudes. As global warming takes hold, soil carbon concentrations are almost certain to fall significantly, with carbon returning to the atmosphere as carbon dioxide through the process of bacterial and fungal respiration (in other words, decay), fuelling further global warming. This is an example of a *positive feedback*, an interaction within a system that enhances change so that the output is greater than it would otherwise have been.

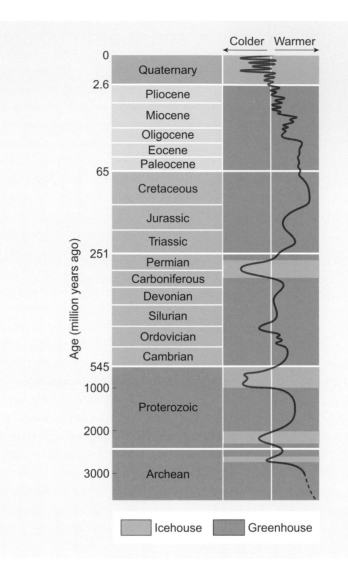

Figure 1.15   Temperature fluctuations over the Earth's history. The age axis is not to scale (Source: based on Marshak, 2008, p. 815)

Furthermore, while forests are at present absorbing carbon dioxide, thus slowing atmospheric warming, this will only continue to happen beneath a certain temperature threshold. The exact temperature will differ for different species of trees and other plants, but photosynthesis becomes difficult for many species much above 40 °C as the chemical processes are temperature sensitive. When this happens, forests will take up less carbon dioxide from the atmosphere, fuelling further warming. A related risk is that warming will greatly increase the likelihood of forest fires in the tropics, which would release huge amounts of carbon dioxide into the atmosphere. Finally, the world's oceans, like soils and forests, are better carbon sinks in colder temperatures than warmer ones because carbon dioxide is more soluble in colder water.

In short, the functioning of the Earth's carbon sinks, which over the last two or three centuries have overall acted as a negative feedback to mitigate climate change, is, given the current trends, almost certain to become less effective and may even switch to positive feedback. Furthermore, the timescale over which this positive feedback is likely to operate could be longer than the period of negative feedback that we are currently living through. Archer and Ganapolski (2005) suggest that the current period of anthropogenic climate change will ward off the next period of glacial advance which, they claim, was due in approximately another 50,000 years but is now likely to be delayed for 500,000 years.

Understanding how the carbon cycle operates helps explain how, over tens of millions of years, a period of global warming can be reversed and tip into a period of planetary cooling, and vice versa (Figure 1.15). Climate scientists are confident that ultimately the present period of anthropogenic warming will be reversed; but it could take millions of years.

8   Summary

Through exploring the relationship between climate change and the carbon cycle over the Earth's history you have gained an insight into the question for this block: *Why are environmental issues so difficult to resolve?*

You have seen that the natural world moves to its own rhythms and temporalities. The transfer of carbon dioxide into the world's atmosphere through human activity would not be a problem if the Earth's carbon cycle were able to process carbon dioxide at the same rate we are adding it, removing it from the atmosphere and sequestrating it in forests, soils, oceans and rocks so that the long-term mean temperature of the planet remained more or less stable. But that is not the case. Left to its own devices, the natural world will remove carbon dioxide from the atmosphere, but only over millions of years. Clearly, this is not quickly enough to avoid global warming during this century.

So, can anything else be done to solve the problem? Humans have shown that they can intervene in the carbon cycle by extracting carbon-rich fossil fuels, such as oil, coal and gas, from underground. The burning of these fuels adds carbon dioxide to the atmosphere. But we have yet to demonstrate that we can reverse the process, intervening in the carbon cycle to extract carbon dioxide from the atmosphere, at least on a sufficient scale to counter the carbon dioxide that we have added. This does not mean that there is nothing that can be done. It does, however, suggest two things which apply not only to climate change but also to other environmental issues.

First, human agency can set in motion natural processes, sometimes unintentionally, that have consequences and risks that are not fully understood. Second, there are limits to what humans can do to solve environmental problems. We certainly cannot assume that if humans cause an environmental problem it is within our capacity to solve it. While the natural world responds to our interventions, there are ecological processes that take place independently of what humans do. We can interfere in nature, but we cannot control it. This suggests that when taking actions that affect the natural world humans should be mindful of the possible consequences of our agency and how we may, or may not, be able to manage these consequences. This requires a willingness to consider in advance the uncertainties of the exact consequences of human action and how the risks of our action may play out over space and time.

References

Archer, D. (2010) *The Global Carbon Cycle*, Princeton, NJ, PrincetonUniversity Press.

Archer, D. and Ganapolski, A. (2005) 'A movable trigger: fossil fuel CO_2 and the onset of the next glaciation', *Geochemistry, Geophysics and Geosystems*, vol. 6, no. 5 [online], DOI: 10.1029/2004GC000891 (Accessed 1 October 2012).

Breining, G. (2010) *Super Volcano: The Ticking Time Bomb Beneath Yellowstone National Park*, St Paul, MN, Voyageur Press.

Hobbs, P. V. and Radke, L. (1991) 'Airborne studies of the smoke from the Kuwait oil fires', *Science*, vol. 256, no. 5059, 15 May, pp. 987–91.

Intergovernmental Panel on Climate Change (IPCC) (2001) *Climate Change 2001 – The Scientific Basis, Contribution of Working Group I to the Third Assessment Report of the IPCC*, Cambridge, Cambridge University Press [online], http://www.grida.no/publications/other/ipcc_tar/ (Accessed 21 November 2012).

Intergovernmental Panel on Climate Change (IPCC) (2007) *Climate Change 2007 – The Physical Science Basis, Contribution of Working Group I to the Fourth Assessment Report of the IPCC*, Cambridge, Cambridge University Press [online], http://www.ipcc.ch/publications_and_data/ar4/wg1/en/contents.html (Accessed 1 October 2012).

MacDougall, D. (2004) *Frozen Earth: The Once and Future Story of Ice Ages*, Berkeley, CA, University of Los Angeles Press.

Marshak, S. (2008) *Earth: Portrait of a Planet* (3rd edn), New York, W. W. Norton.

Paillard, D. (2001) 'Glacial cycles: toward a new paradigm', *Reviews of Geophysics*, vol. 39, pp. 325–46.

Riebesell, U. (2004) 'Effects of CO_2 enrichment on marine phytoplankton', *Journal of Oceanography*, vol. 60, no. 4, pp. 719–29.

Royal Society (2005) *Ocean Acidification Due to Increasing Atmospheric Carbon Dioxide*, policy document 12/05, June, London, Royal Society [online], http://royalsociety.org/uploadedFiles/Royal_Society_Content/policy/publications/2005/9634.pdf (Accessed 1 October 2012).

Schneider, S. H., Rosencranz, A., Mastrandrea, M. D. and Kuntz-Duriseti, K. (eds) (2010) *Climate Change Science and Policy*, Washington, DC, Island Press.

Steinfeld, H., Gerber, P., Wassenaar, T., Castel, V., Rosales, M. and de Haan, C. (2006) *Livestock's Long Shadow: Environmental Issues and Options*, Rome, Food and Agriculture Organization.

Warr, K. (2007) S250 *Science in context*, Topic 5, Climate Change, Milton Keynes, The Open University.

Chapter 2   Oil culture and oil politics

David Humphreys

Contents

1   Introduction

The movement of carbon in the global carbon cycle depends almost entirely on biophysical processes that lie outside human control. However, since the dawn of the Industrial Revolution humans have intervened in the carbon cycle by excavating and burning fossil fuels, which is the primary cause of contemporary climate change. In this chapter we examine some of the interconnected cultural, economic and political forces that drive and sustain the fossil fuel industry. In so doing we will gain a further way of thinking through the question: *Why are environmental issues so difficult to resolve?*

Using the oil industry as a case study, it will be argued that environmental issues become progressively more difficult to resolve the more that people have an interest in continuing the social practices that generated the issue. Most people on the planet rely on oil in one way or another to lead their lives. So addressing the problems of the greenhouse gas emissions from burning oil does not simply mean focusing on the oil industry. It inevitably means that a majority of the world's people must confront and adapt their own lifestyles and values.

2 Culture, values and peak oil

The use of oil dates back thousands of years. In about 3000 BC, bitumen, an oil-based residue that had seeped to parts of the Earth's surface, was first used as building mortar in what is now the Middle East. In AD 700, the Byzantine Empire used a petroleum mix – called 'Greek fire' – to set alight enemy ships (Figure 2.1). However, it was not until the mid nineteenth century that humans first extracted oil from underground. An American industrialist, George Bissell, had an original idea: to drill for oil. On 27 August 1859, Edwin Drake, employed by Bissell's Pennsylvania Rock Oil Company, drilled to a depth of 21 metres and struck oil in Titusville, Pennsylvania. As political scientist Daniel Yergin (2009, p. 13) writes, 'Drake's discovery would, in due course, bequeath mobility and power to the world's population, play a central role in the rise and fall of nations and empires, and become a major element in the transformation of human society.'

Figure 2.1 The navy of the Byzantine Empire used a petroleum mix to set ablaze the ships of its enemies

In 1859, all this lay in the future. Yet just a century later the first predictions were made of the end of the oil era. In 1969, oil geologist M. King Hubbert argued that global oil production would reach a peak after which after which production would enter a period of terminal decline (Figure 2.2). The term now used to denote this theory is **peak oil**. Hubbert predicted that global oil production over time would assume the shape of a bell curve, beginning at a low rate when the industry was in its infancy, then increasing as more oil fields were discovered, oil extraction technology became more advanced and demand increased, before steadily declining after peak oil as reserves became exhausted (Figure 2.3). Peak oil, Hubbert predicted, would be reached at the latest by 2000 (Hubbert, 1969).

Peak oil
The point at which global oil production reaches its maximum, after which the rate of production enters a period of terminal decline.

Figure 2.2   The American geologist M. King Hubbert published a seminal paper in 1969 that predicted peak oil would be reached no later than 2000. The International Energy Agency has suggested peak oil may have been reached in 2006

At some stage in the twenty-first century, society is likely to pass – indeed, may already have passed – the point of peak oil. However, there is uncertainty on just how much oil remains underground and how easily humans can access it. According to the International Energy

Agency (2010), oil production may have peaked in 2006. This suggests that over the course of the twenty-first century human societies will need to adapt as the world's oil becomes progressively more scarce and expensive. However, according to Harvard University's Belfer Center for Science and International Affairs, the world is experiencing a surge of oil production, vast oil resources remain to be discovered and peak oil is not imminent (Maugeri, 2012).

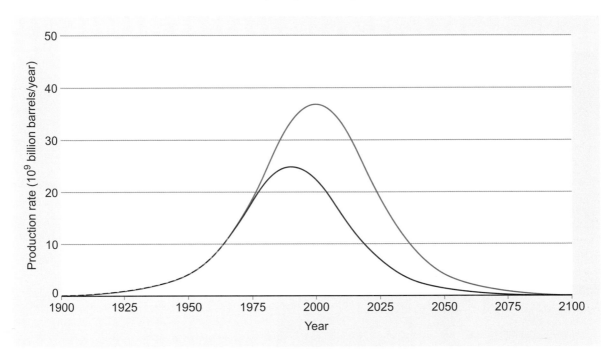

Figure 2.3   Hubbert predicted that, over time, oil production will assume the form of a bell curve. This graph shows two possible scenarios for oil production in Hubbert's 1969 paper. For both scenarios, Hubbert predicted that oil supply would effectively be exhausted by 2100 (Source: based on Hubbert, 1969, p. xiv)

Throughout human history, technologies have come and gone. The relationship between technology and culture is captured in terms such as Stone Age, Bronze Age and Iron Age. These terms denote that when humans learnt to make tools using stone and metals their social organisation and culture also changed. Human ecologist Alf Hornborg argues that over history technological systems are situated not just in time, but also in cultural space. This is also true of the technology of the fossil fuel era; oil is integral to the culture and organisation of the contemporary world. Technology embodies power relations: those who control the development, deployment and use of technology have a source of power, in both a thermodynamic sense (e.g. electricity and motor power) and an economic and political sense. Technology is embedded in networks of social and economic relations, promoting cultural values and discourses that are often unquestioned by those who use the technology so that they are considered 'normal' and 'rational' (Hornborg, 2001).

Take, for example, the use of the motor car. According to Matthew Paterson (2007), the values that legitimise 'car culture' include individuality, freedom to travel and a belief in modernity as progress. Most people in industrialised countries, and probably a majority of the world's population, rely in some way on the automobile for personal transport or to carry the goods they consume. Cars have enabled not only personal mobility (the ability of individuals to travel) but also social mobility (the ability of people to take employment and social opportunities they were previously unable to take). Motorised transport, therefore, enables people to travel through space and society in ways that were not possible before. The production and use of cars is thus a manifestation of cultural power, and this power is legitimised by social values that are both widespread and underpinned by global oil consumption. Fast cars with larger engines which use more fuel are often seen as a status symbol. Overcoming the problems that 'technologies' such as cars cause and the broader problems generated by oil consumption therefore involves challenging some deeply held cultural values and ways of life.

Activity 2.1   Oil and culture

Can you think of other ways in which oil has led to changes in contemporary Western culture? Spend a few moments thinking about this question before reading on.

Comment

Oil is not like other products that are traded and used: it is absolutely central to the functioning of the global economy (Lerch, 2010). Oil is vital to manufacturing, transport and agriculture. It has enabled the development of city suburbs far from the main public transport routes, whose residents rely on motorised private transport for mobility (Figure 2.4). And a vast range of consumer products such as aircraft interiors, computers and medical devices are manufactured using oil-based compounds (Box 2.1).

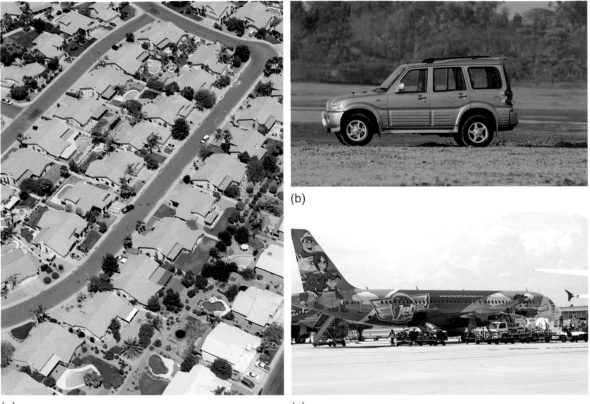

(a)

(b)

(c)

Figure 2.4   Fuelled by oil: (a) Suburban housing in the USA; (b) Scorpio sports utility vehicle; (c) Air Asia budget airline jet. These technologies are seen as rational in the cultural space and time of the twentieth and early twenty-first centuries. In a post-peak oil world, will they be replaced by other technologies?

I've chosen the quote in Box 2.1 as it illustrates in satirical form the serious point that actions that may appear mundane, normal and routine in one cultural space and time may appear bizarre and incomprehensible in another. The quote also reminds us that some profound social changes are inevitable in a future, oil-scarce world.

Box 2.1   Oil-based products

In 2003, the American author and film-maker Michael Moore wrote about a conversation he may have with his granddaughter later this century when oil is scarce:

> We made everything from oil by turning it into plastic. Furniture upholstery, grocery bags, toys, bottles, clothes, medicines, even baby diapers were made from oil. The list of what was made with oil and by-products of oil was endless: aspirin, cameras, golf balls, car batteries, carpet, fertilizers, eyeglasses, shampoo, glue, computers ... – you name it, and it came in some way from oil. Man, we were hooked on the stuff. We would take a drink from a plastic bottle and throw it away. We might burn a gallon of oil to drive to a drink store for a gallon of milk (which came in a plastic bottle, too). ... And yes, it's true we even wrapped our garbage in plastic and tossed it out.
>
> (Moore, 2003, p. 88)

Global struggles for political and economic power, such as that over oil, involve a complex mix of cooperation and conflict. To help understand the subject of oil politics it is helpful to consider a field of study called **political economy**. To political economists, an understanding of power requires an awareness of both politics and economics: those who wield economic power need to take into account political factors such as government policy, while the exercise of political power depends on the economic context. Political economists argue that there is a complex iterative relationship between political and economic power, with decisions and events in one area impacting on the other. For example, usually in international politics the government of a country with a strong and stable economy will tend to exert more power politically than the government of an economically troubled country. Another example is that the chief executives of powerful businesses may be able to exert influence on political leaders.

In the remainder of this chapter we consider the relationships between governments and oil business corporations and how these relationships have changed over time. This illustrates the importance of economic and political power in maintaining an oil-based way of life. Any attempt

Political economy
An area of study in which the exercise of political power and economic power are seen as interrelated.

to address climate change induced by this carbon-based lifestyle will require shifts in these power relations.

3 Introducing international oil politics

What are the political and economic forces that have driven the rapid and intensive exploitation of oil? In the rest of this chapter we consider three sets of actors that have been central to the extraction, refining, transport and retailing of oil: transnational oil corporations; oil-producing countries; and the governments of the main oil-consuming countries, especially in North America and western Europe. In this section, we explore the first actor, transnational corporations, and in the following two sections we look at the other two actors.

A **transnational corporation** (TNC) is a business organisation that controls assets in two or more countries. (Some authors refer to TNCs as multinational corporations.) Transnational corporations are central to the study of political economy. Decisions made in one space (e.g. at the head office of a TNC) can result in actions being taken in another space that can have significant local consequences. Corporate decisions to invest in a country may affect, positively or negatively, the local economy and environment. TNCs may transfer capital, such as finance and technology, to countries where it is relatively scarce. They may extract natural resources from one country and transfer them, and profits, to other countries.

Transnational corporation
A business that controls assets in two or more countries.

The decisions of TNCs that control productive assets such as oil affect multiple countries, and the world's largest TNCs, including oil corporations, exercise power at an international scale. This is because the production, consumption and trade of oil is a vital part of the global economy. In 2008 the global oil trade accounted for almost 80 per cent by value of all trade in natural resources (Ruta and Venables, 2012). Oil forms a significant part of many countries' imports and exports, so that the global price of oil can have a significant influence on national economies. Most oil is traded in US dollars, not in the currency of those selling or buying oil. Oil-importing countries therefore have to acquire dollars in order to buy oil. The state of the US economy and the value of the US dollar in the global foreign exchange market thus depend to a significant degree on the trade in oil.

Oil corporations from the USA and Europe have invested heavily in transferring technology to oil-producing countries. They have contributed to the economic development of countries with oil reserves, providing employment and enhancing the political power of local elites. The infrastructure that has been developed by and for the oil industry –

such as oil wells, refining plants and pipelines – transports oil across the globe, literally fuelling industrial development in countries around the world (Figure 2.5). This infrastructure helps to shape our agency as social actors. Without it, many of the routine, everyday practices that we engage in – such as turning on the central heating or air-conditioning, storing food in refrigerators, travelling to work and working on computers – would not be possible. Many people believe that to live their lives they have, in effect, no choice but to continue carrying out actions that generate fossil fuel emissions.

(a)

(b)

(c)

(d)

Figure 2.5   A vast infrastructure has developed around the global oil industry, mining and refining oil and transporting it across vast distances to the end-user, including: (a) refineries (Fawley oil refinery, England); (b) pipelines (Trans Alaska); (c) tankers; (d) petrol stations (Esso station near London)

This oil-based way of life, which has spread globally, is however dependent on oil production in just a few countries. In international oil trade there is an interdependence between oil producers, oil corporations and oil consumers, all of which benefit from this trade. **Dependence** is where one actor relies on another; for example, for the supply of a particular good or service. **Interdependence** exists when actors are mutually dependent on each other. But a state of interdependence does not necessarily mean that dependence between actors is symmetrical, with each depending on the other to the same degree. Interdependence is often asymmetrical, with one actor more dependent on the relationship than the other.

In other words, within any relationship one actor may have more power than the other. The history of oil politics can be understood as one in which actors have sought to increase their power at the expense of other actors. Over time this has led to shifts in the patterns of interdependence between producer governments, the oil corporations and the consumer governments. While there has been cooperation between these actors, there has also been intense competition over the ownership and production of oil and the sharing of the wealth it generates. To develop the argument that actors in the oil industry both cooperate and compete, I first introduce you in Box 2.2 to some ideas – such as utility and Pareto optimality – from economic theory. The significance of these ideas for the oil industry will become clear as the remainder of the chapter unfolds.

Dependence
Where one actor relies on another actor.

Interdependence
A state when two or more actors are mutually dependent on each other.

Box 2.2 Cooperation, competition and Pareto optimality

In economic theory, **utility** denotes the satisfaction, or instrumental value, that a consumer derives from consuming a good or service. Utility is an abstract concept that cannot be measured directly. However, the concept is central to economic theory. Economists argue that the greater the utility a consumer derives from consuming a good or service, the greater the price they are prepared to pay.

Imagine an economy with just two types of goods. Consumer S grows strawberries, while Consumer L grows lemons. Consumer S has more than enough strawberries for his own consumption needs. He wants some lemons and is willing to offer some strawberries in exchange for them. Meanwhile, Consumer L is seeking some strawberries in exchange for his surplus lemons. The two decide to cooperate and trade some of their wares.

By trading, each gains utility. In other words, they derive increased satisfaction. Once they have started trading, the two fruit consumers will continue to seek new trading relationships that will further

Utility
The satisfaction, or instrumental value, that a consumer derives from consuming a good or service.

Pareto improvement
Any situation that will lead to at least one actor being better off, with neither being worse off.

Pareto optimality
Any point at which it is no longer possible for both actors to increase their utility.

increase their utility. They will do this as long as a **Pareto improvement** is possible. A Pareto improvement is any situation that will lead to at least one actor being better off, with neither being worse off. The term is named after the Italian economist Vilfredo Pareto (1848–1923). Pareto improvements are possible only when both actors agree voluntarily to a change in the trading arrangement.

When no more Pareto improvements are possible, a state known as **Pareto optimality** has been reached. Pareto optimality is a theoretical idea and is a point at which it is no longer possible for both actors to increase their utility. This is any point where utility for both actors has been increased so that it is not possible to allocate the resources differently without making at least one actor worse off. At this point, no change in the trading relationship is possible. This is depicted in diagrammatic form for Consumer L and Consumer S in Figure 2.6 as a utility possibility diagram, a diagram that plots all the possible combinations of utility for two consumers engaged in trade. Note that this diagram shows the utility for the consumers (and not the quantities of fruit traded). In this diagram all possible points of Pareto optimality appear on what is known as the *Pareto frontier*.

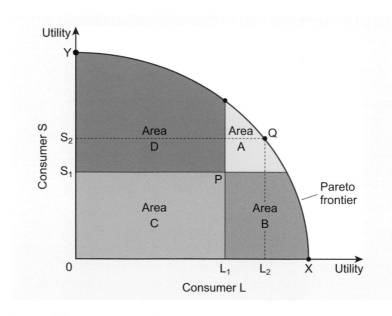

Figure 2.6   A utility possibility diagram showing trades between a strawberry grower and a lemon grower

This diagram has two axes. The horizontal X axis shows the utility of the lemon seller and the Y axis that of the strawberry seller. At point 0 there is no trade between the two fruit consumers. Point P represents a hypothetical trading arrangement and the utility each individual has gained from the arrangement. At this point the utility for Consumer L is L_1 while that for Consumer S is S_1. However, as you can see, the lemon seller is gaining more than the strawberry seller. Point P is a **Pareto sub-optimal outcome**, an outcome where further mutual gains in utility from increased trade are possible. Note that, for any Pareto sub-optimal outcome, a new arrangement with mutual gains for both the fruit growers is only possible when there is a movement to the right and upwards on the diagram. From point P this is within area A.

By trading, the two fruit consumers have developed an interdependent relationship. Each relies on the other for the improvement in their utility. However, an interdependent relationship is rarely one with symmetrical interdependence. Usually, one actor is more dependent on the other. As you can see, the arrangement agreed at point P provides more utility for Consumer L than Consumer S. So Consumer L gains more from the arrangement than Consumer S, but at the same time L is more dependent on S than S is on L.

Let us now assume that the two consumers agree a new arrangement at point Q. The two have each gained utility, with Consumer L's utility increasing to L_2 and Consumer S's utility increasing to S_2. Point Q is on the Pareto frontier, so no further Pareto improvements are possible. The two consumers will not agree to move to a different position on the Pareto frontier, as this would entail a gain for one and a loss for the other.

Pareto sub-optimal outcome
An outcome where further mutual gains in utility from increased trade are possible.

Activity 2.2 Reading a utility possibility diagram (1)

Look again at Figure 2.6. Four areas are shown: areas A, B, C and D. Moving from point P, which of these four areas would represent a new position whereby Consumer S gains while Consumer L loses?

Comment

This area is represented by area D. So, from point P a shift to any point in area D would represent less utility for Consumer L and more utility for Consumer S.

Similarly, a shift from point P to area B would represent a gain for Consumer L and a loss for Consumer S. The two would not agree to move voluntarily from P to any point in area C as both would lose.

You have seen that point Q is on the Pareto frontier. From point Q, any movement along the Pareto frontier from right to left would represent a loss of utility for Consumer L and a gain for Consumer S. Similarly, moving from left to right would represent a loss for Consumer S and a gain for Consumer L.

However, no actor would voluntarily agree to move to a position that represented a loss. But Consumer S could, for example, be forced to accept a loss if Consumer L were to become more powerful, and could impose exploitative terms that S would not freely agree to. This power might take the form of a threat of physical violence or blackmail.

Activity 2.3   Reading a utility possibility diagram (2)

Look again at Figure 2.6. Moving along the Pareto frontier from Point Q, what point would represent a position where Consumer S maximises his utility at the expense of Consumer L?

Comment

This would be point Y. Because Consumer L would not agree to move from Q to Y, this will only happen when Consumer S has power in the relationship, exploiting Consumer L unjustly, perhaps by obtaining L's fruit illegally or using the threat of force.

Similarly, at point X, Consumer L has maximised his utility at the expense of Consumer S, who now derives no utility from the relationship.

The relationship just described between consumers L and S is an example of a model. It greatly simplifies reality but can be used to explain and theorise some complex social interactions. For example, suppose two business executives are negotiating a renewal of their existing trading arrangement. Each bargains hard, trying to obtain concessions from the other. The two want to gain as much as they can for their business, but a voluntary agreement is possible only when a Pareto improvement can be realised. Similarly, two governments may negotiate a complex trade deal, each trying to secure goods and services that benefits their country as far as possible.

However, agreements in business and politics are not always made completely voluntarily. Power is often a factor. Because no rational actor will freely move to a new arrangement where they lose utility (areas B and D in Figure 2.6), such a movement is possible only when the relationship between the actors involves an element of coercion as well as cooperation, when one actor can deploy power to leverage the other to make concessions they would not make freely.

This model can be used to help explain the history of oil politics in the Persian Gulf. The remainder of this section and the next will show how governments and corporations have cooperated to secure access to oil and the wealth it generates. Over time, new arrangements have been negotiated, but not all these arrangements have represented Pareto improvements. While the actors involved in the Gulf oil industry have cooperated they have also competed, each exercising power in different ways. They have obtained and controlled oil-producing territory, made agreements, and used the threat of conflict to extract concessions from each other.

When oil was discovered in the Persian Gulf in the 1930s, the countries of the region were colonised and had very limited economic power. They also had limited access to the technology, investment capital and managerial skills needed to extract and sell oil. Actors that did have these economic capabilities were the oil corporations that had been created in the nineteenth and early twentieth centuries, such as Standard Oil (founded in 1870 in the United States), Burmah (founded in 1886 in the UK), Royal Dutch Shell (a Dutch–UK enterprise founded in 1907), and Total (founded in 1924 in France). So the Gulf oil countries entered into commercial relationships with Western oil corporations known as concession agreements. A **concession agreement** is a business agreement whereby one actor grants certain rights to another. In the case of the oil industry, the host government grants an oil corporation the right to extract and sell its oil. The concession agreement stipulates the rules that both parties should observe and the rate of tax the corporation should pay to the host government. So keen were some oil corporations to work in the Gulf that they created new businesses. Standard Oil of California and the Texas Oil Company (later Texaco) created the Arabian American Oil Company (Aramco), which in the 1930s was granted the concession to exploit the Saudi Arabian oil fields (Parra, 2010).

Concession agreement
A legal contract whereby one actor grants certain rights of exclusivity to another actor.

When agreeing the early pre-Second World War concessions, the oil corporations exerted their power and expertise in the oil trade, bargaining hard with the new producer countries, in effect imposing terms that favoured the corporations, which retained well over half the profits from oil sales. In the post-war period, the producer governments grew more confident in negotiations, and by the 1950s the 50/50 concession agreement had become widespread, with half of the revenues going to the corporation and half to the host government. This was still a sizeable return on the investments of the corporations. Meanwhile, the governments of the producing countries gained a substantial source of tax revenue which was used to promote economic development.

The next section explains how the producer governments joined together to improve their negotiation position.

4 The Organization of the Petroleum Exporting Countries (OPEC)

The relationship between producers and oil corporations began to change owing to a shift in global economic relations in the 1950s, leading eventually to the collapse of the concession system in most oil-producing countries. During the 1950s and 1960s, many of the European colonies in Asia and Africa had gained their independence, and the governments of these newly independent countries became more assertive, arguing that the prices they received for their commodities were unfairly biased in favour of the countries of the global North. This had an impact on international oil politics.

The Organization of Petroleum Exporting Countries (OPEC) was founded in 1960 to promote better oil prices for producing countries (Figure 2.7). OPEC's most important members are the Gulf oil producers, with its largest historical and current producer being Saudi Arabia. These countries argued that too much revenue from oil sales was concentrated in the hands of foreign business and they argued for 'shared ownership' of the corporations to which they had granted concessions. In 1968, OPEC agreed a statement supporting shared ownership whereby the governments of producer countries would hold shares in oil corporations such as Aramco (Parra, 2010).

Figure 2.7 The first OPEC conference was held in Baghdad in September 1960

Facing an assertive and united OPEC, the largest oil corporations, in particular the 'Seven Sisters' (a term often used to describe the seven largest Western oil corporations, and which in the early 1970s comprised businesses from the USA, Britain and the Netherlands), joined forces and in 1971 proposed that OPEC negotiate collectively with the corporations to agree a simultaneous settlement of all OPEC claims. However, OPEC pointed out that the legal relationship in question was the concession agreement between individual corporations and individual producer governments. The producers asserted that they were under no obligation to negotiate collectively with the corporations through OPEC, and they refused to do so, depriving the corporations of bargaining leverage. OPEC was, however, successful in maintaining its own united front, with all the Gulf producers, backed by Algeria and Libya, insisting on shared ownership and increased tax rates (Yergin, 2009).

The oil corporations then appealed to the governments of the USA and western Europe to intervene on their behalf. Governments from the global North have a history dating back to the colonial era of protecting the claims made by their businesses to natural resources in other countries, sometimes using military force. But throughout this period Western governments (with the exception of the Netherlands) decided not to become involved in the dispute. The USA was unwilling to risk jeopardising good relations with the Gulf governments; neither did it want to risk causing problems for its national economy, and the global economy in general, by becoming embroiled in a conflict that could interrupt oil supplies. The USA urged producer governments and oil corporations to compromise and settle on terms that were affordable to both sides and which kept the oil flowing. Deprived of the opportunity to negotiate collectively, with no support from their host governments and unwilling to sour relationships with the producers lest they lose all, the oil corporations eventually accepted some losses and agreed to shared ownership of the oil, settling with the producers as favourably as possible.

Throughout the dispute the oil producer governments sought to maximise their power. Their control over oil gave them bargaining power which they translated into financial gains. The unspoken threat was that the corporations should agree to these terms or lose their favoured position in the producer countries.

The demand for shared ownership was quickly followed by demands from the oil-producing governments for full ownership of oil corporations based in OPEC countries. Throughout the 1970s, many Western-owned oil businesses passed into public ownership in the producing states, with the parent businesses in Europe and North America receiving compensation in exchange. Today, the largest oil corporations in the world are the nationally owned businesses of the largest oil-producing countries. Aramco was bought by the Saudi Arabian government and since 1980 has been known as Saudi Aramco (Figure 2.8).

Figure 2.8   Saudi Aramco's headquarters in Dhahran, Saudi Arabia

By the early 1970s, the OPEC producers, more confident in their relations with the West, were prepared to use their newly found bargaining power to achieve broader political goals. This became clear when, on 6 October 1973, a coalition of Arab countries (Egypt, Syria and Jordan, with some Iraqi forces contributing) invaded Israel during the Jewish holiday of Yom Kippur. After achieving early territorial gains the coalition was pushed back, with Israel eventually gaining territory from its neighbours. The Arabic OPEC oil producers then came under pressure from the invading coalition to deploy the 'oil weapon' by embargoing oil exports to Western countries supporting Israel, in particular to the main supplier of weapons and financial aid to Israel; the USA. On 17 October, OPEC announced it would cut production by 5 per cent every month until Israel withdrew from the occupied territories of Gaza, the Golan Heights and the West Bank (Merrill, 2007). The Saudi government told executives of US oil corporations that their positions in Saudi Arabia were at risk and they could lose everything because of US policy towards Israel. Texaco, Mobil and Chevron, which just a few years earlier had been looking to the US government for support in its dealings with OPEC, subsequently lobbied for a change in US policy in the Middle East (Yergin, 2009).

The ensuing six months saw the power of the USA and its allies pitched against the power of OPEC. One crucial difference between this crisis and the early dispute between OPEC and the oil corporations on shared ownership was that most Western governments were not prepared to yield to OPEC demands. The USA was not prepared to abandon its Middle Eastern ally, Israel. To do so would alienate the vocal pro-Israel domestic lobby in the USA. A further factor in the dispute was the Cold War between the USA and the Soviet Union. A weakened Israel would have left the Soviet Union with more influence in the region than the USA.

In Western countries the phrase 'energy crisis' entered the vocabulary. The crisis presented Western governments with a problem of uncertainty: how to keep the economy running with uncertain supplies. In the USA, a national speed limit of 55 mph was introduced, backed by a national advertising campaign – 'Don't be fuelish' – urging fuel conservation and increased energy efficiency. The crisis led to a notable, although short-lived, increase in research into fuel-efficient cars in the USA. The USA sought to manage the risks of zero oil production from the Gulf through a more diversified supply, seeking better relations with producers such as Nigeria and Venezuela.

After six months of negotiations between Western governments and OPEC, and between the USA and Israel, OPEC lifted the embargo in exchange for a partial Israeli withdrawal from territory captured in the Yom Kippur war. OPEC had failed to secure a complete Israeli withdrawal, and in this respect the crisis revealed the limits of the broader political bargaining leverage of the oil producers if the consumer governments held firm and sought additional oil supplies. The outcome of the dispute revealed the interdependence of producers and consumers: an oil-producing country needs a secure consumer base just as an oil-consuming nation needs a secure supply.

Nonetheless, the 1973–74 oil crisis led to a fourfold increase in oil prices, the benefits of which accrued almost exclusively to the oil-rich countries. The producers were now firmly in control of supply and price and had again improved their material position relative to that of the Western corporations.

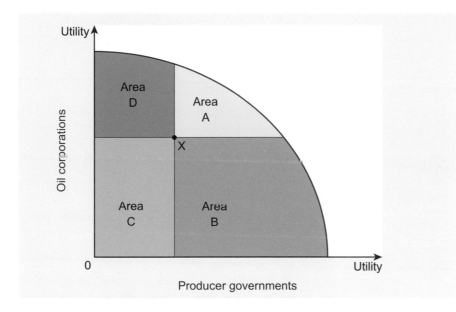

Figure 2.9   A hypothetical utility possibility diagram showing the aggregated utility of oil corporations and oil-producer governments in the Persian Gulf before the 1973–74 oil crisis

Activity 2.4   Reading a utility possibility diagram (3)

Imagine that the utility the oil corporations gained from the Persian Gulf oil industry immediately before the 1973–74 oil crisis could be aggregated, as could that of the oil-producer governments. This may be expressed in Figure 2.9, with point X representing the position immediately before the Yom Kippur War.

In which area – A, B, C or D – would you expect to see the situation after the dispute was settled in 1974?

Comment

As with previous disagreements over shared ownership, the outcome was one whereby the oil-producer governments improved their position at the expense of the oil corporations. This would represent a shift to somewhere in area B.

Since the 1973–74 oil crisis, both producer governments and oil corporations have continued to benefit from the Gulf oil industry. However, disputes between oil-rich countries and Western corporations on the sharing of oil revenues continue. For example, a cable sent from the US embassy in Baku, Azerbaijan, in 2007 details disagreement between the Azerbaijani government of President Ilham Heydar oglu Aliyev and BP, with Aliyev claiming that 'BP is stealing our oil' (Leigh and Harding, 2011, p. 303) (Figure 2.10).

Figure 2.10   The oil fields of Baku and the Caspian Sea have long been prized by outsiders. Nazi Germany made an unsuccessful bid to seize the fields during the Second World War in an effort to deprive the Soviet Union of oil. Access to the region's oil remains politically contentious to this day

You have seen that the pervasiveness of oil and oil-based commodities in our daily lives has made oil the object of political and economic struggles. These struggles have shifted over time with changing relationships between the actors concerned. In the next section, you can deepen your understanding of cooperation and conflict by considering another model, the Prisoners' Dilemma.

5   Cooperation and conflict

The history of oil politics in the Persian Gulf reveals that competition does not rule out cooperation, and vice versa. The OPEC oil producers compete for market share in the international economy and thus are rivals. Yet when faced with what was perceived as a common external 'threat', namely Western oil corporations and Israel, they have combined their power by cooperating. But while the OPEC members have cooperated when it is in their collective interests to do so – higher profits mean more revenue for all members – the individual members also compete against each other in the global marketplace. Even while cooperating to realise collective gains, individual countries may continue to search for gains relative to other producers, and this helps explain why the 1973–74 oil embargo failed to achieve its aims. The embargo was harming the economic interests of the producers, and ultimately not all producers supported the embargo over the long term. This erosion of support led to the collapse of the embargo.

One model that seeks to explain cooperative and competitive behaviour is the Prisoners' Dilemma. The model illustrates that individual actors do not determine outcomes in complex social situations alone. Outcomes, rather, are the result of how the decisions of different actors intersect. The Prisoners' Dilemma is an economics model that explains why two businesses who reach an agreement on market share have an incentive to cheat, generating a situation that is in neither's interest. It is similar in some respects to the tragedy of the commons. Both models show that incentives to act in individual interests may result in collective detriment. (You may find it helpful here to refer back the description of the tragedy of the commons in Book 1, Chapter 2, Section 4.)

In the Prisoners' Dilemma, two men are arrested for a crime they committed together. Both have agreed neither to confess nor to implicate the other. The prisoners are held in isolation and thus cannot communicate after their arrest. The police have no evidence, so can secure a conviction only if one or both men confess. However, they have enough evidence to convict both men of a lesser charge. Let us suppose that:

- If neither prisoner makes a statement, both are convicted of the lesser charge and each serves five years in jail.
- If one prisoner makes a statement implicating the other, the police will drop the charges against that prisoner, who then goes free. The

police will use the statement to secure a conviction against the other prisoner, who receives a 20-year sentence.

- If both make a statement implicating the other, each will receive a ten-year sentence.

This can be represented as a matrix. In the matrix representing the Prisoners' Dilemma it is common to show the sentence in years for Prisoner A in the top left-hand corner of each cell, and that for Prisoner B in the bottom right-hand corner (Table 2.1):

Table 2.1   A Prisoners' Dilemma matrix showing years served in jail

	Strategy	Prisoner B	
		Cooperate with A (no statement)	Defect against A (make a statement)
Prisoner A	Cooperate with B (no statement)	5 5	20 0
	Defect against B (make a statement)	0 20	10 10

So if prisoner A sticks to the original agreement and makes no statement, but B defects and makes a statement, this will be depicted in the top right-hand cell, with A receiving a 20-year sentence and B going free.

Activity 2.5   The Prisoners' Dilemma

What is the best collective outcome for the two prisoners in terms of years served?

Comment

The best collective outcome is where the total years served in jail is the lowest at just ten, when both prisoners cooperate with each other and say nothing to the police. This is depicted in the top left-hand corner, with each prisoner serving five years each. For every other outcome the total years served exceeds ten.

However, each prisoner wishes to reduce the risk of receiving the lengthy 20-year sentence and to increase the opportunity of going free. Each realises that if they cooperate with the police by making a statement against their associate they will serve some jail time (at least 5 years, maybe 20). Keen to avoid the 20-year sentence, each is prepared to defect by making a statement. Each reasons that:

1   He will gain his freedom if the other prisoner does not defect.

2   If the other prisoner also defects, the worst sentence will be ten years.

So the only way definitely to avoid the 20-year sentence is to make a statement. Because under the terms of the game both prisoners will reason like this, the game will settle at what economists call the **Nash equilibrium**, the point at which no actor can gain by changing his strategy (named after John Nash, an American mathematician and game theorist). In this case the Nash equilibrium is when each serves ten years in jail.

Nash equilibrium
The point at which no actor can gain by changing strategy.

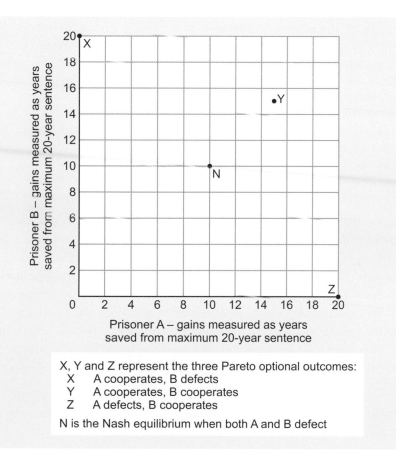

Figure 2.11   A utility possibility diagram depicting the Prisoners' Dilemma scenario in Table 2.1 showing years saved for both prisoners

This particular Prisoners' Dilemma model is depicted as a utility possibility diagram in Figure 2.11. Note that the diagram depicts utility in terms of years *saved* from the maximum 20-year sentence.

Activity 2.6   Pareto optimality

Which of the outcomes of the game depicted in Figure 2.12 may be considered Pareto optimal?

Comment

Recall that a Pareto outcome is one where it is not possible to move to a new position without making at least one person worse off. A study of Figure 2.12 reveals that there are three such positions: X, Y and Z. Figure 2.12 also illustrates that, of the various Pareto optimal outcomes, the point where the collective gains are greatest is Y (when both cooperate). At this point, each prisoner serves five years and thus saves 15 years off the maximum sentence, a collective total of 30 years (compared with points X and Z where the total is just 20 years). In theory, each prisoner can significantly improve his own individual position at the expense of the other, yet when both try to do so they end up in the only position that is Pareto sub-optimal, namely point N (the Nash equilibrium). (Note that because there are only three Pareto optimal points in Figure 2.12 it is not possible to draw a continuous Pareto frontier as in Figures 2.6 and 2.9.)

The Prisoners' Dilemma is not just a puzzling hypothetical situation. Such dilemmas arise all the time in social life, including among prisoners (Figure 2.12). As indicated below, OPEC members face Prisoners' Dilemma-type temptations. However, like all models, the Prisoners' Dilemma has advantages and disadvantages. By focusing on how rational people behave in a particular situation, the Prisoners' Dilemma illustrates how sub-optimal outcomes can be reached through lack of cooperation and why cooperation can be difficult to achieve. But as a model it cannot fully represent the complexity of the real world.

Since the mid 1970s, the various OPEC producers have cooperated, passing resolutions on production quotas intended to maximise the revenue of all producers. Sometimes OPEC has agreed to cut production to force the price of oil up. In effect, individual producing countries are asked to accept less revenue today for a higher market price, leading to more revenue tomorrow. If OPEC producers only cooperated and never competed they could agree on production quotas that realised the greatest possible profit for the OPEC membership. But there is always the temptation among some individual producing countries to 'defect'; in other words, to produce more oil than they have agreed and thus earn more money. However, if too many producers do this the supply of oil to the global marketplace will increase, and oil prices will fall. According to one estimate, oil production in the 1980s and 1990 was some 20 per cent above the agreed production quotas (Seeking Alpha, 2007).

Figure 2.12   The former head of New York's Gambino crime family, John Gotti (left) with his underboss, Salvatore 'Sammy The Bull' Gravano (right). Along with various associates, the two men were arrested in 1990. Each faced similar charges of murder and extortion. Gotti received a sentence of life without the possibility of parole. Gravano received a reduced sentence of five years after turning state's evidence and testifying against Gotti

Such Prisoners' Dilemma-type defections suit the consuming states, as they lead to an increased supply of oil at a cheaper price than would otherwise be the case. Over the long term, all OPEC members lose from such behaviour. Trust is therefore an important issue. Many OPEC governments do not keep the agreements they have reached with their fellow producers. The Prisoners' Dilemma game helps explain why this is so. This has had important environmental consequences: carbon dioxide emissions from oil consumption have been significantly higher than they would have been had the production quotas been observed.

6 Summary

Since the start of the Industrial Revolution, technological and economic development has been fuelled by energy accumulated in plants and marine life millions of years ago. When the oil era ends it will have lasted just a few centuries, a brief moment of time in the history of the Earth. It will be remembered as an era that had a profound impact on how societies are organised.

Oil is cheap in economic terms but costly in environmental terms. In this chapter you have seen that oil is now the basis of a modern way of life. Politics and economics are structured around a culture of oil use. While most people benefit from oil consumption, people share these benefits to different degrees. This chapter has shown that while cooperation between actors is necessary in order for these benefits to be reaped, cooperating actors often relate to one another competitively, leading to the enhanced exploitation of the resource. The case study used to illustrate this point is the oil industry in the Persian Gulf, although the mix of cooperative and competitive relationships you have explored in this chapter also drives the exploitation of other environmental resources. Oil corporations and states have cooperated to exploit oil because they each have an interest in doing so. Neither are motivated by environmental values. Oil corporations gain profits and increased market share, while governments use oil to promote economic growth. That such power relations are so entangled and embedded offers one very important response to our question *Why are environmental issues so difficult to resolve?*, and has profound consequences for attempts to shift away from oil-based ways of life.

References

Hornborg, A. (2001) *The Power of The Machine: Global Inequalities of Economy, Technology, and Environment*, Walnut Creek, CA, Alta Mira.

Hubbert, M. K. (1969) 'Energy resources', in National Research Council Committee on Resources and Man, *Resources and Man*, San Francisco, CA, W. H. Freeman.

International Energy Agency (2010) *Energy Outlook 2010*, Paris, OECD/ International Energy Agency.

Leigh, D. and Harding, L. (2011) *Wikileaks: Inside Julian Assange's War on Secrecy*, London, Guardian Books.

Lerch, D. (2010) 'Making sense of peak oil and energy uncertainty', in Heinberg, R. and Lerch, D. (eds) *The Post-Carbon Reader: Managing the 21st Century Sustainability Crisis*, Healdsburg, CA, Watershed Media.

Maugeri, L. (2012) *Oil: The Next Revolution: The Unprecedented Upsurge of Oil Production Capacity and What It Means for the World*, Cambridge, MA, Harvard Kennedy School [online], http://belfercenter.ksg.harvard.edu/files/Oil-%20The %20Next%20Revolution.pdf (Accessed 2 October 2012).

Merrill, K. R. (2007) *The Oil Crisis of 1973–1974*, Boston, MA, Bedford St Martin's.

Moore, M. (2003) *Dude, Where's My Country?*, London, Allen Lane.

Parra, F. (2010) *Oil Politics: A Modern History of Petroleum*, London, I. B. Tauris.

Paterson, M. (2007) *Automobile Politics: Ecology and Cultural Political Economy*, Cambridge, Cambridge University Press.

Ruta, M. and Venables, A. (2012) 'International trade in natural resources: practices and policy', World Trade Organization Working Paper, ERSD 2012-07, Geneva, WTO.

Seeking Alpha (2007) *Understanding OPEC: Cheaters Never Win* [online], http:// seekingalpha.com/article/32217-understanding-opec-cheaters-never-win (Accessed 2 October 2012).

Yergin, D. (2009) *The Prize: The Epic Quest for Oil, Money and Power*, New York, Free Press.

Chapter 3   Low carbon energy technologies

David Humphreys

Contents

1 Introduction

In the last chapter you saw that the political and economic aspects of oil production have shaped the infrastructures that govern our lives and have influenced individual agency of people and organisations. We focused on the oil industry, noting how an oil-based way of life generates carbon dioxide emissions that contribute to climate change.

In this chapter we consider how infrastructures may change. History teaches us that new infrastructures can be developed and implemented rapidly. Sometimes a new technology may become widely adopted, replacing other technologies before itself being replaced by even newer inventions. We consider how society may shift from carbon-intensive energy infrastructures towards the large scale development and deployment of other infrastructures that meet our energy needs with low, preferably no, net carbon dioxide emissions.

Exploring the subject of infrastructure change will enable us to consider in more depth the block question *Why are environmental issues so difficult to resolve?* You will explore some of the problems associated with developing low carbon energy technologies and how they can be scaled up. The term **scaled up** refers to the expansion of a technology or a system so that it can handle an increased capacity of work over a wider spatial area. While low carbon technologies currently exist, they operate only at localised scales, supplying a very small percentage of energy needs. We will consider three low carbon technologies: solar, wind and tidal. We will examine the technical principles by which these technologies work and some of the uncertainties associated with them. You will see that the three technologies offer many benefits but also pose social and technical concerns, and that managing our energy needs while reducing flows of carbon dioxide into the atmosphere is a difficult and challenging matter.

Scaling up

The process of expanding a technology or a system to handle an increased capacity of work over a wider spatial area.

2   Agency, infrastructure change and time

Do you know where the electricity comes from that lights and heats your home?

I asked myself that question and realised that I do not know the answer. I live in Canterbury in the south-east of England and my electricity could come from a number of sources, including the Dungeness nuclear power station, an offshore wind farm near Thanet, an oil-power station at Grain and the gas-powered Damhead Creek power station. These power stations have very different levels of greenhouse gas emissions and types of environmental impact. Or my electricity could come from much further afield, including France. It is likely that my electricity comes from different sources at different times of the year, depending on the demand for electricity elsewhere on the grid and the planned maintenance schedules of the power stations in my region.

I would prefer my electricity to come from sources that cause little, preferably no, environmental damage. Our household has sought to exercise our agency responsibly by installing solar hot water panels on our roof, which decreases the electricity used for our water heating. This meets some of our hot water needs, although overall I don't feel I am doing as much as I would like to reduce my **carbon footprint**. A carbon footprint is defined as the greenhouse gases emitted by an individual, organisation or a country, or the greenhouse gases needed to produce a particular product.

Carbon footprint
The greenhouse gases emitted by an individual, an organisation or a country, or the greenhouse gases needed to produce a particular product.

This leads on to some broader points. Our actions (and their environmental consequences) are not simply shaped by our intentions and personal values, but are determined in large part by commitments inscribed in cultural practices. For example, I live in a modernist European culture that is highly reliant on electrical appliances. As an individual living within this culture my agency is shaped by it to a significant degree. I do not want to contribute to greenhouse gas emissions when I use an electrical appliance, such as the computer on which I am writing this chapter, but I consider that my work and current lifestyle leave me with few other feasible alternatives.

That is largely because when living my life I rely on the infrastructures that are embedded within my culture. Looking beyond the electricity industry, other examples of infrastructure include roads, phone systems and water networks. Infrastructures set many of the choices that are available to us when we seek to exercise agency. We contribute to carbon emissions not because we are 'bad' or because we want to, but because our energy supply comes mainly from fossil fuels. So our options for action, and the environmental consequences of these options, are to a large degree prescribed and proscribed by the material infrastructures within which we are embedded. We inherit infrastructures from the past and bequeath them to the future.

Our interest in this chapter is in energy infrastructures, particularly electricity infrastructures. Today's energy infrastructures began on a small, localised scale. The early electrification of shopping districts was the niche in which local electricity networks were first established and from which they then spread out and linked up, eventually coalescing into modern nationwide grids (Geels, 2011). Just as these infrastructures were created, so too they can change. Through their actions, people and organisations may act to maintain and renew existing infrastructures, passing them on to the future more or less as they found them. Or they can exercise agency to reconfigure infrastructures so that over time their negative environmental impacts are reduced. In this respect the future is shaped in the present. The agency that the present generation exercises today will help shape the environmental consequences of the agency exercised by future generations. What we do has consequences not just for us but for our descendants. The exercise of agency and infrastructural change should be seen as interrelated; they go together.

3   Some low carbon technologies

An understanding of the first two laws of thermodynamics is necessary to understand energy technologies. The *first law of thermodynamics*, also known as the *law of conservation of energy*, holds that energy cannot be created or destroyed. However, the form in which energy exists may change. Energy can be converted from one form to another. In the case of **low carbon energy technologies**, the intention is to produce useful forms of energy, such as electricity and heat, with only minimal emissions of carbon dioxide. The low carbon energy technologies we are examining in this chapter are solar, wind and tidal power. These are also examples of **renewable energy technologies** that convert environmental energy flows, such as solar energy (sunshine) or wind, into energy that people can use. Other types of low carbon energy technologies are nuclear power, and fossil power stations which capture carbon dioxide emissions and pump them to a secure underground location, thus preventing their discharge to the atmosphere.

The *second law of thermodynamics* involves a concept called **entropy**. Entropy is a measure of the disorderedness of energy. A state of low entropy exists when energy is highly concentrated, while a high entropy state exists when energy is dispersed. The most useful energy sources are those with low entropy. The water in a boiling kettle has low entropy as the heat energy is concentrated in a small volume at high temperature. But if the water in the kettle is poured into a swimming pool the energy is dissipated, leading to a state of higher entropy. This means the energy is much less useful. The second law of thermodynamics holds that when energy is converted from one form to another, entropy will increase. For example, a car engine will convert some of the chemical energy in petrol into motion, but also generate heat. The first law tells us that the heat energy still exists, but the second law tells us it has been dispersed and is, therefore, not available for reuse. This is why energy cannot be recycled. It also explains why, even though the first law tells us that energy cannot be destroyed, ensuring that human societies have continuing access to useful energy supplies is problematic.

The second law of thermodynamics applies to any isolated system. An isolated system is one that does not exchange matter or energy with its environment. But the Earth is not an isolated system. If it were, entropy would increase until all energy on the planet had been dissipated. The Earth is a **closed system**, namely one that exchanges energy, but not

Low carbon energy technologies
Technologies that produce useful energy with minimal or zero carbon emissions.

Renewable energy technologies
Technologies that convert constant or recurring environmental energy flows, such as solar energy or wind, into useful energy.

Entropy
A measure of the disorderedness of energy.

Closed system
A system that exchanges energy, but not matter, with its environment.

matter, with its environment. An *open system*, by contrast, exchanges both energy and matter with its environment (Figure 3.1). Life forms are examples of open systems as they take in food from, and excrete waste to, their environment. The Earth receives energy from the sun. Solar radiation can be used directly to heat water, or converted into electricity using photovoltaic panels. It also drives the world's weather, providing wind, wave and ocean current energy that can be converted to electricity. This energy could help to wean human society from its dependence on fossil fuels. By 2008, however, renewable energy technologies provided only 12.9 per cent of global primary energy supply (Figure 3.2).

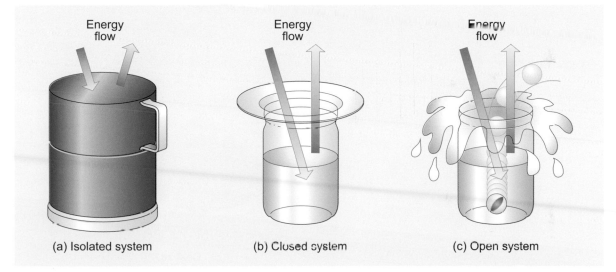

Figure 3.1   (a) An isolated system allows neither energy nor matter to cross its boundaries. Isolated systems do not really exist; (b) A closed system allows energy but not matter to cross its boundaries. Closed systems are rare; but the Earth is an example of a closed system, to a close approximation; (c) An open system allows both energy and matter to cross its boundaries. Open systems are common; most of the Earth's subsystems are open systems. The arrows represent energy flows

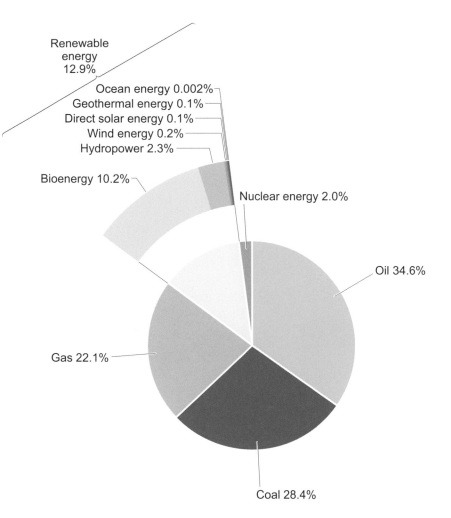

Figure 3.2   Shares of energy sources in total global primary energy supply, 2008. According to the IPCC, renewable energy provided just 12.9 per cent of global primary energy supplies in 2008. Of this, the bulk was from bioenergy. Deployment of renewable energy technology has increased since then – but so too have global greenhouse gas emissions (Source: based on IPCC, 2011, p. 10)

We now examine three types of low carbon energy technology to see how this energy can be harnessed for human use.

3.1   Solar energy

Solar energy is an abundant energy resource with massive unrealised potential. There are two main solar energy technologies, each relying on a different type of solar panel to convert the energy in sunlight into a form that is useful to humans. The first is a solar hot water system, or solar thermal. In this system a carrier fluid (usually water) is heated by the sun and the heat is transferred to an insulated water storage tank. A solar thermal system may be 'active', with pumps and a control mechanism to circulate the carrier fluid (Figure 3.3), or 'passive', with no pumps or controls. The panels can be installed either on the roofs of the building which will use the hot water, or on land close to it.

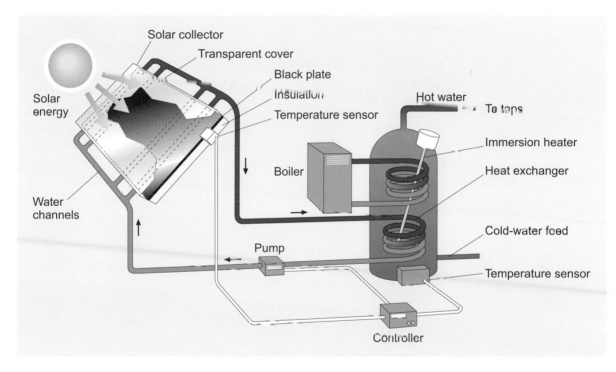

Figure 3.3 An active solar hot water system with a pump and control mechanism to circulate the carrier fluid (Source: based on Arvizu et al., 2011a, p. 348, Figure 3.4)

The second solar energy technology involves a different type of solar panel – the photovoltaic panel – that converts solar radiation into electricity through the **photovoltaic effect**. The photovoltaic effect is the generation of electricity across a junction between two layers of a semiconductor on exposure to light. Semiconductors are materials that have some degree of electrical conductivity. They conduct more electricity than an insulator, which conducts no charge, but less than conductors, such as metal. Elements that may be used in solar photovoltaic panels are silicon, gallium and indium. Silicon is the most commonly used element, so is used in the example below.

Photovoltaic effect
The generation of an electric current across a junction between two layers of a semi-conductor on exposure to light.

Photovoltaic panels consist of a series of linked solar cells made out of two layers of silicon. Each solar cell has both a positively and a negatively charged layer of silicon. Positively charged silicon can be manufactured by doping pure silicon with the element boron. Doping is the process of introducing an impurity into a semi-conductor with the intention of altering its electrical properties. Negatively charged silicon can be manufactured by doping pure silicon with phosphorous. When the two layers of silicon are placed together an electrical field is created. Solar panels are installed with the negative (phosphorus-doped) layers of the solar cells facing the sun. The positive and negative layers are connected by an electrical wire.

Solar energy from the sun strikes the panel. This energy is made up of photons, small particles of solar energy. Some of the photons that strike the negative layer of silicon have sufficient energy to dislodge electrons from their atoms. Electrons have a negative charge and are thus attracted to a positive charge. These electrons flow across the electrical field to the positive side (boron-doped) layer, thus creating an electric current. The electric current then flows into the electrical wire (Figure 3.4). Solar photovoltaic panels are increasingly widely used (Figure 3.5).

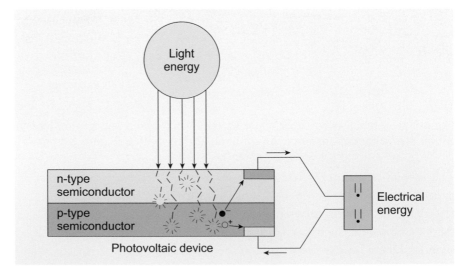

Figure 3.4   The photovoltaic effect is the process through which a photovoltaic cell converts sunlight into electricity. The energy of the light is transferred to an electron in an atom of the semiconductor device. The energy allows the electron to escape from its normal position associated with a single atom in the semiconductor to become part of the current in an electrical circuit

(a)

(b)

(c)

Figure 3.5   Photovoltaic panels on (a) the International Space Station; (b) the Centre for Alternative Technology in Wales; (c) a speed warning sign

Activity 3.1   Solar energy

Apart from variations in cloud cover, what factors may affect the amount of energy that solar panels can collect? You may find it helpful to think about this question in terms of variations over space (i.e. across the Earth's surface) and time (i.e. different times of the day or year).

Comment

The amount of solar radiation that can be collected for solar thermal and solar photovoltaic applications varies over time and space in three respects.

- Low latitude (equatorial) regions receive more sunlight relative to high latitude (polar) regions. The curvature of the Earth means that the sun's rays strike the Earth's surface more or less directly in the equatorial latitudes and more obliquely in polar areas. As a result, the same amount of sunlight covers a larger land area towards the poles (Taylor, 2004) (Figure 3.6).

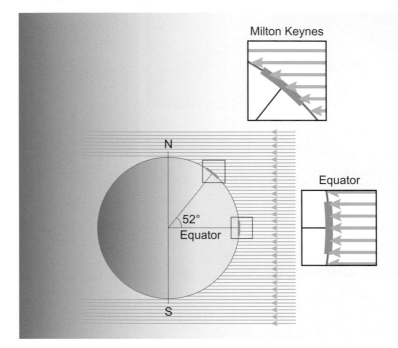

Figure 3.6   The density of sunlight striking a square metre at the equator at a given time of day is greater than that striking the same area at higher latitudes. The sunlight that strikes a square metre at the Open University campus in Milton Keynes is about 60 per cent of that at the equator (Source: based on Mackay, 2009, Figure 6.1, p. 38)

- The amount of solar radiation striking any given part of the Earth will vary with the Earth's orbit around the sun. The Earth's polar axis is tilted in relation to the Sun so that in June the northern hemisphere is tilted towards the Sun, while in December it is tilted away from the sun. (Figure 3.7). This means that the Sun's rays strike the ground more perpendicularly in June in the northern hemisphere giving more solar radiation, and more obliquely in December giving less radiation.
- The collection of solar energy will depend on the orientation and angle of tilt of the solar panels. Panels directly orientated towards the Sun's position at local midday (for example, on south-facing roofs in the northern hemisphere, and on north-facing roofs in the southern hemisphere) will collect more energy than panels that are angled

away from the Sun. Similarly, panels tilted away from the vertical so that they directly face the Sun will collect more energy than those that are tilted in other directions. The angle of tilt that optimises the collection of solar energy will also vary according to the time of year, being greater in summer (when the Sun is high in the sky) and lower in winter (when the Sun is low) (Figure 3.8).

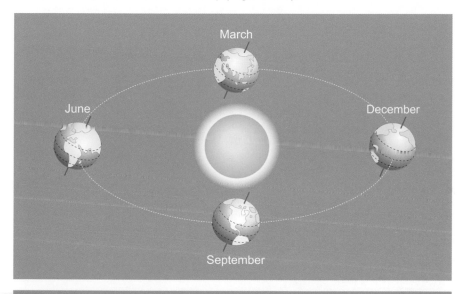

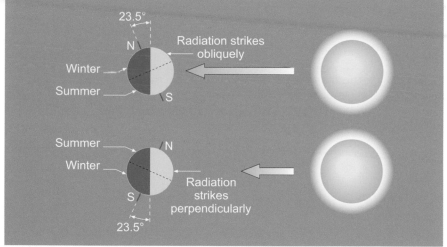

Figure 3.7   The Earth's rotation around the Sun creates seasons, with the northern hemisphere tilted towards the Sun in June, and the southern hemisphere tilted towards the Sun in December

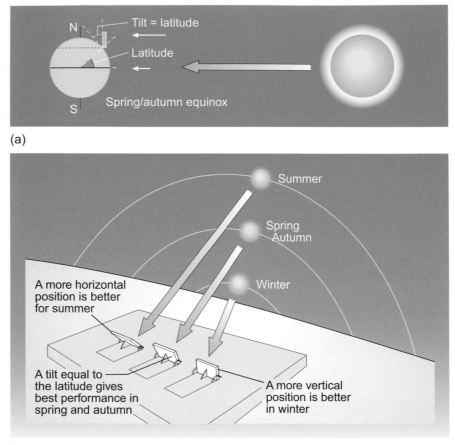

(a)

(b)

Figure 3.8   (a) To maximise the energy collected by solar panels at higher latitudes, the angle of tilt should be adjusted as the Earth orbits the Sun; (b) The intention is that the solar panels should be perpendicular to the Sun wherever possible

3.2   Wind energy

A wind is a movement of air around the planet. Winds are driven by changes of atmospheric pressure around the globe caused by the heating of the atmosphere by the Sun. As air becomes warmer it expands, becoming less dense and rising to higher altitudes. When cooled, for example at night, air contracts, becoming denser and falling in altitude. Air movements from areas of high pressure to areas of low pressure interact with the rotation of the Earth, which deflects wind flows.

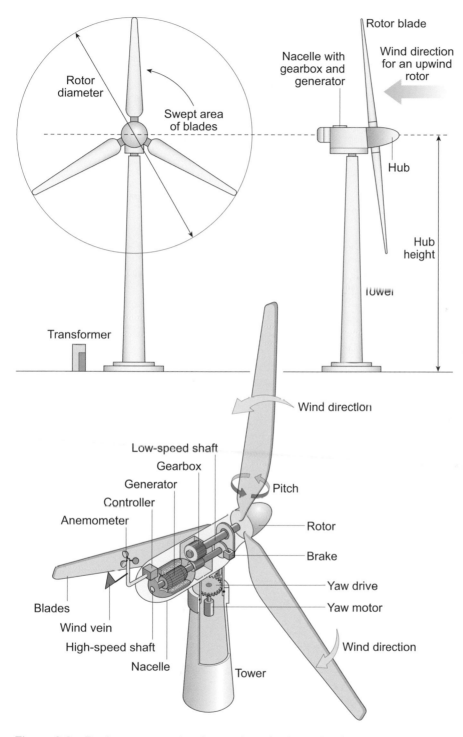

Figure 3.9   Basic components of a modern, horizontal-axis wind turbine with a gearbox (design by the National Renewable Energy Laboratory (NREL)) (Source: based on Wiser et al., 2011, p. 552, Figure 7.5)

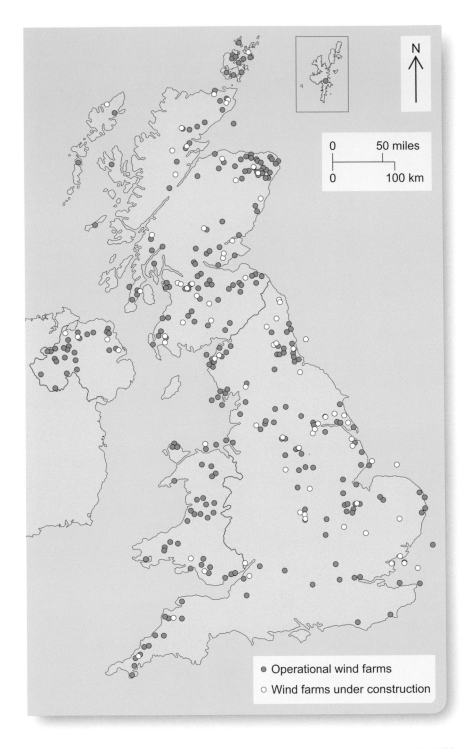

Figure 3.10   By 2010, 77 wind farm projects had been approved in the UK (Source: UK Wind Energy Database, 2012)

Wind has been used for energy for thousands of years. Modern wind turbines are very similar in principle to windmills of old in that they convert the energy of the wind into a rotational motion. While in the windmills rotation was used to grind grain or draw up water from wells, modern turbines use the rotation to generate electricity. Early modern wind turbines came in a variety of designs, including both horizontal and vertical axis turbines. Most contemporary wind turbines have a horizontal axis. Figure 3.9 shows the components of a modern wind turbine with a gearbox.

An increasing number of wind farms are being built in the UK (Figure 3.10). The towers of wind turbines have been getting higher since the first commercially manufactured devices were installed in the 1980s (Figure 3.11). Taller towers provide access to better quality wind resources because wind flows tend to be slower near ground level and increase in speed with altitude. Taller towers are also more cost effective. Towers are likely to increase in height in the future, although not indefinitely. The limits to tower height include engineering constraints, the costs and difficulties of transporting large blades and tower components by road, and the hazards of lifting them into place on site (Wiser et al., 2011).

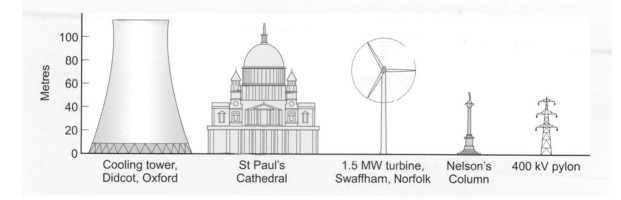

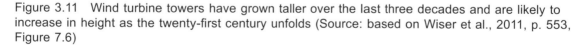

Figure 3.11   Wind turbine towers have grown taller over the last three decades and are likely to increase in height as the twenty-first century unfolds (Source: based on Wiser et al., 2011, p. 553, Figure 7.6)

Wind turbines take **kinetic energy** (in other words the energy of the movement of something, in this case air) and convert it, via a generator, into electricity. The energy taken out of the atmosphere by a wind turbine will reduce the wind speed behind the turbine. It can also introduce air turbulence that can affect bird life.

Kinetic energy
The energy of motion of a moving body.

3.3 Tidal energy

The oceans can provide energy from tides, from waves and from ocean currents. Here the focus is on one particular form of ocean energy, tidal energy.

The energy that can be harnessed for tidal power is derived from the gravitational forces of the Earth–Moon–Sun system. The height of tides will vary according to three different but interacting cycles:

- the rotation of the Earth on its own axis (once every 23 hours and 56 minutes approximately)

- the orbit of the Moon around the Earth (once every 27.3 days approximately)

- the orbit of the Earth around the Sun (once every 365.24 days approximately).

These movements are highly predictable over the very long term, hence the world's tidal flows are also predictable.

Two interacting forces explain the tides: gravity and centrifugal force. The gravitational force of the Moon is highest on the side of the Earth that is closest to the Moon. This force pulls the oceans in a bulge towards the Moon. On the opposite side of the Earth, the oceans are also being pulled towards the Moon, although to a lesser extent as gravitational force reduces with distance.

Centrifugal force arises because the Earth and the Moon rotate around each other, similar to a dumb-bell being twirled. Because the Earth is much larger than the Moon, the centre of rotation of the 'dumb-bell' is not between the Earth and the Moon but is just beneath the surface of the Earth (Figure 3.12). This rotation produces a centrifugal force on the Earth directed away from the Moon. This is why the Moon and the Earth stay more or less the same distance from each other – the gravitational force that pulls them towards each other is exactly countered by the centrifugal force pulling them apart. However, on the outer side of the Earth the centrifugal force pushing the oceans outwards exceeds the gravitational force pulling them towards the Moon, resulting in a net tide-producing force directed away from the Moon. On the moon-side, the gravitational force is stronger than the centrifugal force, so the net effect is to pull the seas towards the Moon. Thus, on both sides of the Earth the oceans bulge away from its surface, in line with the Moon–Earth axis (Figure 3.12). As the Moon moves relative to the Earth's surface, the bulges follow it in a westerly direction. So these two forces – gravitational force and centrifugal force – interact to produce high tides on the parts of the Earth facing directly towards and directly away from the Moon.

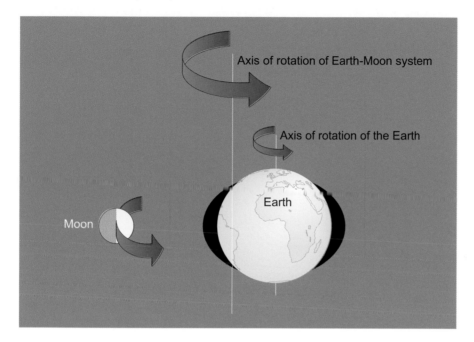

Figure 3.12 Relative rotation of the Earth and the Moon (not to scale)

There are a variety of ways that tidal energy can be harnessed. The two most common are the building of barrages across rivers and estuaries, and the use of submerged turbines to capture energy from tidal streams. Tidal barrages consist of a barrage built across a suitable estuary. As the tide rises and falls, water passes through the barrage. The turbines within the barrage convert the kinetic energy of the flowing water into rotational energy that is then used to drive an electricity generator, thus producing electricity.

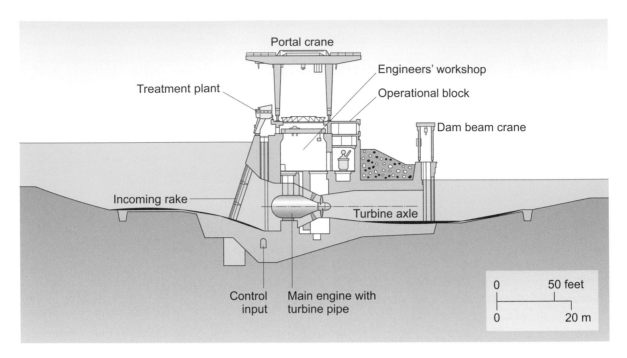

Figure 3.13 A cross-section diagram of a horizontal bulb turbine

One example of such a barrage is at La Rance, France. This was completed in 1967, and contains 24 turbines. The tidal range at La Rance is high, averaging 8 metres. The turbines are located within the barrage, each in a water passageway through which water flows upstream during the flood when the tide rises, and downstream during the ebb when the tide falls (Figure 3.13). The La Rance barrage has sluice gates that can be opened during high tide then closed, storing the water behind the barrage which is then released during the next ebb tide. The turbines will operate in both directions and can thus generate electricity during both ebb and flood tides. At La Rance the generator is embedded within the turbine. However, there are alternative turbine models, including the tubular turbine which has a shaft running from the turbine to a generator within the barrage (Figure 3.14).

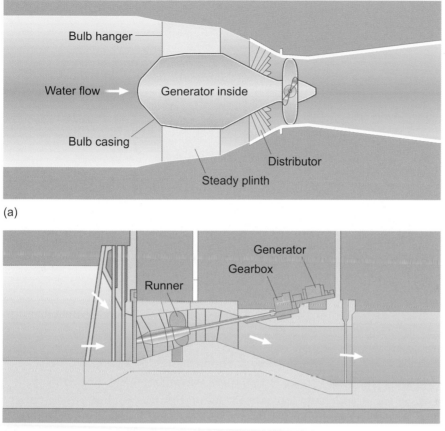

(a)

(b)

Figure 3.14   Cross-sections of: (a) The bulb turbine used at La Rance; (b) A tubular turbine

Tidal barrages can damage ecosystems. The barrage at La Rance has led to silting of the river in a similar way to the problems of silting and ecological damage caused by dams. Because of this, and because tidal barrages involve major capital-intensive structures with high upfront costs, most interest in tidal power now focuses on tidal stream technologies, which have lower environmental impact than barrages. Tidal stream systems consist of submerged turbines that capture the kinetic energy in tidal streams and can also be used to capture energy from non-tidal ocean currents. Some designs resemble wind turbines (Figure 3.15). Although such turbines may be costly to maintain and must be protected from the risk of saltwater corrosion, interest in the use of this technology has grown in recent years.

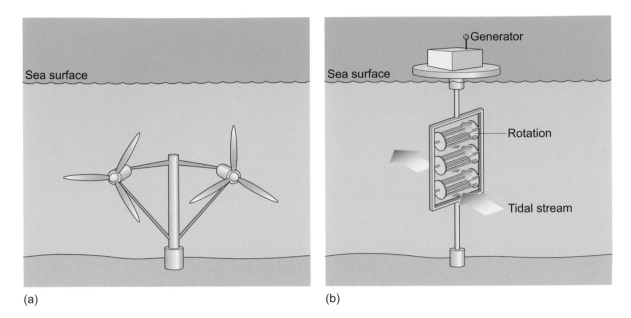

(a)   (b)

Figure 3.15   Tidal current energy converters: (a) Twin turbine horizontal axis device; (b) Cross flow device (Source: based on Lewis et al., 2011, p. 511, Figure 6.8)

Biomimicry
Technology that learns from natural processes and ecosystems.

An alternative tidal stream design, though one that has yet to be developed past field trials, is based on the principle of **biomimicry**, namely technology that learns from natural processes and ecosystems. The Australian company BioPower Systems has designed and tested a tidal current generator with a tail that resembles a fish (Figure 3.16). During tides the 'tail' will swing from side to side mimicking the swishing motion of a fish's tail. The company claims high energy conversion efficiency.

Activity 3.2   Climate change and low carbon energy technologies

Low carbon energy technologies are being designed and developed to reduce the risk of climate change. Can you think of any ways that climate change may affect the future capacity of these technologies to provide energy?

Comment

Under climate change, cloud composition and extent will vary with unpredictable consequences for solar energy, with areas experiencing a greater extent of cloud cover being less suitable for solar energy collection. Climate change could increase the severity and frequency of storms. Wind turbines have a maximum wind speed at which they can

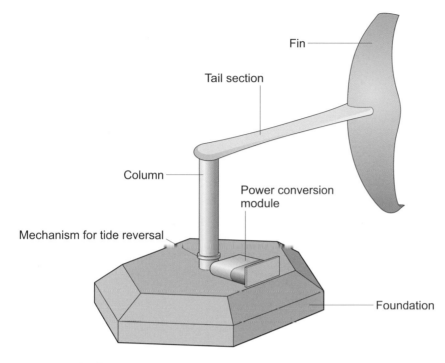

Figure 3.16   The Australian company BioPower Systems has developed a tidal power generator that resembles the tail of a fish (Source: based on BioPower Systems, 2011)

safely operate, and an increase in storm levels could lead to greater amounts of time during which turbines have to be shut down to avoid damage.

4   The problems of scaling up

If low carbon energy technologies are to replace fossil fuels as the main energy source they must be capable of being scaled up. Isolated, small-scale wind, solar or tidal energy projects will not reduce society's dependence on fossil fuels or the risk of climate change from future greenhouse gas emissions. For that to happen the technologies must be introduced on an accelerated timescale around the world. This section introduces you to four potential problems and risks involved in scaling up. These relate to the energy invested in manufacturing low carbon technologies relative to the energy these technologies return; the risk of intermittency of supply; problems associated with location; and how the money should be raised for investing in these technologies.

In the past, new inventions have sometimes led to global technological transformations in a very short time. The manufacture and use of motor vehicles spread rapidly around the world throughout the late nineteenth and early twentieth centuries. Within a decade of the first powered flight in 1903, aircraft were being manufactured in several countries around the world. Similarly, in the late twentieth century, home computer and internet technology spread swiftly around the globe in little more than a decade. It may be argued that low carbon energy technology may similarly spread, in particular if the technology attracts start-up funding from government and is seen as attractive to private investors. However, the widespread uptake of the technological innovations that led to cars, aircraft and computers was only made possible because oil was available and energy was cheap. For reasons that are now clear, the use of oil and other fossil fuels needs to be minimised when producing low carbon energy technologies.

4.1   Energy Return on Energy Invested (EROEI)

Substantial inputs of energy are necessary before a low carbon energy device becomes operational. The concept of Energy Return on Energy Invested (EROEI) is helpful here. To make environmental sense a device must return more energy (energy return) during its lifetime than is invested in its manufacture, transport, installation, maintenance and decommissioning (energy invested). The following formula is used for measuring EROEI:

$$\text{EROEI} = \frac{\text{Energy Return}}{\text{Energy Invested}}$$

The EROEI needs to be greater than 1 – indeed it should be significantly higher than that – for the technology to be feasible. The same is true in the natural world. Predators such as tigers, sharks and eagles must gather more energy from consuming their prey then they expend on hunting. If an individual predator were continually to expend more energy hunting than they received from prey caught they would eventually starve to death.

Activity 3.3   Energy Return on Energy Invested

150 megawatt hours (MWh) is invested to make a wind turbine operational and to decommission the turbine at the end of its life. Over its life the turbine generates 3000 MWh of electricity. What is the EROEI of the turbine?

Comment

3000 MWh divided by 150 MWh gives an EROEI of 20.

Note that any energy device that has an EROEI of less than 1 has not returned the energy invested. This makes no sense in environmental terms and, unless the carbon debt is zero, such a device will lead to an increase in the atmospheric concentration of greenhouse gases (Box 3.1).

There is no global standard for calculating EROEI and comparing the EROEIs of different energy technologies. Methodologies for calculating EROEI are contested, as there is no firm agreement on what should be included or how it should be measured. For example, should the energy invested in mining iron for the steel used to make tidal turbines be included, and should the energy used in manufacturing the concrete and steel for tidal barrages be included? Keeping track of all these many energy expenditures would be a complicated and time-consuming business.

Box 3.1   Carbon and energy technologies

To make the greatest contribution to reducing greenhouse gas emissions, energy technologies would ideally be *zero carbon*; that is, no carbon emissions would take place during the life cycle of a device, from manufacture, through operation and maintenance, to decommissioning. However, this is not easy to achieve. Some emissions may be inevitable. Any carbon emitted during manufacturing an energy device, say a wind turbine, and transporting it to its place of operation can be seen as a *carbon debt*.

The term *carbon debt* has various applications in environmental politics. It can mean the use – by a country, an organisation or an individual – of more than their 'fair share' of the world's carbon sequestration capacity (the absorption of carbon dioxide by vegetation, soils and oceans). Fair share is defined in per capita terms, with every person on the planet entitled to an equal share. Populations that use more than their fair share of the Earth's carbon sequestration capacity through high emissions can be seen as owing a carbon debt to those who use less than their fair share.

The meaning here of the term 'carbon debt' applies to technology. If a technology is to contribute to global carbon emissions reduction it must repay its carbon debt by generating significantly more energy from fossil fuels than was used in its manufacture, transport, installation, and so on. The higher the EROEI and the lower the carbon debt, the greater the contribution a low carbon technology can make to meeting energy demand while replacing more carbon-intensive forms of energy and therefore reducing overall carbon emissions.

Despite this some useful comparisons have been made. Figure 3.17 shows some estimates calculated by David Fridley of the Lawrence Berkeley National Laboratory in California. The EROEI of Middle East crude oil is high, approaching 30. The problem, however, is that this energy comes with huge carbon emissions. Of the low carbon energies, wind has the highest EROEI. Tidal energy is not shown because the EROEI of tidal energy varies greatly from case to case. However, we do know that the energy expended in building a tidal barrage will take several years to repay, and the EROEI will be measured over the several decades during which the scheme will be operational. Again, as

much as possible of the energy invested in bringing low carbon energy
devices on stream must come from non-carbon sources in order to
minimise the carbon debt.

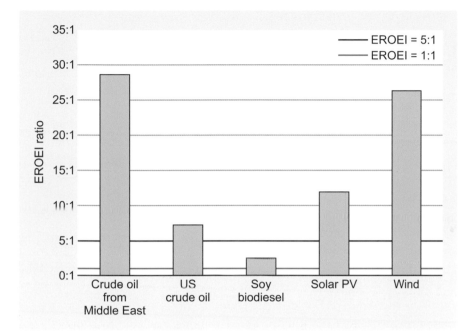

Figure 3.17   Estimated EREOI (sometimes referred to as 'net energy') for
some energy sources (Source: based on Fridley, 2010, Figure 18.3, p. 244)

One technology that needs significant investments in energy before it
can generate electricity is solar. Although silicon is one of the most
plentiful elements on Earth, the process of refining it to yield pure
silicon that is suitable for solar panel use is energy intensive and
expensive (Goodall, 2008). However, producers in China have begun
producing large volumes of silicon, leading to a fall in the price. Even
so, the global industrial capacity to produce photovoltaic panels will
need to increase significantly if solar energy is to increase from the 0.1
per cent of global energy it supplied in 2008 (Figure 3.2 above).

4.2   Intermittency

Intermittency is the problem of interruption. Some renewable energy
technologies cannot operate on a continuous basis. There are periods
when energy can be generated followed by periods of interruption.

Activity 3.4   Intermittency of supply

All three low carbon energy technologies that we have considered so far have an intermittency problem. For which of the three are the interruptions the easiest to predict?

Comment

Tidal flows are the easiest to predict, as the movements of the Earth and the Moon that give rise to tides are known. For any place on Earth it is always known when the Sun will rise and set, but in many places uncertainties over cloud cover mean that predicting when solar energy might be available can be difficult. Similarly, wind flows at any given location are often difficult to predict in advance.

The intermittency problem means that a back-up supply is needed; for example, when the wind doesn't blow or the sun isn't shining. The most straightforward technical solution to intermittency is to ensure that there is a sufficiently large back-up supply that can be used when the main supply is interrupted. For electricity, one solution is to make sure that there are sufficient fossil fuel-powered stations available to supply electricity when the wind isn't blowing or the sun isn't shining. There are three issues with this. First, we would still be using high carbon sources of energy for some of the time. Second, this implies a large overall increase in investment in the energy supply system but with lower usage of individual power stations. And third, we would need highly responsive power stations that could be called on to generate electricity at very little notice.

Another possible solution is storage, so that power can be generated when the low carbon sources are available and then stored for later use. At its simplest, this storage could be achieved in batteries, although batteries can only store small amounts of energy and are usually only useful in local and isolated situations. Other alternatives include pumped hydropower stations, such as those at Dinorwig and Blaenau Ffestiniog in Wales. In these stations, surplus electricity during periods of low demand is used to pump water uphill into a large reservoir; then, during periods of high demand, the water can be released to flow downhill through turbines that generate electricity. Similar storage technologies using surplus electricity to compress air, which is then released through turbines to generate electricity on demand, are currently being developed. These types of power station can respond to the need for more electricity within seconds. However, this would add to the cost of the overall system. Furthermore, the second law of thermodynamics tells us that when energy is being converted from one form to another, there is always some loss of energy and thus a lowering in the overall efficiency of the system.

Finally, one idea for tackling the problem of intermittency is the use of 'smart' grids. The idea here is for the electricity network to be developed to be far more capable of responding to the balance between supply and demand. If demand were increasing at a time when supply was limited, the grid would be used to send signals to some end-users and through these to reduce demand. For example, a householder might own a washing machine that was designed to respond to these signals. The householder would load the machine, set the programme and then decide what time they needed the wash to be complete. The grid system would then be left to determine when the machine actually ran – within the end time constraint set by the householder – so that peaks in demand were avoided. Another smart grid idea is to use electric vehicles as a storage mechanism within the system: the vehicles would be left connected to the grid when not in use and, when there was surplus supply, their batteries would be charged. When there was a supply deficit, the vehicle batteries could feed power back into the system. As in the previous example, the vehicle owner would of course be able to specify times when they would expect the vehicle to have a full battery.

The overall idea of a smart grid is really one of averages: if you have lots of supply points (ranging from large wind farms to electric cars parked outside people's homes) and lots of controllable demand, it should be possible to even out variations in supply and demand across the whole system.

4.3 Location

This problem occurs when the desired energy resources are at a considerable distance from the populations that would benefit from the resources. Areas with a high wind density may be several hundred miles from dense population centres. Indeed, they are often found offshore. Similarly, solar rich areas may have very low population densities; examples include Libya and Algeria.

Activity 3.5   Low carbon energy technologies and uncertainty

The problems of intermittency and location both relate to problems of uncertainty: we cannot always be sure that low carbon energy resources will be available in the place and at the time when they are needed. Can you think of any ways in which these uncertainties can be reduced?

Comment

One possible solution is an expansion of the transmission capacity of electricity grids; in other words, increasing the capacity of a grid to transmit energy over long distances, from source to consumer. But this would involve extra costs. For example, if Algeria were to become a major supplier of electricity to Europe, it would be necessary to transmit electricity from North Africa to a European distribution network, entailing additional financial and energy costs. Similarly, in the case of remote wind farms, extra grid capacity would be needed to transmit the electricity from wind farm to consumer.

Location can be a partial solution to the problem of intermittency, as well as a problem in itself. For example, although it cannot be said with any certainty that the wind will be blowing in any given part of the UK at a certain time, it is almost certain that it will be blowing somewhere within the whole of the country and its nearby areas of sea. Locating wind farms in many different locations can therefore help to ensure that there is some level of power generation at any given time. Using widely varied locations for low carbon generation can therefore be part of a 'smart grid' solution.

4.4   Investment

One dimension of risk is the risk borne by financial investors. New technologies create opportunities for new businesses, while those businesses with a vested interest in old infrastructures may offer resistance to infrastructural change.

New technologies always bring with them a degree of risk to those who invest in their research, development and manufacture. Investors must balance the potentially high profits if demand for a technology or product is high against the risk of losing their investment if the technology proves unprofitable. The private sector is unlikely to invest significant sums of money into low carbon energy technology unless it considers the risks of losing its investment to be low. This requires political stability and a secure economic climate for investors. Government can play a role in mitigating investor risk. It can spread the risks for the private sector; for example, by underwriting any debts incurred from research and development and thus stimulating investment.

Government can also provide a policy environment that signals support for low carbon energy and enhances the probability that investors will secure returns on their investment over the time frame for which the investment is made. Examples include tax breaks for the research and development of low carbon technologies (thus lowering the costs of manufacture), grants to householders who install solar panels, and long-term public sector contracts to manufacturers. One of the most important elements of government policy in this context is uncertainty. Governments may change. A business operating in a sector that is heavily reliant on government support is exposed to policy risk: if the subsidies or tax breaks supporting the market are removed, the business may well collapse. For this reason, the business response to government support may not be as large or enthusiastic as could perhaps be expected.

However, the involvement of the public sector brings with it other risks. Large sums of taxpayers' money may be spent on technologies that prove to be commercially unsuccessful, and this in turn brings environmental risks: if the transfer to low carbon energy should prove sluggish then economies may remain reliant on fossil fuels for a longer period, with the increased risk to climatic instability that this would entail.

Another risk is that a strong renewable technology sector could *increase* the demand for fossil fuels by some actors. The more renewable energy that is generated, the lower will be the global demand for fossil fuels, and hence the lower the price. This could lead to an increase in the use of fossil fuels in other countries where renewable energy resources are limited (Arvizu et al., 2011b).

5   Summary

This chapter has considered the development of low carbon energy technologies as possible alternatives to fossil fuel energy technologies. It has been argued that, while such technologies have the potential to provide some of our energy needs, there are some problems with scaling up these technologies so as to provide secure and predictable energy supplies. Assuming that these problems cannot be overcome, there would appear to be two alternatives. The first is that human societies should prepare for a future in which collectively we use less energy. The second is that we accept that we can only achieve a partial transition to a low carbon economy and that for the foreseeable future some fossil fuel consumption is inevitable. The first alternative poses economic risks, while the second poses continued risks to the environment.

An appreciation of risk helps us to understand why environmental issues are so difficult to resolve. As you saw in Book 1, Chapter 2, risk is not simply a matter of calculating probabilities. It is also a matter of perception, with different actors viewing different types of risk differently. Private investors, local communities, environmental campaigners and scientists all view risk in different ways. Risk may also vary over time as environmental conditions change. Investing in an offshore wind farm may be low risk today, but could be high risk in another 30 years if the frequency of severe storms increases owing to climate change. And as you saw earlier in the module, different actors may discount risk differently over time.

For a low carbon technology to be low risk in environmental terms, the energy returned must exceed the energy invested in bringing the technology on stream, with as much additional energy as possible being generated. But there are investor risks at stake too: to make commercial sense, investors in low carbon technologies must be persuaded that they will make a profit that is commensurate with the risk of their investment.

The problem here is that the risks of climate change and the risks that arise from developing and using low carbon energy technology are differentiated over different actors across time and space: while all people will suffer in the long term, some actors will suffer more than others in the short term, and future generations will suffer more than the present generation. In an ideal world, there would be a coherent global political process that weighed up the various risks associated with mitigating climate change, and which selected the least risky option. The choice any rational political process should make would, it would appear, seem obvious: there should be massive and sustained investment in low carbon technologies accompanied by the rapid phasing out of fossil fuels.

The fundamental problem, however, is that different risks are assessed in different institutions. There is no institution – be it corporate boardrooms, national legislatures or international organisations – that assesses all the risks at stake in energy and climate policy. In this respect the problem of climate change is an institutional one, with different institutions making different risk assessments in isolation from each other. There is no coherent political decision-making process that can make judgements on all the different dimensions of the issue and enforce decisions in the interests of those actors who will be most affected but who have no voice in climate and energy policy – future generations.

References

Arvizu, D., Balaya, P., Cabeza, L., Hollands, T., Jäger-Waldau, A., Kondo, M., Konseibo, C., Meleshko, V., Stein, W., Tamaura, Y., Xu, H. and Zilles, R. (2011a) 'Direct solar energy', in Edenhofer, O., Pichs-Madruga, R., Sokona, Y., Seyboth, K., Matschoss, P., Kadner, S., Zwickel, T., Eickemeier, P., Hansen, G., Schlömer, S. and von Stechow, C. (eds) *IPCC Special Report on Renewable Energy Sources and Climate Change Mitigation*, Cambridge and New York, Cambridge University Press [online], http://srren.ipcc-wg3.de/report (Accessed 15 October 2012).

Arvizu, D., Bruckner, T., Chum, H., Edenhofer, O., Estefen, S., Faaij, A., Fischedick, M., Hansen, G, Hiriart, G., Hohmeyer, O., Hollands, K. G. T., Huckerby, J., Kadner, S., Killingtveit, Å., Kumar, A., Lewis, A., Lucon, O., Matschoss, P., Maurice, L., Mirza, M., Mitchell, C., Moomaw, W., Moreira, J., Nilsson, L. J., Nyboer, J., Pichs-Madruga, R., Sathaye, J., Sawin, J., Schaeffer, R., Schei, T., Schlömer, S., Seyboth, K., Sims, R., Sinden, G., Sokona, Y., von Stechow, C., Steckel, J., Verbruggen, A., Wiser, R., Yamba, F. and Zwickel, T. (2011b) 'Technical summary', in Edenhofer, O., Pichs-Madruga, R., Sokona, Y., Seyboth, K., Matschoss, P., Kadner, S., Zwickel, T., Eickemeier, P., Hansen, G., Schlömer, S. and von Stechow, C. (eds) *IPCC Special Report on Renewable Energy Sources and Climate Change Mitigation*, Cambridge and New York, Cambridge University Press [online], http://srren.ipcc-wg3.de/report/IPCC_SRREN_TS. pdf (Accessed 15 October 2012).

BioPower Systems (2011) 'bioSTREAM' [online], http://biopowersystems. com/biostream.html (Accessed 5 October 2012).

Fridley, D. (2010) 'Nine challenges of alternative energy', in Heinberg, R. and Lerch, D. (eds) *The Post Carbon Reader: Managing the 21st Century's Sustainability Crises*, Healdsburg, CA, Watershed Media.

Geels, F. (2011) 'The role of cities in technological transitions: analytical clarifications and historical examples', in Bulkeley, H., Castán Broto, V., Hodson, M. and Marvin, S. (eds) *Cities and Low Carbon Transitions*, Abingdon, Routledge.

Goodall, C. (2008) *Ten Technologies to Fix Energy and Climate*, London, Green Profile.

IPCC (2011) 'Summary for policymakers', in Edenhofer, O., Pichs-Madruga, R., Sokona, Y., Seyboth, K., Matschoss, P., Kadner, S., Zwickel, T., Eickemeier, P., Hansen, G., Schlömer, S. and von Stechow, C. (eds) *IPCC Special Report on Renewable Energy Sources and Climate Change Mitigation*, Cambridge and New York, Cambridge University Press [online], http://srren.ipcc-wg3.de/report (Accessed 15 October 2012).

Lewis, A., Estefen, S., Huckerby, J., Musial, W., Pontes, T. and Torres-Martinez, J. (2011) 'Ocean energy', in Edenhofer, O., Pichs-Madruga, R., Sokona, Y., Seyboth, K., Matschoss, P., Kadner, S., Zwickel, T., Eickemeier, P., Hansen, G., Schlömer, S. and von Stechow, C. (eds) *IPCC Special Report on Renewable Energy*

Sources and Climate Change Mitigation, Cambridge and New York, Cambridge University Press [online], http://srren.ipcc-wg3.de/report (Accessed 15 October 2012).

MacKay, D. J. C. (2009) *Sustainable Energy: Without the Hot Air*, Cambridge, UIT.

Taylor, D. (2004) 'Wind energy', in Boyle, G. (ed.) *Renewable Energy: Power for a Sustainable Future*, Oxford, Oxford University Press/Milton Keynes, The Open University.

UK Wind Energy Database (UKWED) (2012) *Renewable UK* [online], available at http://www.renewableuk.com/en/renewable-energy/wind-energy/uk-wind-energy-database/index.cfm/maplarge/1 (Accessed 15 October 2012).

Wiser, R., Yang, Z., Hand, M., Hohmeyer, O., Infield, D., Jensen, P. H., Nikolaev, V., O'Malley, M., Sinden, G. and Zervos, A. (2011) 'Wind energy', in Edenhofer, O., Pichs-Madruga, R., Sokona, Y., Seyboth, K., Matschoss, P., Kadner, S., Zwickel, T., Eickemeier, P., Hansen, G., Schlömer, S. and von Stechow, C. (eds) *IPCC Special Report on Renewable Energy Sources and Climate Change Mitigation*, Cambridge and New York, Cambridge University Press [online], http://srren.ipcc-wg3.de/report (Accessed 15 October 2012).

Chapter 4   Geoengineering

David Humphreys

Contents

1   Introduction

In this block we are examining two problems associated with managing carbon. The first is how increasing atmospheric concentrations of carbon dioxide are leading to the challenge of anthropogenic climate change. The second problem is the reduced presence of carbon-rich fossil fuels in the Earth's crust and the question this raises over future energy security. The problem of climate change is proving difficult to resolve because the biogeochemical processes of the carbon cycle work too slowly to remove carbon dioxide from the atmosphere by natural means (Chapter 1). Yet despite the problem of climate change, humans continue to extract and burn fossil fuels such as oil. Oil is not only a chemical compound; it is also a matter of political and economic competition and conflict (Chapter 2). Chapter 3 explored how attempts to resolve the problem of energy security also involve trade offs technical and social – because of the different values and risks associated with low carbon technologies.

In this chapter we return to the first of these two issues: climate change. We do so by exploring some proposed technical responses to the problem of increasing atmospheric concentrations of carbon dioxide. These responses, still largely speculative, are collectively called geoengineering.

The origins of geoengineering as an idea stem from a growing belief among climate scientists and policy makers that there is a serious risk of conventional greenhouse gas mitigation measures (such as the low carbon energy technologies discussed in the previous chapter) failing to avert dangerous climate change. Admittedly, there have been some successes: increased energy efficiency, improved building insulation and the growth of the renewable energy sector have led to some emissions reductions. But with greenhouse gas emissions in many countries continuing to rise, many scientists and policy makers are concluding that conventional mitigation measures will not work fast enough to avert catastrophic climate change, and that it is now time to think of a 'Plan B' (Figure 4.1).

Extreme and risky action the only way to tackle global warming, say scientists

The Guardian, 1 September 2008

Climate scientists: it's time for 'Plan B'

The Independent, 2 January 2009

Plan B: scientists get radical in bid to halt global warming 'catastrophe'

The Sunday Times, 15 March 2009

Figure 4.1   Newspaper headlines from the British media on geoengineering

Geoengineering
A set of proposed techniques for manipulating the environmental processes that affect the Earth's climate.

Geoengineering may be defined as a set of techniques for the intentional large-scale manipulation of environmental process that affect the Earth's climate in an attempt to counter the effects of global warming. Geoengineering of the climate has not yet taken place: it remains an idea rather than an existing strategy or set of practices. But the possibility of geoengineering is being taken increasingly seriously. This chapter introduces you to the various techniques that have been proposed to date for controlling the climate. You will examine the scientific principles behind these techniques and consider some of the risks and uncertainties for the climate and for people that the implementation of geoengineering techniques might entail.

2   Introducing geoengineering

Anthropogenic climate change is taking place because human activities have led to an increase in the atmospheric concentration of greenhouse gases, in particular carbon dioxide (Chapter 1). Remember that it is the energy balance between incoming and outgoing radiation that determines changes in global temperature. Sunlight warms the Earth's surface, which then emits longer-wave infrared radiation. Rather than being emitted into space, much of this long-wave energy is absorbed by greenhouse gases, leading to a warming effect.

All things being equal, the planet will thus warm when one or both of the following changes occur, leading to more energy entering the atmosphere than going out:

- The amount of incoming short-wave solar radiation that is absorbed by the Earth's surface and is therefore re-radiated back from the Earth as long-wave radiation increases.

- The atmospheric concentration of greenhouse gases increases.

Two main types of geoengineering techniques have been proposed to date, each of which seeks to control one of these two variables. **Solar radiation management (SRM)** techniques aim to increase the planetary albedo (reflectivity) and thus reduce the amount of outgoing long-wave radiation that can be trapped by greenhouse gases. **Carbon dioxide removal (CDR)** techniques aim to remove carbon dioxide from the atmosphere. We consider these two techniques in the rest of this section.

2.1   Solar radiation management

Solar radiation management (SRM) techniques aim to increase the planetary albedo. The long-term average planetary albedo of the Earth is approximately 0.31. If the atmospheric concentration of carbon dioxide at the time of the Industrial Revolution were to double (the so-called '$2 \times CO_2$ world'), the resultant warming could in theory be offset by shielding or reflecting approximately 1.8 per cent of incoming solar radiation (Govindasamy and Caldeira, 2000). This would require an increase in the planetary albedo from approximately 0.31 to 0.32 (Royal Society, 2009).

Solar radiation management (SRM) Techniques that aim to increase the planetary albedo.

Carbon dioxide removal (CDR) Techniques that aim to remove carbon dioxide from the atmosphere.

SRM techniques may operate in three spaces:

- outer space
- the Earth's atmosphere
- the Earth's surface.

We now examine these techniques in turn.

First, highly reflective material could be placed in outer space in a position that would reflect solar radiation from the Earth. One proposal is to insert a large reflective shield in an orbit, where the forces of gravity between Sun and Earth cancel each other out. Such an orbit is called a Lagrange orbit after the astronomer and mathematician Joseph-Louis Lagrange (1736–1813). There are five Lagrange points. A solar shield would be placed at the L1 point where it would orbit the Sun in a direct line between Sun and Earth (Figure 4.2).

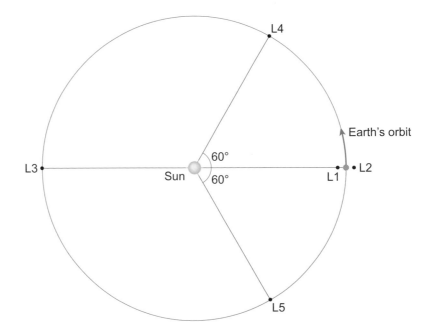

Figure 4.2   The astronomer and mathematician Joseph-Louis Lagrange identified five points – L1 to L5 – at which an object can orbit at a fixed distance from two objects of larger mass. A solar space shield would be placed at the L1 point (diagram not to scale) (Source: NASA, n.d.)

An alternative is to place reflective shields in near-Earth orbits. However, a shield in a Lagrange orbit would be more effective for two reasons: it would be closer to the Sun and could thus reflect more solar radiation than a shield in near-Earth orbits; and it would be in permanent sunlight, unlike near-orbit shields which would be in darkness for part of their orbit. However, it would be cheaper and easier to place a reflective shield or shields in near-Earth orbit. At the time of writing, humans have yet to attempt placing an object in a Lagrange orbit (Figure 4.3).

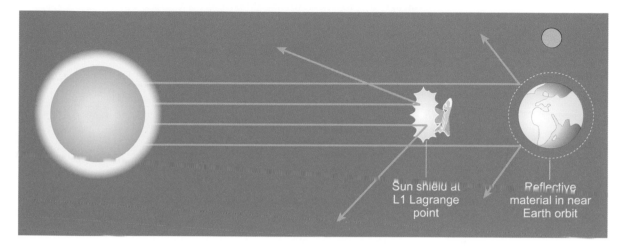

Figure 4.3   Diagram of the Sun, Earth and Moon showing a space mirror at the L1 Lagrange point and reflective material in a near-Earth orbit, some of it in the Earth's shadow (not to scale)

The second space in which SRM could operate is the atmosphere. Two main atmospheric SRM techniques have been proposed. First, sulphate particles – a type of aerosol – could be injected into the stratosphere (Figure 4.4), thus producing a cooling effect similar to that caused by volcanic eruptions. A number of methods have been proposed for injecting sulphates into the stratosphere, including firing artillery shells and releasing sulphates from jet aircraft or giant balloons (Figure 4.5) (Robock et al., 2009).

Figure 4.4   Layers of the atmosphere including the stratosphere

(a)   (b)

Figure 4.5   (a) Aircraft vapour trails (or contrails) have a cooling effect, reflecting incoming solar radiation. However the effects usually last only a few hours; (b) Spraying sulphates or other aerosols from aircraft into the stratosphere would lead to a cooling effect lasting several days. Note that in this hypothetical image, the condensation trails do not come from the engines but from wing tanks purpose-built to hold sulphates or other aerosols. An aircraft with sulphate wing tanks has yet to be built

The second proposed atmospheric SRM technique aims to change the world's cloud cover. White clouds have a high albedo, reflecting some solar radiation that strikes them. Spraying droplets of seawater into low-level maritime clouds from fleets of remote-controlled boats would make clouds whiter, increasing their albedo and thus reflecting more short-wave solar radiation before it strikes the Earth's surface (Latham et al., 2008; Salter et al., 2008) (Figure 4.6).

Figure 4.6   An artist's image of a remote-controlled boat spraying saltwater into the air to whiten existing clouds

Activity 4.1   Clouds and the greenhouse effect

As well as having a cooling effect by reflecting sunlight, clouds also have a warming effect. From your reading in Chapter 1 of this book, can you explain why this is so?

Comment

Clouds are composed of water vapour, which is an important greenhouse gas. Note that the overall effect (warming or cooling) of clouds is complex and difficult to predict with certainty. Generally, however, higher clouds tend to have a net warming effect, trapping more long-wave radiation than low-level clouds, which tend to have a net cooling effect.

The third space in which SRM techniques would operate is on the surface of the Earth. Proposed techniques include painting the roofs of buildings white and installing desert reflectors to increase the Earth's surface albedo (Figure 4.7). These techniques would be most effective in solar-rich countries. It has also been suggested that planetary albedo could be increased through the genetic modification of plants to breed lighter species of vegetation.

Figure 4.7   All white now: white roofs will reflect more incoming short-wave solar radiation into space. The buildings will be cooler in summer, which could reduce the energy used on air conditioning

2.2   Carbon dioxide removal

In contrast to SRM, carbon dioxide removal (CDR) techniques seek to reduce the atmospheric concentration of the main greenhouse gas, carbon dioxide. Four main CDR techniques have been proposed:

- terrestrial biological sequestration
- ocean fertilisation

- enhanced mineral sequestration
- carbon capture devices.

These techniques, which we examine below, aim to interfere in the carbon cycle, taking carbon dioxide out of the atmosphere to compensate for anthropogenic emissions.

The main proposed CDR technique is terrestrial biological sequestration, in particular increasing the global extent of forest cover to enhance the Earth's carbon sink capacity. In many respects this is a conventional mitigation activity, although it is often included in geoengineering studies. In this respect, the boundary between mitigation and geoengineering is somewhat fuzzy. The pressure on land for urban settlements and organised agriculture means that the limited land space available for reforestation is further decreasing.

Another proposal is sequestering carbon through the production and burying of biochar: carbon-rich charcoal produced from tree, biomass and crop waste through pyrolysis (Lehmann et al., 2006). As you saw in Book 1, Chapter 3, pyrolysis is the heating of material in an oxygen-deprived environment. Pyrolysis is very different from burning in an oxygenated environment such as the Earth's atmosphere. You will recall that when trees and biomass are burned in the atmosphere, carbon dioxide is emitted. No carbon dioxide is emitted through pyrolysis. (You may find it helpful here to refer back to the treatment of biochar and pyrolysis in Book 1, Chapter 3, Section 5.)

Pyrolysis produces charcoal, an inert form of carbon that cannot be broken down by bacteria and which will remain inert for a millennial timescale if mixed with soil or buried underground. One proposal is to pay farmers to grow trees with a fast growth rate, such as willow, which are then felled when they reach maturity, turned into biochar and buried underground. James Lovelock, who developed the Gaia hypothesis (see Book 1, Chapter 8, Section 5), has argued that we can let plant photosynthesis take carbon dioxide out of the atmosphere and then turn plant matter into biochar if every farmer has a charcoal maker (Lovelock, 2009; see also Black, 2010). An added benefit of biochar is that it absorbs water and nutrients and thus improves the fertility of sandy soils.

The second CDR technique, ocean fertilisation, is the addition of nutrients such as iron or nitrogen fertiliser to the oceans in order to seed oceanic uptake of carbon dioxide through the enhanced growth of photosynthetic marine species, such as phytoplankton and algae

(Lampitt et al., 2008). Dead plankton and algae often sink, carrying sequestered carbon to the seabed. However, there are doubts about the long-term effectiveness of ocean fertilisation. Experiments have been carried out in the Southern Ocean, including from the German research ship *Polarstern* (Figure 4.8). Some of these experiments reveal that while fertilisation can lead to increased uptake of carbon dioxide, the uptake is similar to that of natural blooms, thus making very little difference to global carbon budgets (Buesseler et al., 2004). Two scientists from the University of East Anglia have suggested that ocean fertilisation is only likely to be effective in stabilising the climate if sustained over a millennial timescale (Lenton and Vaughan, 2009).

Figure 4.8   In 2009 the German research ship *Polarstern* conducted iron fertilisation experiments in the Southern Ocean

A third CDR proposal, enhanced mineral sequestration, is human activity to promote the sequestration of carbon in minerals and rocks at a rate greater than that which occurs naturally. As you saw in Chapter 1 of this book, the sequestration of carbon in minerals takes place naturally over extremely long periods of geological time in the rock cycle. For this to take place, carbon dioxide first needs to be dissolved in water.

Activity 4.2 Carbon dioxide and the formation of carbonate minerals

Can you recall from Chapter 1 the process by which carbon dioxide from the atmosphere is locked up in carbonate sediments in the oceans?

Comment

From Sections 5.2 and 5.3 of Chapter 1 you will recall that carbon dioxide in the atmosphere can dissolve in the ocean, which in turn can be used by marine plants for photosynthesis. These plants can be eaten by marine animals. When marine plants and animals die they fall to the seabed (sometimes being cycled by being eaten by other animals on the way). The calcium carbonate skeletons or shells of the organisms accumulate on the ocean floor, eventually forming carbon-based rocks when buried.

While this process takes millennia to occur naturally, experiments in Iceland have shown that carbon dioxide sequestration into rocks (called mineral sequestration) can be speeded up by injecting carbon dioxide under pressure into basalt aquifers (Kunzig and Broecker, 2008; Matter et al., 2009; Oelkers et al., 2008). When injected into a basalt aquifer the carbon dioxide dissolves in water and then reacts with rock minerals to become carbonates. Under such conditions, mineral sequestration takes place considerably faster than under natural conditions. When no underground water is present, water needs to be injected alongside the carbon dioxide (Schuiling, 2006). The advantage of mineral sequestration is that, once the carbon dioxide has been converted into a stable solid state, it cannot escape from underground as gaseous carbon dioxide and is, in effect, sequestered on a long timescale (Goldberg et al., 2001) (Figure 4.9). However, there are many technological and economic challenges to be overcome, and this technique is only likely to be able to sequester a minute fraction of the anthropogenically produced carbon dioxide (Oelkers et al., 2008).

Finally, a fourth proposed CDR technique, suggested by Klaus Lackner, is 'artificial trees': carbon capture devices in towers in windswept areas that would physically remove carbon dioxide from the atmosphere (Figures 4.10 and 4.11). Air would flow into the tower and through a sorbent (a material that can trap liquids or gases). The sorbent should be CO_2-selective, capturing carbon dioxide but not other gases. A good sorbent is environmentally benign and can withstand repeated recycling (Lackner et al., 1999). The best sorbent identified so far for removing atmospheric carbon dioxide is a polypropylene sheet in which particles of resin are embedded. Exposing the resin to water releases the carbon dioxide, creating a stream of the gas that can be compressed to pipeline pressures and pumped to a secure location (Lackner, 2009). Lackner's intention is to design a device that can be mass-produced and fit into a standard shipping container.

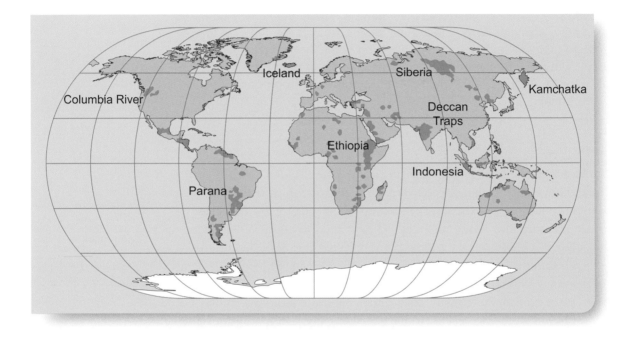

Figure 4.9   Locations of continental basalts that could serve as mineral carbonation sites (Source: Oelkers et al., 2008, p. 335, Figure 2)

Unlike real trees, artificial trees would not break down the carbon dioxide by photosynthesis, storing the carbon and releasing oxygen. The carbon dioxide would need to be securely stored; for example, by pumping it underground, perhaps into old oil wells or coalmines secured by an impermeable cap rock. Another alternative is to pump the carbon dioxide into underground chambers in basalt formations where the gas will react in the presence of water to form carbonates. However, at present no anthropogenic CDR technique is as effective as photosynthesis at removing carbon dioxide from the atmosphere. Literally millions of artificial trees would be needed to remove the anthropogenically produced carbon dioxide produced each year.

Figure 4.10 Professor Klaus Lackner of Columbia University, New York has dedicated much of his career to developing innovative solutions to climate change

Figure 4.11 Highway to the future? An artist's image of a motorway lined with wind turbines and artificial trees to extract carbon dioxide from the atmosphere. Is this a realistic vision? And how will the vehicles using these roads be powered? (Source: BBC, 2009)

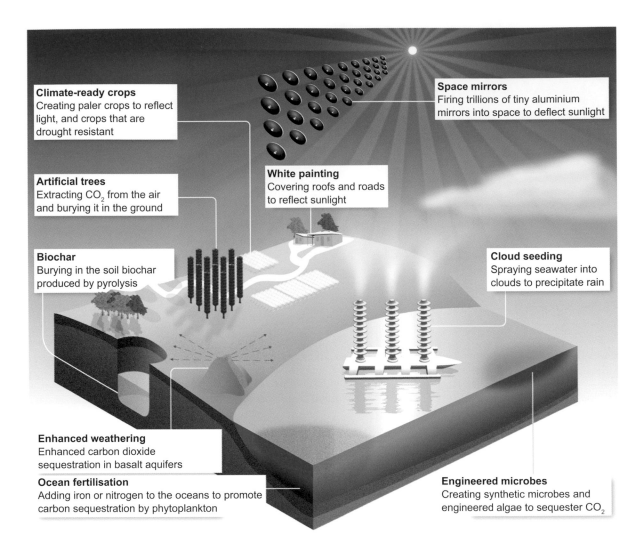

Climate-ready crops
Creating paler crops to reflect light, and crops that are drought resistant

Space mirrors
Firing trillions of tiny aluminium mirrors into space to deflect sunlight

Artificial trees
Extracting CO_2 from the air and burying it in the ground

White painting
Covering roofs and roads to reflect sunlight

Biochar
Burying in the soil biochar produced by pyrolysis

Cloud seeding
Spraying seawater into clouds to precipitate rain

Enhanced weathering
Enhanced carbon dioxide sequestration in basalt aquifers

Ocean fertilisation
Adding iron or nitrogen to the oceans to promote carbon sequestration by phytoplankton

Engineered microbes
Creating synthetic microbes and engineered algae to sequester CO_2

Figure 4.12   How geoengineering plans to combat climate change (Source: *The Guardian*)

A geoengineered world would be very different from the world we live in now. There would be some significant differences to the sights we see on land, at sea and in the sky (Figure 4.12). And geoengineering would bring with it significant risks and uncertainties. We now explore some of these.

3   Risk, uncertainty and the precautionary principle

This section gives you a flavour of some of the complex and demanding questions with which scientists and policy makers must grapple when making judgements on the various risks and uncertainties of environmental problems. While the area of discussion is geoengineering, the discussion is typical of the sorts of questions that inform other environmental issues too.

To approach this discussion, let's begin with one of the most cited principles in international environmental law, to which you were introduced in Book 1, Chapter 2, Section 4: the precautionary principle. This principle, which appears in the 1992 Rio Declaration on Environment and Development, holds that lack of full scientific certainty should not be used as a reason to postpone measures to protect the environment (UNEP, 1992).

Activity 4.3   The precautionary principle and geoengineering

In your view, does the precautionary principle permit geoengineering? When you have thought about this question for a few moments, read on.

Comment

A precaution is a course of action taken to prevent an undesirable or dangerous event. The answer to this question depends on what it is that we wish to prevent. One view is that intervening to control the global climate may be seen as a risk management activity intended to prevent the greater harm of anthropogenic climate change. A second view is that geoengineering itself is fraught with uncertainties and should be prevented as it could lead to significant environmental risks. The first view might suggest that, although geoengineering involves uncertainties, it should be permitted to safeguard the planet from a greater hazard, namely runaway climate change. The second view is that geoengineering is a risky strategy which should not be undertaken if other, less risky, options are available, such as emissions reduction and investment in low carbon energy.

In 2007, the Intergovernmental Panel on Climate Change (IPCC) concluded that geoengineering is 'largely speculative and unproven, and with the risk of unknown side-effects' (IPCC, 2007, p. 15). This raises the question of what side effects are acceptable when implementing geoengineering. For instance, should stratospheric aerosol injection be permitted if the fallout of sulphates were to cause acid rain damage to local environments? (See Box 4.2 on acid rain, in Section 4 below.) These questions bring to the fore questions of environmental values. Which environments matter the most? Should some damage to local environments be sacrificed for the 'greater good' of avoiding catastrophic climate change?

This debate illustrates a more general problem when dealing with major environmental problems. The risks of the proposed solutions could in theory be greater than the hazards they are designed to remedy. A rational risk management strategy would evaluate the available knowledge on the different policy options and select the option that has the greatest probability of securing the desired outcome with the least risk of unacceptable adverse consequences. A problem here, however, is that many geoengineering ideas exist as theoretical propositions that have yet to leave the design board; hence a well-developed knowledge base on which to calculate risk does not exist.

So, should field trials be permitted: for example, experiments to evaluate the effects of ocean fertilisation in seeding phytoplankton growth? According to one interpretation of the precautionary principle, there should be a moratorium on all ocean fertilisation activities pending clear scientific knowledge that fertilisation will not cause damage to the wider marine environment. On this view, field trials would not be permitted. A second view is that it is impossible to assess whether a moratorium is scientifically justified until experimental trials have taken place. This was the justification for the experiments in the Southern Ocean from the *Polarstern*. Taking this view, some small-scale and localised risks are acceptable in order to gain scientific knowledge that will permit a more informed assessment of the risks.

This then raises definitional questions, such as what risks are 'acceptable', and how much knowledge is needed to make an 'informed' decision? Even the best field trials can only result in the development of a limited knowledge base. Scientific research often reveals new areas of uncertainty where new research is needed. For example, while the *Polarstern* trials yielded new knowledge on ocean fertilisation at a particular set of locations in the Southern Ocean, this knowledge provided no clear indication of how effective ocean fertilisation would be in different marine environments, such as nearer the equator in the Indian Ocean or the Pacific Ocean.

The discussion so far raises an important question about the relationship between risks and uncertainties: what risks from field trials can be tolerated today to eliminate scientific uncertainties that enable better decision making tomorrow? While this question has been discussed here in the context of geoengineering, it is relevant to other environmental issues. Different scientists may make different judgements in response. This suggests that no blanket application of the precautionary principle to geoengineering is possible. Instead, arguably the precautionary principle should be applied not so much to geoengineering as an overall strategy, but separately to different geoengineering techniques, each of which would involve different risks and uncertainties over time and space.

A reliance solely on solar radiation management would mean that atmospheric concentrations of carbon dioxide would remain dangerously high. Solar radiation management would need to be continued indefinitely and, should there be an interruption to SRM for any reason, global temperatures would start to rise again. Furthermore, solar radiation management would do nothing to counter the growing risk of ocean acidification caused by anthropogenic emissions of carbon dioxide. A sole reliance on SRM would thus deal with the symptoms of climate change, but not the problem of high atmospheric concentrations of carbon dioxide. A high carbon dioxide/SRM world would behave very differently from, and more unpredictably than, a low carbon dioxide/non-SRM world. In short, SRM is the riskier strategy. The Royal Society, the UK's oldest scientific academy, argues that CDR should be the favoured option, although it should accompany efforts to mitigate greenhouse gas emissions rather than substitute for them (Royal Society, 2009).

While some techniques are more desirable than others, different techniques have different degrees of affordability and effectiveness. SRM may entail more risks, but at present it is more viable than large-scale CDR. Carbon dioxide removal techniques such as artificial trees and mineral sequestration would need significant long-term investment and a lead time of decades before they would make an appreciable difference to carbon dioxide levels. The same can be said for some SRM techniques. For example, installing solar shields at the L1

Lagrange point in space would require decades of planning and massive investments of finance and resources.

However, injecting stratospheric sulphates could be done relatively quickly and inexpensively and, if implemented on a large enough scale, could lead to a net planetary cooling effect within days. So while CDR compares more favourably with SRM in terms of risk, some SRM techniques compare more favourably with CDR in terms of feasibility, lead time and cost. However, calculating the various permutations of risk is no easy matter, not least because perceptions of risks will vary between actors over space and time.

In terms of variations over space, perceptions of the risk of geoengineering will vary around the globe. Some local communities will perceive the risks of climate change as more severe than others. They may therefore favour countering climate change with geoengineering, perceiving the risks of geoengineering as less severe than communities that do not face climate change-induced risks. Ultimately, of course, no community will be able to insulate themselves indefinitely from climate change.

In terms of variations over time, those communities most at risk from the immediate and short-term effects of climate change, such as coastal populations facing sea-level rise, and communities at risk of drought, are likely to perceive geoengineering as less risky than communities for whom the negative effects of climate change will happen only in the distant future. So much depends on how soon the consequences of risky behaviour may be realised. A risk today will be valued more highly than a risk tomorrow. Another way of saying this is that risks that will occur in the distant future are discounted and valued less highly than risks that people face today. This has consequences for intergenerational equity (Book 1, Chapter 1, Section 3). The shorter the time span between behaviour and consequence, the higher the perceived risk.

For example, most people tend to avoid high-voltage electricity as they know there is a strong, virtually certain, likelihood of immediate death. That is, the risks are high and the uncertainty is low. But many people smoke as they judge the risks of consequences that may accrue in the future less highly than risks that will have consequences today. Furthermore, not everyone dies from smoking. So compared with contact with high-voltage electricity, the risks of smoking are low and the uncertainties are high. A complicating factor with smoking is that there are benefits, many smokers argue, from smoking as a form of relaxation which should be weighed against the risks.

Similarly, geoengineering brings with it the promise of potential benefits as well as risks. Policy makers must judge the risks that are acceptable in relation to the likely benefits. To illustrate this, the example of stratospheric aerosol injection is relevant.

Figure 4.13   Under a blood-red sky. Did the eruption of Krakatoa in 1883 inspire Norwegian artist Edvard Munch to paint *The Scream*?

Scientists can predict some of the most immediate effects of stratospheric aerosol injection from studying volcanic eruptions. One effect is sky whitening. Aerosols reflect some incoming solar radiation back into space, but scatter the rest. This leads to a whitening effect in the sky. This would mean that for most regions of the planet blue skies would become a thing of the past (MacCracken, 2006). However, sunsets and sunrises would become more brilliant, with the scattering of near-horizon sunlight by aerosols producing some spectacular oranges and reds. It has been suggested that the striking sky in Edvard Munch's painting *The Scream* (Figure 4.13) was inspired by dramatic sunsets in Oslo following the spreading of aerosols around the world after the eruption of Krakatoa in 1883.

While more spectacular sunsets may be welcomed, the loss of blue skies could have a profound effect on the psyche and sense of well-being of many people. Would people accept this? The loss of blue skies might seem a low cost to pay for the chance of averting the worst consequences of climate change, but the costs could be significant if a large number of people were to suffer emotional or mental disorders from such a significant change to their everyday environment. The question of values is important here. How much value should decision makers place on the possible negative social and emotional consequences of their policies? How much value should we place on blue skies? If the sky had always been white would we value a blue sky? Should we place a value on blue sky for future generations based on a set of emotions which future generations might not share?

Two points emerge from this discussion. From the standpoint of intergenerational equity, some judgement is needed on the acceptability of the costs and risks that should be borne by today's generations in return for the benefits to future generations, and on how these various costs and risks should be valued and distributed across generations. This relates to a second point, namely public acceptability. Governments may consult the public on geoengineering; alternatively, governments could simply impose geoengineering. However, the public will be unwilling to accept the risk and the financial costs of geoengineering today unless they can be persuaded that it is necessary to deal with a more serious risk in the future, such as catastrophic climate change. Public acceptance of geoengineering is, at the very least, desirable, and is essential if some geoengineering schemes are to function. Roof whitening and biochar sequestration, for example, will only be effective on a global scale if local communities around the world are persuaded or incentivised to implement them.

Another factor that will shape judgements on which geoengineering techniques are preferred is the energy used in their manufacture. Any energy expended on manufacturing geoengineering technologies should preferably come from low carbon energy technologies so that the carbon debt of any one technique is as low as possible. And while some carbon emissions may be unavoidable, the carbon removed from the atmosphere by any one device should exceed the carbon expended in the manufacture, transport, installation, maintenance and decommissioning of the device. It would clearly make no sense if more carbon dioxide were emitted in manufacturing an artificial tree and pumping the captured carbon dioxide to a secure location than was captured from the air during the lifetime of the device.

In this section you have seen that how risks are perceived will play a role in determining the political feasibility of geoengineering. You have gained a sense of the sorts of questions that feed into political discussions on geoengineering. In the next section we explore the international politics of the subject in more depth.

4   The international politics of geoengineering

In this section we consider some of the political challenges that geoengineering is likely to present to governments and other actors.

One important question on which people are likely to disagree is the desired end point of geoengineering. At first sight, it might appear that the goal would be to return the climate to a perceived 'natural' state, such as the Earth's temperature before the Industrial Revolution. However, the world's land surfaces have changed enormously since then, with significant forest loss and worldwide increases of urban settlements and organised agriculture. Some might argue that it is more desirable to stabilise the planetary temperature at another level that is more agreeable to human activities (Jamieson, 1996). However, different scientists and politicians would probably disagree on what the desired mean temperature should be. In any case, it is highly unlikely that humans will be able to implement geoengineering so as to calibrate the temperature of the planet with any degree of precision.

The very idea of geoengineering is inescapably global in nature, suggesting that a system of global governance for geoengineering is essential. Yet at present there is no internationally agreed mechanism with overall responsibility for research and development on geoengineering, and its implementation and regulation. There are, however, a number of international legal instruments that could claim responsibility for individual geoengineering techniques.

The most relevant instrument is the Framework Convention on Climate Change of 1992 and its Kyoto Protocol of 1997. The International Maritime Organization and parties to the Convention on Biological Diversity have both taken an interest in ocean fertilisation, and parties to the United Nations Convention on the Law of the Sea (UNCLOS) of 1982 could also claim a legitimate interest in this area. There is scientific concern that stratospheric aerosol injection could harm the ozone layer, which could bring this technique under the purview of the 1987 Montreal Protocol on Substances that Deplete the Ozone Layer (Box 4.1). Parties to the 1979 Convention on Long-range Transboundary Air Pollution (LRTAP) could also become involved in debates on sulphate aerosols, which in the past have caused acid rain damage to forests and buildings (Box 4.2). The United Nations Forum on Forests could claim an interest in reforestation and biochar sequestration. While many of these organisations have overlapping memberships, with many governments party to several instruments, each organisation has its own particular mandate and is not permitted to stray into decision making on a subject that is governed by another legal instrument. In the absence of an international coordination mechanism on geoengineering, decision making is likely to be fragmented and incoherent (Figure 4.14).

Figure 4.14   A number of international organisations have mandates that are relevant to individual geoengineering techniques, but none has oversight responsibility for all techniques

Box 4.1   The ozone layer

The ozone layer is the region of the stratosphere lying between 18 and 35 km above the Earth's surface with the highest concentration of ozone molecules. An ozone molecule is made up of three oxygen atoms, so its chemical formula is O_3. Stratospheric ozone protects life on earth by absorbing high-energy solar ultraviolet radiation, in particular UVB, a type of radiation that can cause skin cancers for humans and damage other species. Ozone concentrations in the stratosphere can be depleted by the presence in the atmosphere of certain chemical compounds, including chlorofluorocarbons (CFCs). States agreed to phase out the production of CFCs and other ozone-depleting chemicals under the Montreal Protocol on Substances that Deplete the Ozone Layer of 1987. Note that, as well as depleting the ozone layer, CFCs are also greenhouse gases and thus contribute to climate change.

Ozone is also found at the lowest stratum of the atmosphere, the troposphere, where it can be created by human activities; it is a component of smog, for example. In high concentrations, tropospheric ozone is toxic and is considered a pollutant.

Box 4.2   Acid rain and acidic depositions

Acid rain is rain containing acidic particles, such as sulphur and nitrous compounds, that cause damage to buildings, soil, crops and forests, pollution to rivers and lakes and respiratory problems to humans and other species (Figure 4.15). Acid rain has a pH value of less than 5. Note that while the term 'acid rain' has entered popular usage, depositions of acidic compounds may also be dry (in the form of particles) as well as wet (within rain droplets, hail or snow). The term acidic deposition encompasses both wet and dry depositions.

Figure 4.15 Acidic depositions can cause serious damage to trees by weakening the cell tissues and leaving the trees more vulnerable to attack from pests and disease

The politics of geoengineering is further complicated as the various geoengineering techniques span the global commons, broadly defined to include outer space in addition to the atmosphere and oceans, as well as those parts of the territory of independent sovereign states that are important components in global systems, such as some major forests and rivers. (You were introduced to the global commons in Book 1, Chapter 2, Section 4.) In principle, all states have an equal right of access to the global commons, and strictly speaking no state should take action that could lead to the degradation of the global commons and that could affect other states. However, it might be argued that geoengineering is intended to conserve the global commons, and that if some states are willing to take action from which all will benefit then they should be permitted to do so.

Activity 4.4   Categorising geoengineering techniques

Try to complete Table 4.1, which provides a simple way of categorising geoengineering techniques, divided between SRM and CDR, and between approaches which are commons-based and territorial-based. When you have done so, compare your responses with mine at the end of the chapter. Note that you are being asked to consider where the techniques would be based and not the impact of their use, which in both cases (SRM and CDR) would be global.

Table 4.1   A categorisation of geoengineering techniques

	Solar radiation management	Carbon dioxide removal
Commons-based techniques		
Territorial-based techniques		

The effects of geoengineering would vary across the globe and in the short term some may win more than others, while others will lose. For example, large-scale cloud whitening could affect global rainfall patterns, with some states receiving more rainfall and others receiving less, possibly leading to crop failure. Should the losers be entitled to compensation? A problem here is uncertainty about causation (Davies, 2009). In a system as complex as the global climate, it would be difficult to determine with any degree of certainty which countries were suffering environmental stress as a result of geoengineering.

The question of power – political and economic – is an important consideration with commons-based techniques. Having a legal right of access to the commons (which all states are entitled to in principle), and the actual capability to achieve access, are two different things. Only a small number of states have the technological capability to install solar reflectors in outer space, such as the USA, Russia, and China. Similarly, only a few states have the capability to inject stratospheric sulphate aerosols on the scale required to cool the planet. These countries may seek international agreement before they act, although they would not need international cooperation, in that they could act without the consent of other states.

States capable of deploying such techniques unilaterally may not take into account the risks such actions could create for other countries and ecosystems. Smaller states are unlikely to take unilateral action: even if they had the technological capability, they would be reluctant to act unilaterally without the approval of more powerful states that could impose political and economic costs, such as sanctions or diplomatic isolation.

Commons-based and territorial techniques would require very different forms of governance. Both would be ineffective unless deployed on a sufficiently large scale. Territorial techniques would make little difference if implemented by one state alone. For example, roof whitening in just one country would not significantly increase the Earth's albedo, nor would biochar production in one country lead to carbon dioxide sequestration on the scale needed to cool the planet. These techniques would constitute a collective action problem, a problem that cannot be solved by one country alone and which would require international agreement. International cooperation to implement these techniques would face the problem of Prisoners' Dilemma-style defections that have bedevilled international environmental cooperation in the past.

Activity 4.5   The Prisoners' Dilemma and geoengineering

You were introduced to the Prisoners' Dilemma game in Chapter 2 of this book. Using international cooperation on territorial-based geoengineering techniques as an example, how might the game be used to explain how states may behave?

Comment

Under the terms of the Prisoners' Dilemma, individual states would perceive they will gain by agreeing to international cooperation on geoengineering, but then not implementing their international commitments, thus 'free riding' from the beneficial effects of other states' actions. If all governments perceive they can benefit by such a strategy, then the dominant strategy is not to cooperate.

However, this does not mean that international cooperation is doomed to fail. Under the terms of the Prisoners' Dilemma that we have considered so far, the prisoners make their decisions in isolation from each other and neither knows what moves the other is making.

However, if the prisoners were allowed to confer so that each knew what the other would do when making their moves, the outcome would be different. The outcome would not settle at the Nash equilibrium but would instead be closer to the Pareto frontier (Chapter 2, Section 3, Box 2.2).

This suggests two things for international environmental politics. First, there should be transparency. Governments should not implement international agreements in isolation from each other but should share information and cooperate on their tactics. Second, there should be binding implementation and compliance provisions (Barrett, 2003). If governments know that 'defecting' from an agreed course of action will incur costs, such as fines or international sanctions, then they will be more likely to implement their commitments.

However, governments are not the only relevant actors. Many territorial techniques, such as roof whitening, desert reflectors and biochar burning, would require the active support of local authorities and communities if they were to be successful. The form of governance required would therefore need to be both decentralised and participatory, yet also regulatory, with states reporting on the implementation of any commitments internationally. Territorial techniques thus call for a different form of governance from commons-based techniques.

Any international mechanism tasked with implementing geoengineering would have to grapple with some scientifically and politically complex questions. For example, which states should undertake which activities? Different countries are better suited to specialising in different techniques, depending on their geographical attributes. Algeria and Saudi Arabia are solar-rich countries that could specialise in installing desert reflectors, while forest-rich countries could specialise in biochar. But this then leads to another question: who will pay? Should countries engaged in geoengineering be expected to bear the costs alone? Or should they receive compensation, and if so from whom?

The concepts of time and space are particularly relevant here. In 1992, at the United Nations Conference on Environment and Development, governments agreed the international legal principle of **common but differentiated responsibilities** in the Framework Convention on Climate Change. This principle deals with the question of responsibility over time: it holds that while all states have a common responsibility to address environmental problems, those that have done most to cause the problem in the past should do the most to solve it in the future.

This suggests that those states that have been responsible for producing the most greenhouse gas emissions since the start of the Industrial Revolution should pay the most for addressing the problem. Overall, the countries of North America and western Europe have emitted more greenhouse gases over time – both in absolute terms and per capita – than those in South America, Africa and Asia. However, while there is agreement on common but differentiated responsibilities in principle, there is no agreement on how it should be applied in practice.

Many countries of the global South may argue that they are entitled to receive international assistance if they are prepared to undertake geoengineering activities. For example, it may legitimately be argued that it would be unfair for a tropical forest country with low historical emissions to incur costs by producing biochar for burial in the twenty-first century in order, in effect, to sequester emissions made in the nineteenth and twentieth centuries by countries that have reaped benefits from fossil fuel burning in terms of economic development. It would violate the principle of intergenerational equity if emissions at one time and in one space were to benefit the polluter, yet CDR activities at another time and in another space were not rewarded, especially when the latter provide a global public goods function which benefits all countries.

Common but differentiated responsibilities
A principle of international law which holds that states that have done most to cause an environmental problem should do the most to solve it.

5   Summary

If, as seems likely, the world's politicians and businesses are unable to bring greenhouse gas emissions under control through greenhouse gas mitigation policies such as the large-scale use of low carbon energy technologies, geoengineering may seem increasingly attractive as an option. Geoengineering is a theoretical, and as yet untried, global risk management strategy for addressing climate change. Critics of geoengineering argue that the idea is so risky that it should not even be attempted and that political efforts should focus instead on emissions reduction and developing renewable energy.

Using geoengineering as a case study has helped us to think further about the question for this block, *Why are environmental issues so difficult to resolve?* Many of the difficulties that inform the politics of geoengineering apply to other environmental issues too. They include the difficulties and complexities of reaching agreement between multiple actors with varying degrees of political and economic power. The difference in values on a range of questions, such as how scientific uncertainty should be handled, how decisions taken internationally are translated into action at the local level, and how local-level community participation should be managed, also make environmental issues difficult to resolve.

This block has explored some of these issues as they relate to carbon. The biogeophysical processes involved in the carbon cycle, the politics and economics of managing carbon, the technical issues facing the phasing out of carbon-rich fossil fuels and the risks, uncertainties and values that are associated with removing carbon dioxide from the atmosphere all make addressing climate change a complex and challenging issue. This is particularly so due to the embedded nature of carbon and its by-products in the infrastructures around us and thus in our everyday lives. In this block these issues have been explored with regard to two specific challenges: energy availability and increasing atmospheric concentrations of carbon dioxide leading to climate change. The problems caused by climate change and by carbon also affect other aspects of life, such as water (Block 3) and food (Block 5).

Response to Activity 4.4

Table 4.1   (Completed) A categorisation of geoengineering techniques

	Solar radiation management	Carbon dioxide removal
Commons-based techniques	Space shields at the L1 Lagrange point Space shields in near-Earth orbit Stratospheric aerosol Injection Cloud whitening from ocean vessels	Ocean fertilisation
Territorial-based techniques	Desert reflectors Roof whitening Crop genetic modification to yield lighter varieties	Terrestrial biological sequestration (reforestation, biochar) Mineral sequestration (e.g. in basalt aquifers) Artificial trees

References

Barrett, S. (2003) *Environment and Statecraft: The Strategy of Environmental Treaty-Making*, Oxford, OxfordUniversity Press.

BBC (2009) 'Artificial trees: the future for carbon capture?' *BBC World Service*, 28 August [online], http://www.bbc.co.uk/worldservice/news/2009/08/090827_artificial_trees_wup_sl.shtml (Accessed 22 November 2012).

Black, R. (2010) 'Biochar: running the numbers', 23 December, *BBC News* [online], http://www.bbc.co.uk/news/science-environment-12008573 (Accessed 12 October 2012).

Buesseler, K. O., Andrews, J. E., Pike, S. M. and Charette, M. A. (2004) 'The effects of iron fertilization on carbon sequestration in the Southern Ocean', *Science*, vol. 304, no. 5669, pp. 414–17.

Davies, G. (2009) 'Law and policy issues of unilateral geoengineering: moving to a managed world', 29 January, SSRN [online], http://papers.ssrn.com/sol3/papers.cfm?abstract_id=1334625 (Accessed 22 November 2012).

Goldberg, P., Zhong-Ying, C., O'Connor, W., Walters, R. and Ziok, H. (2001) 'CO_2 mineral sequestration studies in US', Paper presented at the First National Conference on Carbon Sequestration, Washington, DC, 14–17 May [online], http://www.netl.doe.gov/publications/proceedings/01/carbon_seq/6c1.pdf (Accessed 22 November 2012).

Govindasamy, B. and Caldeira, K. (2000) 'Geoengineering Earth's radiation balance to mitigate CO_2-induced climate change', *Geophysical Research Letters*, vol. 27, no. 14, 15 July, pp. 2141–4.

IPCC (2007) *Contribution of Working Group III to the Fourth Assessment Report of the Intergovernmental Panel on Climate Change, 2007*: *Climate Change 2007: Mitigation*, Cambridge and New York, Cambridge University Press [online], http://www.ipcc.ch/publications_and_data/ar4/wg3/en/contents.html (Accessed 10 October 2012).

Jamieson, D. (1996) 'Ethics and intentional climate change', *Climatic Change*, vol. 33, pp. 323–36.

Kunzig, R. and Broecker, W. (2008) *Fixing Climate: The Story of Climate Science – and How to Stop Global Warming*, London, Green Profile.

Lackner, K. S., Grimes, P. and Ziock, H.-J. (1999) 'Capturing carbon dioxide from air' [online], http://www.netl.doe.gov/publications/proceedings/01/carbon_seq/7b1.pdf (Accessed 22 November 2012).

Lackner, K. S. (2009) 'Capture of carbon dioxide from ambient air', *European Physical Journal Special Topics*,vol. 176, no. 1, pp. 93–106.

Lampitt, R. S., Achterberg, E. P., Anderson, T. R., Hughes, J. A., Iglesias-Rodriguez, M. D., Kelly-Gerreyn, B. A. and Yoo, A. (2008) 'Ocean fertilization:

a potential means of geoengineering?', *Philosophical Transactions of the Royal Society A*, vol. 366, no. 1882, pp. 3919–45.

Latham, J., Rasch, P., Chen, C.-C., Kettles, L., Gadian, A., Gettelman, A. and Choularton, T. (2008) 'Global temperature stabilization via controlled albedo enhancement of low-level maritime clouds', *Philosophical Transactions of the Royal Society A*, vol. 366, no. 1882, pp. 3969–87.

Lehmann, J., Gaunt, J and Rondon, M. (2006) 'Bio-char sequestration in terrestrial ecosystems – a review', *Mitigation and Adaptation Strategies for Global Change*, vol. 11, no. 2, pp. 395–19.

Lenton, T. M., and Vaughan, N. E. (2009) 'The radiative forcing potential of different climate geoengineering options', *Atmospheric Chemistry and Physics*, vol. 9, no. 15, pp. 5539–61.

Lovelock, J. (2009) *The Vanishing Face of Gaia: A Final Warning*, London, Allen Lane.

MacCracken, M. (2006) 'Geoengineering: worthy of cautious evaluation? – an editorial comment', *Climatic Change*, vol. 77, nos 3–4, pp. 235–43.

Matter, J. M., Broecker, W. S., Stute, M., Gislason, S. R., Oelkers, E. H., Stefánsson, A. and Björnsson, G. (2009) 'Permanent carbon dioxide storage into basalt: the CarbFix Pilot Project, Iceland', *Energia Procedia*, vol. 1, pp. 3641–6.

NASA (n.d.) 'Three classes of orbit' *NASA Earth Observatory*, figure [online], available at http://earthobservatory.nasa.gov/Features/OrbitsCatalog/page2.php (Accessed 12 August 2012).

Oelkers, E. H., Gislason, S. R. and Matter, J. (2008) 'Mineral carbonation of CO_2', *Elements*, vol. 4, no. 5, pp. 333–7 [online], DOI: 10.2113/gselements.4.5.333 (Accessed 9 October 2012).

Robock, A., Marquardt, A., Kravitz, B. and Stenchikov, G. (2009) 'Benefits, risks, and costs of stratospheric geoengineering', *Geophysical Research Letters*, vol. 36 [online], http://www.agu.org/journals/gl/gl0919/2009GL039209/2009GL039209.pdf (Accessed 12 October 2012).

Royal Society (2009) *Geoengineering the Climate: Science, Governance and Uncertainty*, London, Royal Society.

Salter, S., Sortino, G. and Latham, J. (2008) 'Sea-going hardware for the cloud albedo method of reversing global warming', *Philosophical Transactions of the Royal Society A*, vol. 366, no. 1882, pp. 3989–4006.

Schuiling, R. D. (2006) 'Mineral sequestration of CO_2 and recovery of the heat of reaction', in Badescu, V., Cathcart, R. B. and Schuiling, R. D. (eds) *Macro-Engineering: A Challenge for the Future*, Dordrecht, Netherlands, Springer.

United Nations Environment Programme (UNEP) (1992) *Rio Declaration on Environment and Development* [online], http://www.unep.org/Documents.Multilingual/Default.asp?documentid=78&articleid=1163 (Accessed 9 October 2012).

Block 5   Food

Chapter 5 The economic, social and environmental impacts of food

Petr Jehlička and Parvati Raghuram

Contents

1   Introduction

Food is essential to human life, but also a big part of human culture. Human food systems have also always been the most fundamental point of contact between humans and their environments. Since the domestication of crops and animals and the birth of agriculture, food has driven human transformation of the environment. In the present day, food is recognised as one very important element in global environmental transformations, including climate change and biodiversity loss. These issues are driven both by increasing human numbers and by changing tastes and expectations. But food systems are not only causing environmental change; they are, in turn, very prone to being disrupted by changes in climate or depletion of biodiversity.

This module has regularly returned to the risk of increasing amounts of carbon dioxide in the atmosphere causing abrupt and non-linear climate change. Associated with this is the threat of significant changes in biodiversity, disruptions in the water cycle, alterations in the chemistry of seawater and other environmental problems. These current and future changes are not evenly spread throughout the world; nevertheless they raise shared questions about how best to respond. Food, the topic of this block, is one arena where the effects of climate change are likely to be felt most acutely. Agriculture (the basis of most food production) is a major source of carbon dioxide emissions and contributes a substantial portion of other powerful greenhouse gases – about 47 per cent and 58 per cent of total methane (CH_4) and nitrous oxide (N_2O) emissions, respectively (Smith et al., 2007). Hence food systems are intrinsically linked to the causes and consequences of climate change. This chapter explores why food has become a problem, focusing on food security and the impacts of food provisioning on the environment. The following three chapters look at different responses to food production as an environmental issue. They will consider some of the different responses to food insecurity in order to see how environmental issues can be responded to, thus directly addressing the block question *How can we make a difference?*

2   Food security

Food security
The goal of providing physical and economic access to sufficient, safe and nutritious food to meet the dietary needs and food preferences for an active and healthy life for all the world's population.

Food security has been defined as the goal of providing physical and economic access to sufficient, safe and nutritious food to meet the dietary needs and food preferences for an active and healthy life for all the world's population (World Food Summit, 1996). It has been a central problem throughout human history but understandings of it, and hence responses addressing food insecurity, have altered over time. There are many different definitions of food security (Smith et al., 1992). Some of the most prominent from the last 200 years are briefly summarised here.

In the eighteenth and nineteenth centuries, in the UK and in France, economists such as David Ricardo and Adam Smith argued that the best way to achieve food security was through freedom of trade (Nally, 2011). Pro-trade measures began to replace traditional state-centred, anti-scarcity structures aimed at prevention of food shortages (price controls, curbs on exports, the operation of public granaries, and the like). This approach was called laissez-faire.

Experience in the 1930s of food shortages in Europe and North America and of food rationing during and after the Second World War led to a change in emphasis. Food security came to be understood as the need to increase food supply in almost every country in the world. This **productionist paradigm** emphasised technology-driven and specialised food production. Increasing yields of food became a priority for national governments and was promoted by organisations such as the UN World Health Organization (WHO) and the UN Food and Agriculture Organization (FAO) established in the late 1940s (Figure 5.1).

Productionist paradigm
A production-led framework for thinking about food in which increase in the quantity of food prevails over other priorities.

In the late 1970s and early 1980s, the emphasis shifted from state or 'macro' level management to micro food security. The state ceased to be seen as the main guarantor of food security. Responsibility for meeting food needs diversified among a range of actors, including the state, households and individuals. This approach was also supported by many non-governmental organisations (NGOs).

(a)   (b)

Figure 5.1   (a) World Health Organization headquarters (Geneva); (b) Food and Agriculture Organization headquarters (Rome)

Since the 1980s, notions of food security have been influenced by the tendency of governments in the global North and of international agencies to promote trade liberalisation. Its rationale is economic efficiency and, accordingly, it promotes shifting production to areas with the most efficient production. This interpretation of food security is based on one of the core principles of classical economics – the principle of **comparative advantage**. The principle holds that 'territories produce those goods or services for which they have the greatest cost or efficiency advantage over others' (Gregory et al., 2009, p. 105). The outcome is trade in the goods and services in which places specialise.

Even if there is broad agreement about the goal of food security (in other words, the availability and affordability of nutritionally adequate

Comparative advantage

An economic principle according to which particular places specialise in production of goods and services for which they have the greatest cost advantage over other places.

157

and culturally accepted food), different actors see different roles for states, markets and civil society in pursuing it. In the productionist paradigm the state is responsible for ensuring food security; in micro food security approaches it is the farmers, individuals and households; while trade liberalisation approaches place faith in markets. International organisations, above all the FAO, are also involved in trying to produce food security. The many definitions of food security suggest that policies for achieving it are deeply contested.

One example of a strong position on the politics of defining food security is offered by La Via Campesina, a transnational peasant movement, begun in 1993 by farmers in Europe, Latin America and Africa. It prefers to use the term **food sovereignty**. The movement is critical of free trade in foods and agricultural resources and demands that food should be under the control of those who depend on food systems. Actors who hold this perspective champion domestic control of natural and genetic resources and seek to limit international trade in food and natural resources to those commodities that are not available in importing countries. They advocate local food production and the right to wholesome food, fair prices for primary producers and, ideally, national self-sufficiency as a guarantee of feeding the population. This perspective is not unique to peasant movements. Many other communities also adopt similar definitions of food security.

Food sovereignty
A perspective that seeks to limit international trade in food and advocate local food production and fair prices for primary producers.

3 Causes of food insecurity

You may recall from Book 1, Chapter 4 that in 2007–08 there were food riots in more than 30 countries of the world. There were further riots in 2011 (Figure 5.2). However, food riots are not new; they were common in eighteenth-century Europe and have been a popular response to food insecurity. What are some of the often-cited causes of food insecurity? In this section we explore the availability of food, economic factors and climate change as three factors affecting food security.

Figure 5.2   A 2011 food riot in Algiers, Algeria

3.1   Availability of food

The most frequent explanation for food insecurity is the lack of availability of food; that is, the amount of food available in the world is not enough to feed the population. The world's population exceeds 7 billion (and thus increased sevenfold over the last 200 years). The UN *State of World Population 2011* forecast that by the end of the century the world's population could reach 10, possibly 15, billion (UNFPA, 2011), raising the question of whether the Earth has the capacity to produce enough food for such a population.

Some argue strongly that it cannot. In his 1798 *Essay on the Principle of Population*, Reverend Thomas Malthus (1766–1834; Figure 5.3) argued that population when unchecked increases at a geometric rate (1, 2, 4, 8, 16, etc.) whereas subsistence food production only increases at an arithmetic rate (1, 2, 3, 4, 5, etc.). Therefore, the 'power of population is indefinitely greater than the power in the earth to produce subsistence for man' (p. 13). Malthus went on to claim that these 'two unequal powers must be kept equal' (p. 14).

Figure 5.3   Thomas Malthus (1766–1834)

Malthusian model
Population growth leads to the expansion of land used for food production, to resource depletion and ultimately to environmental degradation.

Malthus was concerned with the relationship between population and food supply under conditions where technology and resources in land remained constant. The implication of the **Malthusian model** is that, in the absence of institutional and technological change, population growth leads to the expansion of land used for food production and then to resource depletion and ultimately environmental degradation.

However, in reality, similarly sized populations may make significantly different demands on food supply and other resources. This leads us to question some of Malthus's assumptions. For instance, population growth may result in increasing investment of human, natural and financial capital, and in innovation leading to the development of new technical means of production and hence increases in yields. This is the **Boserupian scenario**, named after the Danish economist Ester Boserup who first offered this hypothesis (Boserup, 1981).

In addition to technology, another important variable that shapes environmental impact is consumption. More affluent societies tend to consume more resources and emit more pollution per capita than do poorer societies. Barry Commoner (1971) has proposed that a given environmental impact (I) is derived from three variables – population (P), per capita consumption or affluence (A), and technology (T); hence $I = PAT$. This approach is often referred to as neo-Malthusian. It adds more variables to Malthus's analysis but, as you will see later in this block, it does not recognise the political and social factors that may be more important than the variables acknowledged in this formula.

Although population is a key variable in food availability, since the beginning of the 1960s there has been remarkable growth in agricultural production, with increases in food production across the world. Since then, aggregate world food production has grown by 145 per cent. In Africa it rose by 140 per cent, in Latin America by almost 200 per cent and in Asia by 280 per cent. The greatest increases have been in China, where a 500 per cent increase in food production occurred, mostly during the 1980s and 1990s. In countries of the global North, production started from a higher base; yet it still doubled (100 per cent increase) in the USA over 40 years (FAO, 2005). Moreover, per capita agricultural production has outpaced population growth. For each person today, there is an additional 25 per cent more food compared with that in 1960. Yet four-fifths of countries are net importers of food (Pretty, 2008). So why is there still so much concern about food security? The cause cannot just be lack of availability.

3.2 Economic factors

Another explanation for concerns about food insecurity is that many people do not have access to food, even if it is available. The Nobel laureate economist Amartya Sen (1993) argued that famines are caused not by food availability decline, but by reduced entitlements to food. This kind of analysis is called the **entitlement** approach. Entitlement to food comes from four sources: production-based entitlement (growing food), trade-based entitlement (buying food), own-labour entitlement

Boserupian scenario
Population growth results in the intensification of production and innovation of the technical means of production.

Entitlement
The set of commodities that can be acquired through the use of the various legal channels of acquisition open to that person.

(working for food) and inheritance and transfer entitlement (being given food by others).

For that half of the world's population that now live in cities, buying food, or trade-based entitlement, is the main way in which food is acquired. As a result, the role of the market or of economic forces in food security is paramount. Hence, because food is widely traded, when food availability is reduced or when the quantity of food circulating in the global market falls, more and more people will go hungry. However, the effect will vary globally. For instance, in 2007–08 as food prices began to rise, major food exporting countries such as China and Argentina imposed taxes or quotas on their rice and wheat exports to prevent local shortages. Rice exports were banned in Cambodia, Egypt, India, Indonesia and Vietnam, so their populations were less exposed to global food price volatility. However, people in countries which did not control prices found it hard to afford food at the higher global prices. Hence, sovereignty over food production or markets can be an integral part of securing food. La Via Campesina's demand for food sovereignty arose from a recognition that in an interconnected world food security for some leads to food insecurity for others.

However, sovereignty is hard to achieve in an urbanising world. It is the urban poor in the global South who are the most food insecure because once they move to cities they are dependent on purchasing food but do not have the purchasing power that urban populations in the global North have. So why is it that prices can suddenly go up? The following newspaper extract gives one journalist's interpretation of that process.

Food speculation: 'people die from hunger while banks make a killing on food'

Just under three years ago [i.e. in 2008], people in the village of Gumbi in western Malawi [Figure 5.4] went unexpectedly hungry. ... Oddly, there had been no drought, the usual cause of malnutrition and hunger in southern Africa, and there was plenty of food in the markets. For no obvious reason the price of staple foods such as maize and rice nearly doubled in a few months. ... It was the same story in 100 other developing countries. ... The explanation offered by the UN and food experts was that a 'perfect storm' of natural and human factors had combined to hyper-inflate prices. US farmers, UN agencies said, had taken millions of acres of land out of production to grow biofuels for vehicles, oil and fertiliser prices had risen steeply, the Chinese were shifting to meat-eating from a vegetarian diet, and climate-change linked droughts were affecting major crop-growing areas. ...

But a new theory is emerging among traders and economists. The same banks, hedge funds and financiers whose speculation on the global money markets caused the sub-prime mortgage crisis are thought to be causing food prices to yo-yo and inflate. ... There has always been modest, even welcome, speculation in food prices and it traditionally worked like this. Farmer X protected himself against climatic or other risks by 'hedging', or agreeing to sell his crop in advance of the harvest to Trader Y. This guaranteed him a price, and allowed him to plan ahead and invest further, and it allowed Trader Y to profit, too. ... When this process of 'hedging' was tightly regulated, it worked well enough. The price of real food on the real world market was still set by the real forces of supply and demand. But all that changed in the mid-1990s.

Then, following heavy lobbying by banks, hedge funds and free market politicians in the US and Britain, the regulations on commodity markets were steadily abolished. Contracts to buy and sell food were turned into 'derivatives' that could be bought and sold among traders who had nothing to do with agriculture. In effect a new, unreal market in 'food speculation' was born. Cocoa, fruit juices, sugar, staples, meat and coffee are all now global commodities, along with oil, gold and metals. Then in 2006 came the US [financial] disaster and banks and traders stampeded to move billions of dollars in pension funds and equities into safe commodities, and especially foods.

(Vidal, 2011, pp. 32–3)

Figure 5.4   A mother and child in the village of Gumbi, western Malawi

Activity 5.1   'What for a poor man is a crust, for a rich man is a securitised asset class' (Vidal, 2011)

Now read the newspaper extract above again, but this time make some short notes under headings of the two sets of module concepts of risk and uncertainty, and time and space, to explain this author's perspective on the emergence of food insecurity.

Comment

This extract shows how it is not only climate but also the vagaries of economics that can influence food security. In particular, it shows how financial speculation is leading to risks and uncertainties in food access. Food is becoming valued as a commodity for financial speculation, not just production and consumption. For most of the twentieth century, only farmers and food producers speculated on food. However, after new regulations in the 1990s, bankers too were allowed to trade in food. Bankers are not actually interested in food as a product for consumption; rather, they use it as a commodity, whose price volatility they bet on. As you saw in Book 1, Chapter 4, they speculate on the changes in food prices: will the price of food items go up or down? They estimate how much a food might cost a few minutes later and then buy and sell accordingly. As such, they never actually buy or sell food. These speculations often bear little or no relation to the availability of food (i.e. whether a tonne of grain exists or not). Powerful economic actors such as bankers, acting within the financial system of global trade markets, are, however, affecting food prices through these actions. They are buying and selling notional quantities of food, and based on the economic value that they give to food they change the prices of food in the global trade markets on a second-by-second basis. These uncertainties in food prices, related to bankers' risk-taking behaviour, change the actual price of food. It has made some food, especially grains such as wheat and rice on which many people depend for their nutrition, increasingly expensive and therefore difficult for poor people to access. The linkages between people suffering from hunger in rural Malawi and the traders speculating in food points to the importance of global connections and the interdependence of societies and communities sharing the planet (raising issues of time and space). It also shows the limits of both Malthusian and neo-Malthusian analyses of food security.

While the kind of food speculation outlined in the extract from Vidal's article was made possible only after changes in financial regulations, trading in food as a commodity has a long history. It became increasingly common from the sixteenth century onwards but most of this trading was local, between food producers and consumers in close proximity. However, over time traders realised that they could get a better price for food by selling it to the urban rich and to consumers in distant parts of the world. This privileging of distant consumers over local populations led to food riots, especially in the eighteenth century. For the historian E.P. Thompson, this is because the moral economy, people's rights to food as a basic moral value, was being challenged by economic forces (Thompson, 1971). He used the term 'moral economy' to highlight the intertwined nature of the economy and moral values. The term moral economy suggests that the operation of markets both depends on and influences social and cultural values.

Marketisation spread globally through colonialism. Colonisers acquired land by force, pushing local people into precarious modes of pastoral cultivation. 'Famines became lethal engines for sweeping the soil of its human encumbrances, preparing the ground for the commodification of the food system' (Nally, 2011, p. 43). The geographer David Harvey calls this 'accumulation by dispossession' (Harvey, 2003, p. 137). These processes resemble the processes of 'land grab' occurring around the world in recent years (Book 1, Chapter 4). Economic policies, adopted through internationally agreed trade liberalisation policies, forced many countries in the global South to allow low-cost exports from Europe and the USA while European and US agriculture was both protected and subsidised. This further devastated agriculture in the global South. For example, subsidised food crops such as wheat from the US were sold cheaply in Africa. Local farmers in Africa, from whom subsidies were simultaneously removed, could not compete with these prices and so gave up farming. Others had to switch from growing food crops to crops that could be sold in the global market as these were often subsidised as part of the trade agreements established by multilateral organisations.

Colonised lands were used for growing single crops (monocultures) rather than providing food for local inhabitants, and these could be traded by colonisers in the world market. Thus, crops such as cotton in Egypt and groundnuts in Senegal replaced more diverse agricultural systems that had developed more gradually in ways that suited the local environmental conditions. As a result, of around 7000 crop species that are grown globally, just 103 species represent 90 per cent of food production (Tomich et al., 2011). Monocultural crops are more prone to disease and pest infestation as pathogens are species specific and thrive in a monoculture because they can easily pass from one organism to another. Chemicals can be used to control these infestations but they are expensive and carry their own hazards in relation to biodiversity loss. This economic and environmental history of agriculture has forced many parts of the world out of a position of food sovereignty and into food insecurity. However, the effects of this have been felt unequally and most overwhelmingly by poor people in the global South.

Although population, affluence and technology influence food availability, this section has shown how the effects of marketisation and of the control over food prices that the market exerts can have much more significant impacts on food systems.

3.3   Climate change

Problems of food availability and accessibility are expected to become more acute in the future on account of global environmental changes, above all climate change. Food is manufactured, processed, transported and eaten on a dynamic, ever-changing planet. Changing weather patterns, failure of rains, flooding and severe winters have always led to changes in the amount of food that is available for consumption. For instance, crops may fail as a result of both flooding and droughts. With the anthropogenically induced climate change that we explored in

Block 4, these patterns of weather may become more uncertain. In particular, it is anticipated that droughts and floods may become more intense, more frequent and less predictable, leading to further food insecurity.

Despite the uncertainties, agricultural economists and plant scientists are seeking to calculate the likely costs of climatic change. For instance, with the possible effects of climate change it is estimated that crop zones will alter and crop yields may drop. Each 'degree day' that a crop spends above 30 °C (a unit that reflects both the amount and duration of heat experienced by the plant) will depress yields (Lobell et al., 2008). These variations will lead to further food insecurity until agricultural practices adapt to the new climatic zones.

4   The food supply chain and its environmental effects

If food production is susceptible to environmental change, it is also a major cause of environmental change. Modern agricultural production, as well as distribution and consumption of food products, causes environmental impacts and natural resource depletion. In this section we look at the environmental effects at each stage of what is called the food supply chain.

Food supply chain
The various stages through which foodstuffs pass from source to consumers.

The **food supply chain** is the various stages through which foodstuffs pass from source (land or oceans) to consumers. Figure 5.5 represents a food supply chain. It also depicts the losses at each stage, such as the rejection of material that is inedible or unacceptable in some way. Accompanying the flow of materials, the various activities also require energy (usually fossil fuel) – for cultivating land, for producing fertilisers, for transport and for processing food – before it reaches the consumer. This is usually termed **embodied energy** to distinguish it from the chemical/dietary energy (used by animals to live and breed), which is present in food material. This embodied energy is currently almost all from fossil fuel sources and can be expressed as energy per unit mass (megajoules per kilogram; MJ/kg) or as the ratio of embodied energy per unit of dietary (food) energy supplied. In most common foods, embodied energy exceeds dietary energy.

Embodied energy
The total amount of energy required to grow, transport, process and store a particular food.

Food production occupies most of the non-urban area of countries such as England and the Netherlands, but even in less intensively farmed countries it occupies a considerable proportion of the land surface. Food-producing land represents a major part of the biophysical environment, so the way food production is organised has direct environmental effects. These effects can be categorised using the concept of the ecological footprint (Wackernagel and Rees, 1996), which was introduced in Book 1, Chapter 3, Section 3.2. Food production needs land directly to grow crops (crop land) together with pastureland for livestock and fishing grounds. It also needs fossil fuel energy for cultivation and processing (energy/carbon storage land). Agriculture changes the nature of the vegetation and other organisms on the land, and therefore affects biodiversity (depicted by the butterfly in Figure 5.5). Food production and processing need water, and also have a water footprint (Book 1, Chapter 10, Section 6).

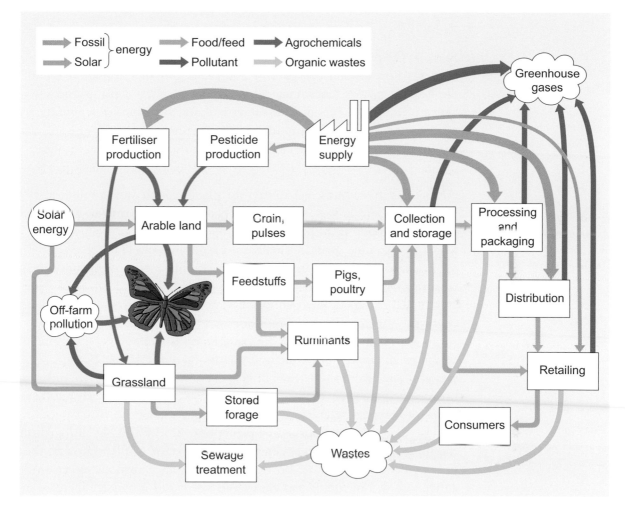

Figure 5.5   The food supply chain shown as a flow diagram

Food provision thus has an unavoidable ecological footprint. Citizens who wish to make a positive difference to their impact on their environment through food choices seek to reduce their footprint. Working through the rest of the section will enable you to begin to evaluate some ways in which food procurement has environmental effects. In Chapters 6 to 8 we will look at ways in which these effects can be reduced.

4.1   Fertilisers

Book 1, Chapters 5 to 12 examined the ways in which water and nutrients flow around ecosystems. The availability of fertilisers is one of the limiting factors that influence the rate of growth of plants and hence the supply of food. In most agricultural situations, the limiting nutrients are nitrogen (chemical symbol N), phosphorus (P) or potassium (K), the so-called NPK familiar to gardeners from fertiliser packets.

Nitrogen is a key nutrient required for plant growth and is found in all living organisms as it is an important component of proteins. Animals get their nitrogen from plants and nitrogen can only be taken up by plants in a soluble form, normally as the nitrate ion. These ions are made available to plants in the soil by a complex series of chemical reactions where decomposing fungi and bacteria break down dead plant and animal material. Nitrogen in the atmosphere (approximately 79 per cent of the atmosphere's composition) can be converted to suitable forms for plant absorption by nitrogen-fixing bacteria. At the beginning of the twentieth century a method was found – the Haber-Bosch process (Smil, 2001) – that could convert atmospheric nitrogen and hydrogen supplied by methane (CH_4) into ammonia (NH_3). By another series of complex reactions this is converted into a form of nitrogen fertiliser that can be absorbed by plants once in the soil. As nitrogen (in the form of nitrates) is very often a limiting factor to plant growth, the development of the Haber-Bosch process had an enormous effect on agriculture worldwide. It was cheap and promoted a massive increase in crop yields.

Since one aim of agriculture is to increase the production of desired crop products and to provide an income for the farmer, it is sometimes desirable and profitable to supply additional plant nutrients in the form of fertilisers. Most crop plants have been selectively bred (i.e. artificially selected to produce specific plant varieties or cultivars with specific traits) to be able to make use of additional nutrients; Figure 5.6 shows a typical curve for the response of a crop to additions of fertiliser. Pause to think about the implications of such a curve for a farmer's decision making about investments in fertiliser.

Figure 5.6 shows that with no fertiliser applied, the yield per unit area (that is, the mass of the desired crop component) is limited by the rate at which the limiting nutrients such as N, P and K become available through natural nutrient cycling. As fertiliser containing N, P and K is added, yield increases, but not by a constant amount; the curve shows what is known as **diminishing marginal returns**, in that the increment in yield for each additional ('marginal') increment in added fertiliser is smaller the more fertiliser is applied in total. There comes a point (M) where the increment is zero; adding more fertiliser beyond this amount provides no additional yield because a shortage of another input – for example, CO_2, water or light – limits growth. This is one of the biological problems of modern agriculture. The applied fertiliser contains the nutrients in highly soluble form so that they can be taken up quickly by the crop. Any nutrient not taken up immediately will be washed out of the soil, ultimately into water courses or groundwater.

Diminishing marginal returns
The process through which the increment in yield from each additional ('marginal') increment in an input becomes progressively smaller the more of that input is applied.

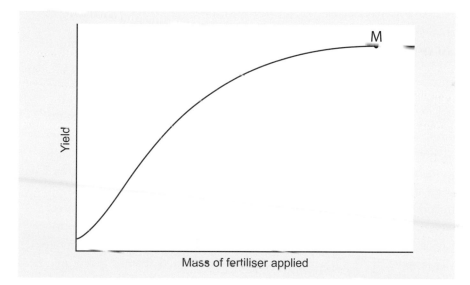

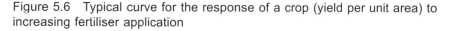

Figure 5.6   Typical curve for the response of a crop (yield per unit area) to increasing fertiliser application

Simple economics would suggest that no farmer would apply more fertiliser than the amount corresponding to point M in Figure 5.6. After point M the farmer continues to spend money on fertiliser but for no additional production. In fact, the point of maximum profit (the difference between cost and income from the crop) occurs at a point some way before M, in theory at the point where the cost of the last increment in fertiliser exactly equals the value of the additional yield that this provides. When fertilisers were cheap, farmers often applied them unnecessarily liberally, resulting in severe pollution in water courses from run-off and progressive degradation of soil structure.

In addition to the effects of off-farm pollution, the manufacture of nitrogen fertilisers uses methane from natural gas and oil or gas to heat to the high temperatures required for the process, thus contributing to carbon dioxide in the atmosphere. The manufacture of nitrogen-containing fertilisers is particularly energy intensive, needing 65 megajoules (MJ) of (usually fossil fuel) energy to produce one kilogramme of fertiliser nitrogen (Gover, 1996). Other micronutrients, potassium and phosphorus, are mined in various areas of the world, again needing fossil fuel energy, estimated at approximately 6 and 8 MJ per kilogramme of nutrient respectively.

4.2   Pesticides

Pesticides
Highly active chemical substances which can be used to control specific pests and pathogens.

Insecticides and herbicides
Insecticides are pesticides with the controlling effect on insects; herbicides control weeds.

Another factor that can determine yields of food materials is the presence or absence of weeds, pests and diseases (of both plants and animals). In the nineteenth century it was discovered that certain compounds could be used to control pests and diseases without damaging the crop. Bordeaux mixture (a mixture of copper sulphate and lime) was used to control fungal diseases in vines, and several other highly noxious materials, including arsenic, were often used for other pests and diseases. Since the 1940s, more sophisticated **pesticides** have been developed to control a range of pest and disease problems, including **insecticides** to control insects and **herbicides** to control weeds. These newer compounds are usually more selective, with low toxicity to non-target organisms such as humans. These have increased yields, potentially allowing more people to be fed from a given area of land. But there are negative consequences for biodiversity. Although the compounds used may be highly specific in their targets, the removal of the indigenous plant and animal species (considered 'weeds' and 'pests' within a crop/herd) disrupts and destroys entire ecosystems. This was highlighted in the book by Rachel Carson, *Silent Spring* (1962), with its vision of a future 'where no birds sing'. The publication of Carson's book, with its mixture of science and evocative and emotional writing, is often considered a key event in the development of the modern environmental movement. Widespread use of some compounds has unexpected side-effects, sometimes leading to their removal from sale. For example, although DDT was a highly effective insecticide it also caused thinning of the shells of some bird eggs. Hence, it was one of the first to be banned (first in the USA in 1972), despite its usefulness in controlling malaria-carrying mosquitoes. This is an example of the dual nature of technology, whereby a development such as DDT saved many lives by killing mosquitoes but also resulted in unforeseen negative consequences. Some countries are now using DDT again as the threat from malarial death is considered so great that this consideration outweighs any others.

4.3   Livestock

The role of livestock in agriculture also became increasingly controversial during the latter years of the twentieth century, with the development of ever-larger farm units that focus exclusively on raising animals. Manure from livestock that are housed over winter can become a pollutant. Wet slurries of animal manure can break down anaerobically (i.e. in the absence of oxygen) to release methane, a powerful greenhouse gas. **Ruminant** livestock such as sheep and cattle are also a source of methane as a result of their specific digestive system. This allows them to make use of grass and other materials comprising mainly cellulose that are indigestible to humans, but they belch out methane in the process. The amount they release depends on their specific diet, and research to limit this is currently a major topic.

A second area of controversy concerning livestock is their competition for food and land space that could be used directly by humans. In 1900, 10 per cent of the world's grain harvest was fed to animals, whereas by the late 1990s this proportion was 45 per cent. National differences remained vast; for instance, the proportion of the grain harvest fed to animals was 65 per cent in the USA and 5 per cent in India (Smil, 2002). While ruminants can live happily on grass alone, their rate of growth or production of milk can be limited where they are fed primarily through grazing. This is the situation for livestock in the hills and uplands of the UK, the pampas of South America and pastoral Australia. Feeding cattle grain, which is potentially food for humans, allows them to grow faster (for meat) or to produce more milk. Although it takes between 2 and 8 kg of grain to produce 1 kg of meat (McDonald et al., 2002), depending, again, on the exact costs and prices involved, this can make economic sense for the farmer. Indeed, there is an efficiency argument for some feeding of grain; any animal needs some food every day just to stay alive, its **maintenance ration**, even if it is not growing or producing milk. If its feeding regime is such that it can only grow slowly, or produce a small amount of milk per day, then the ratio of output to input is low, since most of the input is used just to keep the animal alive. Feeding some grain to allow it to grow faster or produce more milk does not affect the maintenance

Ruminants
A group of animal species (e.g. cattle, sheep, deer) that soften plant food within the first part of their stomach prior to regurgitating the semi-digested mass. Microorganisms in the later chambers of the stomach digest the mass.

Maintenance ration
The amount of food that must be fed to animals to keep them alive, healthy and productive.

ration, but the extra production does mean that the ratio of useful product per unit of feed consumed increases as more grain is fed. So, the productive efficiency of the farm system is increased. If, however, we look at the overall efficiency of the food system, this may be reduced. This shows that any analysis of food systems and their varying environmental impacts needs to consider appropriate system boundaries. Drawing the system boundaries too narrowly, for example around the farm, will miss out important environmental impacts outside the farm. Drawing the boundary too widely will result in a very complex body of information that it might be difficult to base decisions on.

4.4   Environmental effects of food distribution and processing: transport, food packaging and waste

A corollary of the dispersal of agriculture across rural land surfaces and the increasing concentration of human populations in cities and towns is that most foods have to be transported to the point of consumption. The economic principle of comparative advantage suggests that it is most economical to produce certain foods in particular areas, where the climatic, geographical or economic conditions are most favourable, so that costs are lower and outputs higher than elsewhere. It does not make economic (or energetic) sense to try to grow bananas or oranges in the UK, or to grow crops with a high demand for water in a semi-desert. Hence, there is need for transport. However, the transport of food can reach bizarre levels, with, for example, milk products and confectionery manufactured in Germany and France being transported to Britain, passing similar products from different manufacturers in Britain heading in the opposite direction (Figure 5.7).

Food miles
The total sum of the distance travelled by a food commodity 'from farm to fork'.

The desire to communicate the hidden environmental impacts of long-distance food trades has led to the concept of **food miles** (Paxton, 1994), the sum total of the distances travelled by a food commodity 'from farm to fork'. To reduce environmental impact it makes sense that food miles should not be incurred for trivial reasons. Of course, one person's trivial reason may not be trivial for another as each person may have different needs, tastes and values. While the concept of food miles is a useful aid to thought, it is also the case that different forms of transport impose different costs per unit of distance travelled. Table 5.1 shows the energy cost per tonne-kilometre (that is, the cost of transporting one tonne one kilometre) of different modes of transport.

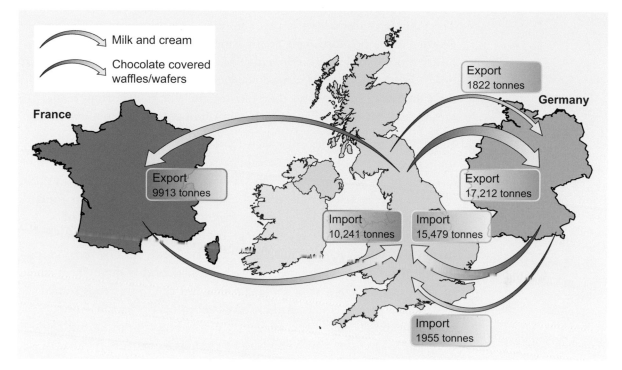

Figure 5.7   Perverse trade flows of milk products and confectionery; UK trade with France and Germany (Source: based on Simms et al., 2006, pp. 16–17 and 23)

Table 5.1   Energy cost of different transport modes (in megajoules per tonne-kilometre)

Transport mode	Energy costs (MJ/tonne-km)
Ship	0.2
Inland barge	0.2
Rail	0.2–0.5
Road	0.9–2.3
Air	7.4

Source: derived from Boustead and Hancock, 1979, and Weber and Matthews, 2008

The table indicates why it is that shipping grain by sea from the grain-growing areas of North and South America or Australasia to drier or hotter areas with lower comparative advantage for grain production can make economic sense. It can be cheaper to grow crops in places which are climatically suitable and then pay for fuel for transporting them, rather than paying for fuel for irrigation pumps and greenhouses.

In addition to the direct energy costs of transport, there may also be indirect costs for processing or otherwise protecting food materials in transit. For fresh foods with high water content, such as fruit and meat, it may be necessary to refrigerate the transport units to prevent **food spoilage** in transit. Spoilage occurs mainly through the action of microorganisms such as yeasts, fungi and bacteria, but insects and mammals such as rats and mice may also be involved. For most crops grown in seasonal environments, the harvest period is quite short (think of apples in the UK), so if there is a demand for these crops out of season, the materials have to be processed to keep them in a fit condition to eat. Such processing may involve heating to kill off the microorganisms that cause spoilage or cooling to restrict the growth of such organisms and also to restrict the continuing changes that occur through the action of **enzymes** that are still active in the food material. Other methods of preservation include the use of **food additives** that restrict spoilage; controlled atmosphere storage, where the makeup of the atmosphere (regulated temperature, humidity and concentrations of oxygen, carbon dioxide and nitrogen) around the product is modified; and drying. These techniques restrict the rate of spoilage of the material, but drying may also affect taste and structure. This may or may not be desirable (think of dried sultanas versus fresh grapes).

An area that has come under increasing scrutiny is food waste, where the supermarkets are considered by think tanks such as the New Economics Foundation (2003) and campaigning groups such as Friends of the Earth to be major culprits. They adhere rigorously to sell-by dates and dispose of large quantities of mostly edible food for health and safety reasons, but they also impose very strict cosmetic standards on the commodities they sell. Apples that have the odd surface blemish or cucumbers that are not completely straight are nutritionally as good as their cosmetically perfect equivalents. The dumping of products that do not meet retailers' cosmetic standards greatly increases food waste. It is estimated that between 40 and 50 per cent of the weight of raw vegetables is discarded at some point of the food supply chain before they reach the buyer (Henningsson et al., 2004). Critics of supermarket

Food spoilage
Damage to food (usually through the action of microorganisms) which renders it unsuitable for eating.

Enzymes
Proteins with catalytic effect that increase the rates of chemical reactions and can lead to food spoilage.

Food additives
Chemical substances added to food to preserve it or to enhance its taste or appearance.

food systems also point to over-packaging that often appears to achieve no more than showing off the product. Producing the packaging takes up energy and disposing of it via the refuse system wastes further resources. However, supermarkets argue that through efficient storage and packaging they reduce the waste that occurs over the chain from supplier to user.

Activity 5.2   Energy inputs in the food supply chain

List some of the major energy-requiring aspects of the food supply chain discussed in this section.

Comment

Fertilisers and farm machinery are major users of energy in agriculture. Energy for heating and cooling are essential in food processing, and, depending on the distances and type of transportation involved, energy for transport is another major use. Packaging is a further energy requirement, particularly in large-scale supermarket-based systems.

4.5   Saving and cooking food

Few foods other than salads and fresh fruit are eaten raw, so in considering the environmental impacts of food we must also consider the effects of cooking; this can make available nutrients from the food that would not be accessible in the raw material and it also makes the foodstuff more palatable. Prior to the twentieth century, most cooking took place in the home; as the twentieth century progressed, more foods were bought pre-cooked, either for immediate consumption or for storage in a domestic fridge or freezer for subsequent heating (Figure 5.8).

Figure 5.8   Domestic fridge and industrial cold store

Activity 5.3   Energy efficiency of domestic and industrial food processing

Processing and storage requires energy from fuels, but doing this on an industrial, rather than domestic, scale may be more energy efficient. Take the example of a cooker. The loss of heat, and hence the additional energy that needs to be supplied to the cooker, depends on the surface area of the heated unit, and on its insulation.

1   Consider a domestic oven that is 0.5 m high, 0.5 m wide and 0.5 m long.

  a. What is the volume?

  b. What is the surface area?

2   Now consider a commercial oven with a cross-section of 1 m by 1 m, and a length of 2 m.

  a. What is the volume?

  b. What is the surface area?

3   How much more food can the commercial oven heat than the domestic oven?

4   How much more heat is lost across the walls of the commercial oven than the domestic oven?

You will find the answers at the end of the chapter.

Concentration of food processing and distribution in larger units may lead to greater energy efficiency in the processing stage. It may also increase transportation costs, as we saw in the example of milk products and confectionery at the start of Section 4.4 above. Again, in considering the environmental impacts of the food system, we need to consider all the processes involved.

5   Summary

This chapter is the first in this series of four to examine one of the closest relationships between nature and society – that between food and agriculture. Agriculture and food production – vital to human well-being – are dependent on the functioning of ecological processes. Any disturbance or changes in ecosystem functioning can have serious repercussions for food security. Declines in agricultural yield caused by changed ecological conditions such as those related to climate change (flooding, temperature rise, storms and spread of parasites), combined with expected population growth, may lead to volatile situations at a local level or even large-scale crises at the national or regional level. Poorer countries are going to be hit particularly hard as they are unable to buy their way out of such crises (Lang and Heasman, 2005). Both subsistence and cash crops are vulnerable to climate change. You have also seen that food crises in particular localities of countries of the global South can be generated by financial speculations in a distant place, a process which illustrates the importance of the concepts of time and space.

Food production and the environment are interrelated and the relationship works in both directions. Not only do changing environmental conditions impact on food production, but individual segments of a food supply chain – production, storage, processing, distribution and consumption – can have serious environmental consequences. These include loss of wildlife habitat, declining water quality, loss of biodiversity, pollution, depletion of non-renewable resources such as fossil fuels and climate change.

Given the importance of food to our well-being, the problem of food production has generated a number of responses. Some of these have been at an individual level but, increasingly, there are attempts to alter food consumption and production in order to reduce their environmental effects. We turn to these in the next chapter.

Response to Activity 5.3

1   (a) 0.125 m^3

   Calculated: 0.5 m × 0.5 m × 0.5 m = 0.125 m^3

   (b) 1.5 m^2

   Calculated:

   - surface area of each side, 0.5 m × 0.5 m = 0.25 m^2
   - total surface area therefore 6 × 0.25 m^2 = 1.5 m^2

2   (a) 2 m^3

   Calculated: 1 m × 1 m × 2 m = 2 m^3

   (b) 0.5 m^2

   Calculated:

   - surface area of top and bottom, 1 m × 1 m = 1 m^2
   - surface area of the four long sides, 1 m × 2 m = 2 m^2
   - total surface area therefore (2 × 1 m^2) + (4 × 2 m^2) = 10 m^2

3   To calculate this we must divide the volume of the commercial oven with that of the domestic oven:

$$\frac{2 \text{ m}^3}{0.125 \text{ m}^3} = 16$$

The commercial oven can therefore heat 16 times as much food as the domestic oven.

4   To calculate this we must divide the surface of the commercial oven with that of the domestic oven:

$$\frac{10 \text{ m}^2}{1.5 \text{ m}^2} = 6.7 \text{ (rounded to one decimal place)}$$

So the commercial oven loses 6.7 times the heat of that lost by the domestic oven.

The commercial oven can therefore cook 16 times as much food at a time, but will only lose 6.7 times as much heat through the oven walls. Therefore, the commercial oven is more than twice as efficient in its energy use than the domestic oven. There is thus an argument that, environmentally, it is more efficient to do most heating of foodstuffs on an industrial, as opposed to a domestic, scale.

References

Boserup, E. (1981) *Population and Technologic Change: A Study of Long Term Trends*, Chicago IL, University of Chicago Press.

Boustead, I. and Hancock, G. F. (1979) *Handbook of Industrial Energy Analysis*, Chichester, Ellis Horwood and New York, John Wiley.

Carson, R. (1962) *Silent Spring*, Boston, MA, Houghton Mifflin.

Commoner, B. (1971) *The Closing Circle: Nature, Man, and Technology*, London, Random House.

Food and Agriculture Organization of the United Nations (FAO) (2005) *FAOSTAT* [online], http://faostat3.fao.org/home/index.html#HOME (Accessed 24 October 2012)

Gover, M. P. (1996) *Alternative Transport Fuels: A Preliminary Life-cycle Study for the UK*, London, HMSO.

Gregory, D., Johnston, R., Pratt, G., Watts, M. J. and Whatmore, S. (2009) *The Dictionary of Human Geography*, Chichester, Wiley-Blackwell.

Harvey, D. (2003) *The New Imperialism*, Oxford and New York, Oxford University Press.

Henningsson, S., Hyde, K., Smith, A. and Campbell, M. (2004) 'The value of resource efficiency in the food industry: a waste minimisation project in East Anglia, UK', *Journal of Cleaner Production*, vol. 12, no. 5, pp. 505–12.

Lang, T. and Heasman, M. (2005) *Food Wars: The Global Battle for Mouths, Minds and Markets*, London, Earthscan.

Lobell, D. B., Burke, M.B., Tebaldi, C., Mastrandea, M. D., Falcon, W. P. and Naylor, R. L. (2008) 'Prioritizing climate change adaptation needs for food security to 2030', *Science*, vol. 319, no. 5863, pp. 607–10.

Malthus, T. R. (1798) *An Essay on the Principle of Population*, London, J. Johnson.

McDonald, P., Edwards, R., Greenhalgh, J. F. D. and Morgan, C. A. (2002) *Animal Nutrition*, Harlow, Prentice Hall.

Nally, D. (2011) 'The biopolitics of food provisioning', *Transactions of the Institute of British Geographers*, vol. 36, no. 1, pp. 37–53.

New Economics Foundation (2003) *Ghost Town Britain II: Death on the High Street* [online], http://www.neweconomics.org/publications/ghost-town-britain-ii-death-high-street (Accessed 11 December 2012).

Paxton, A. (1994) *The Food Miles Report: The Dangers of Long Distance Food Transport*, London, Safe Alliance.

Pretty, J. (2008) 'Agricultural sustainability: concepts, principles and evidence', *Philosophical Transactions: Biological Sciences*, vol. 363, no. 1491, pp. 447–65.

Sen, A. (1993) *Poverty and Famine: An Essay on Entitlement and Deprivation*, Oxford, Clarendon Press.

Simms, A., Moran, D. and Chowla, P. (2006) *The UK Interdependence Report: How the World Sustains the Nation's Lifestyles and the Price It Pays*, London, new economics foundation.

Smil, V. (2001) *Enriching the Earth: Fritz Haber, Carl Bosch, and the Transformation of World Food Production*, Cambridge, MA, The MIT Press.

Smil, V. (2002) 'Eating meat: evolution, patterns, and consequences', *Population and Development Review*, vol. 28, no. 4, pp. 599–639.

Smith, M., Pointing, J. and Maxwell, S. (1992) *Household Food Security: Concepts and Definitions – An Annotated Bibliography*, Development Bibliography No. 8, University of Sussex, Institute of Development Studies.

Smith, P., Martino, D., Cai, Z., Gwary, D., Janzen, H., Kumar, P., McCarl, B., Ogle, S., O'Mara, F., Rice, C., Scholes, B. and Sirotenko, O. (2007) 'Agriculture', in Metz, B., Davidson, O. R., Bosch, P. R., Dave, R. and Meyer, L. A. (eds) *Climate Change 2007: Mitigation. Contribution of Working Group III to the Fourth Assessment Report of the Intergovernmental Panel on Climate Change*, Cambridge and New York, Cambridge University Press.

Thompson, E. (1971) 'The moral economy of the English crowd in the eighteenth century', *Past and Present*, vol. 50, no. 1, pp. 76–136.

Tomich, T. P., Brodt, S., Ferris, H., Galt, R., Horwath, W. R., Kebreab, E., Leveau, J. H. J., Liptzin, D., Lubell, M., Merel, P., Michelmore, R., Rosenstock, T., Scow, K., Six, J., Williams, N. and Louie Y. (2011) 'Agroecology: a review from a global-change perspective', *Annual Review Environmental Resources*, vol. 36, pp. 193–222.

United Nations Population Fund (UNFPA) (2011) *State of World Population 2011*, UNFPA [online], http://www.unfpa.org/public/op/preview/home/sitemap/swp2011 (Accessed 29 October 2012).

Vidal, J. (2011) 'Food speculation: "People die from hunger while banks make a killing on food"', *Observer Food Monthly*, 23 January, pp. 32–3; also available online at http://www.guardian.co.uk/global-development/2011/jan/23/food-speculation-banks-hunger-poverty (Accessed 24 October 2012).

Wackernagel, M. and Rees, W. (1996) *Our Ecological Footprint: Reducing Human Impact on the Earth*, Gabriola Island, BC, New Society Publishers.

Weber, C. and Matthews, H. S. (2008) 'Food-miles and the relative climate impacts of food choices in the United States', *Environmental Science and Technology*, vol. 42, no. 10, pp. 3508–13.

World Food Summit (1996) *Rome Declaration on World Food Security*, UN Food and Agriculture Programme [online], http://www.fao.org/wfs/index_en.htm (Accessed 24 October 2012).

Chapter 6   Food choice, diet and environmental change

Petr Jehlička

Contents

1   Introduction

The previous chapter discussed the relationship between getting hold of food (food provisioning) and environmental change. It considered how these two things are in a close relationship, and that the relationship also dictates the degree of food security that people experience. The environmental implications of food production, processing, distribution and storage were explored using the concept of the food supply chain. In this and subsequent chapters of this block you will examine how the environmental effects of food production and consumption can be reduced. Seeking to respond to the block question *How can we make a difference?*, this chapter will discuss what determines people's choice of food and what difference they can make as individuals by changing their diet. Towards the end, by introducing the discussion of obesity and public dietary guidance, the chapter will highlight the limits to framing food issues in terms of individual actions. The chapter concludes with a discussion of the need to consider the possibility of structural changes in both food systems and social structures.

2   Some examples of choices in food

For consumers who have secure work, obtaining food is largely a matter of visiting a supermarket or other food store and choosing foodstuffs from well-stocked shelves. This has become the mainstay of food provisioning in the global North, although it is increasingly an aspect of life for the middle classes of the global South. For others, especially those in the global South who do not have the chance to grow their own food, such as the increasing populations of urban poor, access to food can be difficult and uncertain. In this chapter, we begin to consider some of the factors that may affect how people choose the food they eat.

The food scholar Warren Belasco, writing about food choices in the USA, argued that people's decisions on what to eat are based on a negotiation between the dictates of identity and convenience with some considerations of responsibility (Belasco, 2008) (Figure 6.1). 'Identity involves considerations of personal preference, pleasure, creativity and the sense of who and where you are' (Belasco, 2008, p. 8). It refers to factors such as ethnic origin, taste, memories, group preferences, desire for authenticity and culinary traditions. Convenience includes practical factors such as food availability, affordability and the skills, time and energy needed for acquiring and preparing food. Responsibility reflects people's values and relates to awareness of the personal, social, environmental and political consequences of food choices. It includes consequences for personal health, for the well-being of other people (farmers, workers in food processing), for the environment (or the ecological footprint of growing, processing and distributing food; sometimes termed 'foodprint'), and for the distribution of power in society. According to Belasco (2008), choosing food responsibly has a strong temporal dimension: it requires considering the environmental consequences that resulted from putting food on the table (the past) and anticipating consequences that have yet to happen (the future). Food choice has an equally important spatial dimension, as food and the resources used to produce it must travel (often significant) distances to reach the kitchen.

Convenience is strongly influenced by people's access to food – to supermarkets, local stores or agricultural land where they can grow their own food. While food is easily accessible for some people, others have their access restricted by the economic, environmental and social barriers with which they live. Responsibility, on the other hand, denotes an effort to understand the relationship between the individual and the food system (Belasco, 2008), with the objective of transforming this relationship into an environmentally and socially more beneficial system.

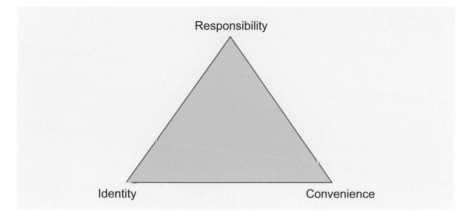

Figure 6.1   The three variables determining the choice of food (Source: based on Belasco, 2008, p. 7)

Why do people eat what they do? A useful model that addresses this question is the 'hierarchy of needs' model of decision making developed by the US psychologist Abraham Harold Maslow (1908–1970). In Maslow's hierarchy of needs, the sourcing of adequately nutritious food – or freedom from starvation – is a first-order (that is, most fundamental) human need. Safety of food – or freedom from bacterial and toxic contamination – is a second-order need. Well-being, for example the consumption of food and drinks for personal and social satisfaction, is a third-order need. Another example is sharing food and drink with others at celebrations, feasts and special occasions. Food-related practices linked to the fulfilment of third-order needs have a strong cultural and identity dimension. This theme will be addressed in some detail in the next chapter. Finally, moral norms (values) and related habits and preferences are an important part of people's identity. Preferences generated by concerns about the environmental and social impacts of food are an example of fourth-order – moral – needs. Values and changes in values are critical factors for the consideration of the block question *How can we make a difference?*

Human nutritional needs could be satisfied relatively easily with a few simple foods such as potatoes, a small range of other vegetables, a few grams of meat or similar source of particular proteins, and some fruit each day. While nutrition science is concerned with the role of foods in

**Organoleptic
properties**
Sensory properties of
food, such as taste,
flavour, mouth feel and
temperature.

the basic operation of human bodies, the actual food people consume is determined by, in Belasco's formulation, other factors such as identity, convenience and responsibility. One element within the 'identity' category is what food scientists and technologists call **organoleptic properties**. These are sensory properties of food, such as flavour, temperature and the feel of food in the mouth. You should also recognise these as an aspect of Maslow's third order in the hierarchy of needs (Figure 6.2). Within Maslow's formulation, economically secure (and hence food-secure) people view the food they eat as much a part of the satisfaction of their higher-order needs as it is of their basic physiological needs. For these people, much of the interaction between food supply and the environment depends on higher-order needs (third or fourth order in Figure 6.2). In other words, environmental impacts of the food system depend at least as much or more on what people actually choose to eat and drink – on diet – as on what they need to eat. Choice of diet at the individual level is one way of responding to the environmental issues that food systems raise, and the first you will explore in response to the block question.

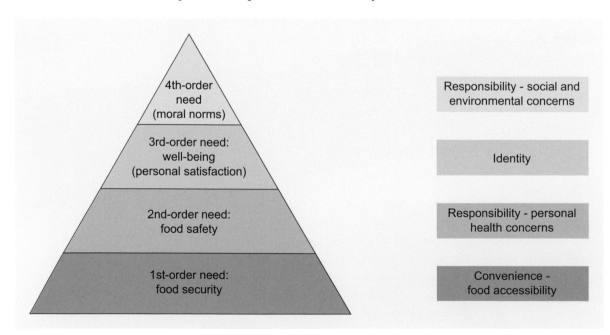

Figure 6.2   Maslow's hierarchy of needs applied to food and its relationship to Belasco's three variables: identity, convenience and responsibility

Since the beginning of the 2000s in the UK, food has developed into a lifestyle subject with newspaper supplements and television programmes dedicated to cooking, eating and culinary cultures. The new culinary culture has manifested itself in both 'food cosmopolitanism', with an increasingly wide range of ethnic restaurants and food shops, and 'food localism' represented by farmers' markets and box schemes supplying locally and/or organically grown food. Yet during the same decade, the consumption of takeaway and fast food increased dramatically. One-fifth of food eaten in households was ready-made meals (Hayward, 2011). The UK has also become the most obese nation in Europe. Similar trends in increasing obesity are observable in the Americas and China.

Both in the realm of national and international public policy and in the media, one very common way of addressing the environmental problems associated with food in terms of social change is through individual choice. According to this line of thinking, the environmental consequences will be reduced when enough people make responsible choices about food. Individual behaviour and personal responsibility are at the centre of this mode of public policy. Belasco's identity–convenience–responsibility triangle introduced above is a more general underpinning of this policy approach. It is helpful at this point to examine some of the variety that exists in people's eating patterns in just one city in the global North.

Activity 6.1   Families and food cultures in one London square

In 2011 the *Observer Food Monthly* published an article on the shopping, cooking and eating habits of four families living in Camberwell in south London (Carpenter, 2011; Figure 6.3). What general observations on food habits can you draw from the summaries on each family below? Take notes on how you can apply Belasco's three variables – identity, convenience and responsibility – to these households. (Please note that the type of household featured in this activity – parents and children – is not typical as households in the UK consisting of children and one or more parents amount to only just over half of the total.)

Family A: Both parents – Regina and Andrew – are actors. Andrew is responsible for all the cooking and shopping. He spends about £100 a week on food, mostly in Iceland (a supermarket chain specialising in frozen food). He makes his own bread. Typical meals are pasta with tinned tomatoes and anchovies, roast chicken, meatballs with rice, ratatouille, *salade niçoise*, pizza. He says: 'For us, it is economy in time, economy in money and economy in effort. I don't let the word "organic" worry me. It's good, functional food but I've never read a recipe in my life.' The family eats the same dish on the same day of the week.

Figure 6.3   Four families living in the same square in Camberwell, London:
(a) Regina, Andrew and children; (b) Nichola, Harold and children;
(c) Spenta, Cyrus and children; (d) Jessamy, Ralf and son (Source:
Carpenter, 2011)

Family B: Nichola (full-time mother) and Harold (a council worker) cook
all meals with ingredients bought as best deals. They use the eggs the
chickens lay in their neighbour's allotment. Their main concern is a

healthy diet for their children with enough fruits and vegetables. Their weekly spend on food is £60 to £70. They have themed weeks – vegetarian, Chinese or no carbohydrates. Typical meals: arrabiata prawns, jollof rice, cassava leaf stew, macaroni cheese, Spanish omelette.

Family C: The weekly food spend of Cyrus (banker) and Spenta (mother and carer) is £139. They typically eat: homemade dansak, M&S oven-ready southern chicken with ready-made mashed potato and coleslaw, fried fish with salad, takeout lamb biriani, takeout shish and doner kebabs, takeout fish and chips, Kentucky Fried Chicken. Spenta says: 'Takeaway food could be rubbish for the children's health, but it is a matter of time and it is a matter that they have something to eat.'

Family D: Ralf (nursery cook) and Jessamy (magazine editor) spend £170 a week on food. Ralf buys organic food at a farmers' market and an organic butcher. Their daughter (not pictured) is a vegetarian. Typical meals Ralf cooks include: Spanish tortilla, goulash, smoked haddock chowder, cold meats, oysters, pork chops, shin of beef, pork belly, and mushroom risotto.

Comment

While one aim of the author of the article, Louise Carpenter (2011, p. 21), was to dispel 'the received wisdom that the middle classes eat well and can cook' while 'poorer people are more likely to be overweight and live on ready meals', the richness of this information enables you to make observations and draw out points that go beyond the immediate concerns of diet, class and income. When the author of this chapter organised their notes on the eating habits of the four families according to a food triangle of three variables – identity, convenience and responsibility (Belasco, 2008; Figure 6.1) – they included the following:

Identity: The diets point to cultural diversity in society – the tastes of the four families were very varied. Most families' diets were an eclectic mix borrowing from a range of national or ethnic cuisines. Some families experiment with their food. Others stick with weekly routines.

Convenience: The four diets reflected differences in weekly expenditures. These different expenditures could be a matter of choice, or they could reflect social inequalities. The highest-spending household spent nearly three times more than the lowest-spending. The organic food diet was significantly more expensive than conventional food. The diet based on ready-made meals – while saving time and labour – was also expensive. Social structures, such as the distribution of wealth, work and caring commitments, and type of shops in the vicinity, significantly influenced food choices.

Responsibility: Different diets have different health and environmental implications. Family D regularly buys organic food and one of the family members is a vegetarian, so that family's ecological footprint, depending on how far the food has travelled, is likely to be one of the lowest. However, as family B showed, lower income can be compatible with a healthy diet and more sustainable (locally produced, in this case) food consumption.

Food choices always have environmental and health impacts, and changing food choices can make a difference in relation to the environment and sustainability, as well as personal health.

3   Environmental impact of changing diets

Activity 6.1 looked at a wide spectrum of diets and the reasons and motivations for choosing those diets. In this section we now consider environmental impacts arising as an aggregate (an adding together) of individual dietary changes that occurred during the shift from largely subsistence to more affluent present-day diets.

The transition from the subsistence to the affluent diet – the process currently occurring in large sections of fast-growing economies such as China – may take place relatively quickly, as the case of post-Second World War western Europe suggests. Analysing changes of diet in the Netherlands from 1950 to 1990, Gerbens-Leenes and Nonhebel (2002) discovered that during these four decades the consumption of meat per capita per year nearly tripled (from 36 kg in 1950 to 85 kg in 1990), the consumption of fats remained the same, the consumption of milk nearly halved but the consumption of cheese tripled. While the consumption of potatoes decreased by more than a quarter, the consumption of citrus fruits increased eightfold.

Gerbens-Leenes and Nonhebel (2002) calculated the change in land requirements that resulted from the changes of food consumption over these four decades. The land requirement changes were calculated by multiplying consumption (kg per capita per year) per food item by the specific land requirement for that item (square metres per kg per year). They found that the 1990 Dutch diet required 28 land units more (100) per person than the diet in 1950 (72 land units), an increase of 39 per cent. The two food categories chiefly responsible for the increase were meat and beverages. A diet high in grain-fed meat also requires approximately 5000 litres of water per person per day, compared with 2500 litres for a vegetarian diet (CTA, 2011). This highlights the role of affluence, and hence changing tastes and expectations, in environmental degradation associated with food production and consumption.

Gerbens-Leenes and Nonhebel argued that land requirements for production of beverages should be included in calculations of the food consumption impacts on the environment. Beverages – beer, wine, coffee and tea – are the category that has undergone the most profound increases. While the consumption of tea remained constant at 1 kg per capita per year, the consumption of coffee increased eightfold, of wine by a multiple of 15 and of beer eightfold over the 40-year period.

Beverage ingredients are produced in agricultural systems and they stake a claim on the same agricultural resources as food. Tea, coffee and fruit juices are obvious examples. The increase in coffee consumption in the Netherlands from 1 kg to 8 kg per capita per year during the 40-year period examined by Gerbens-Leenes and Nonhebel greatly increased the demand for land to produce this commodity (Figure 6.4). Sometimes one ingredient, such as barley, is used for the production of both food and beverages. For example, 28 kg of barley are needed for the production of 100 litres of beer, while 400 kg of barley are needed as pig feed for the production of 100 kg of pork.

Figure 6.4   Interior of a cafe in Amsterdam, the Netherlands

4 Diet, obesity and health

Although the environmental impacts of changing diets have been very significant, it is the consequences for human health of these changes that have captured the attention of politicians and the media in recent years. The issue of obesity is perhaps the most prominent among these health consequences. This is a growing problem in countries such as the UK and the USA, especially in the last three or four decades (Figures 6.5 and 6.6). Body mass index is the most popular indicator for measuring obesity (Box 6.1).

Box 6.1 Body mass index

Body mass index (BMI) is calculated by dividing an individual's body mass (or weight) by the square of their height:

$$BMI = \frac{mass\ (kg)}{height\ squared\ (m^2)}$$

Its use as a method for classifying body weight is shown in Table 6.1.

Table 6.1 Body mass as a measure of obesity

BMI	Classification
Below 18.5	Underweight
18.5–24.9	Normal weight
25–29.9	Overweight
Above 30	Obese

However, there are other ways of measuring obesity: skinfold measurements, underwater weighing and computerised tomography. Unlike the BMI, which can be easily calculated from a person's height and weight, it is prohibitively expensive to collect data from large enough samples using the other methods (Guthman, 2011).

As an indicator of obesity, the BMI has come under criticism:

- As it is a ratio of weight to height, and does not distinguish between lean and fat body mass, BMI does not determine excessive fatness. A bodybuilder with little fat but ample muscle and bone would have a relatively high BMI (Guthman, 2011).

> • BMI's relationship to health is problematic because it cannot distinguish between subcutaneous fat (fat below the skin), considered largely harmless, and visceral fact (fat surrounding internal organs), which is associated with a range of diseases.
>
> As a result, BMI is often considered an insufficiently reliable measure of body fatness (Ross, 2005).

Health professionals, economists and journalists agree that the growing rate of obesity is a very significant public health care concern (Figure 6.6). Being obese and overweight has a number of known health consequences. Visceral fat is associated with diabetes, stroke and cardiovascular disease (Montague and O'Rahilly, 2000), and being overweight puts enormous demands on joints and can lead to high blood pressure. Obesity is a drain on public health budgets as it results in ill health and increased costs to health providers for treatment, transport, extra-large beds, and more. Moreover, as you learnt in the previous section, consumption of food in excess of the needs associated with an adequately nutritious and balanced diet (Box 6.2) has negative environmental consequences. Overeating is bad for both human bodies and the environment.

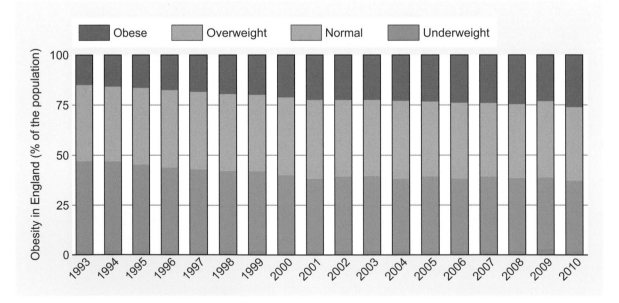

Figure 6.5   Growth in obesity rates in England (Source: based on Office for National Statistics, in Evans, 2012)

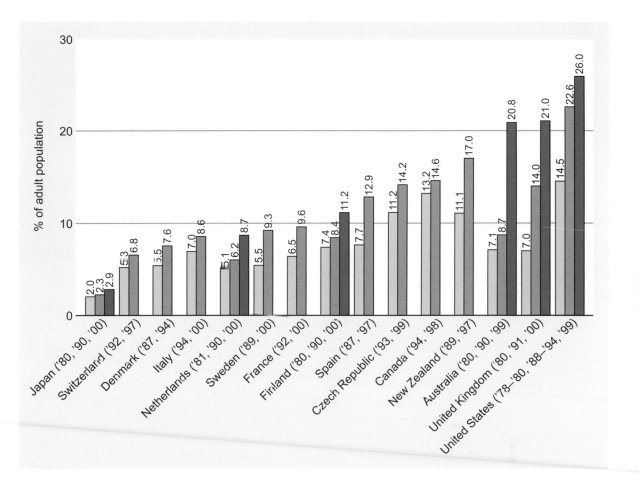

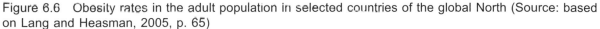

Figure 6.6   Obesity rates in the adult population in selected countries of the global North (Source: based on Lang and Heasman, 2005, p. 65)

So how have societies responded to this problem? In much of the media and in public policy debates, the issue is framed in terms of the individual's lack of information or education about the implications of their eating behaviour. However, as you will see below, this analysis is wholly inadequate.

As Julie Guthman (2011, p. 9) pointed out, 'the current public health consensus is that reducing calorie intake, along with increasing calorie expenditure through exercise, is what must be done'. (Note that Guthman uses an old energy unit – calorie – instead of the joule.) This targets individual changes in dietary behaviour as the primary way of addressing what has become a public concern.

Box 6.2   Recommended daily average food intake

While there is a degree of uncertainty about the average daily food energy intake people need, as the number of joules will depend on factors such as age, gender and lifestyle, there is nonetheless a consensus among nutritionists that in affluent societies the average intake per capita exceeds the recommended amount. The recommended average daily intake of food energy for women is about 8400 kilojoules (kJ) and for men about 10,900 kJ. According to Smil (2004), the difference between the average per capita daily food energy requirements in countries of the global North and the actual, higher level of consumption is about 3000 kJ per capita per day. This difference could supply another 350 million people with the meat and fat-rich diet now prevailing in countries of the global North, or could provide for twice as many people consuming the traditional, largely vegetarian but nutritionally adequate diet common in some parts of Asia (Smil, 2004).

4.1   Diet and dietary guidelines: an opportunity for individual action on the environment?

According to governments worldwide, one way of achieving individual, choice-driven behavioural change is the provision of information. This usually takes the form of some kind of official dietary guidance. This expert knowledge-based dietary guidance is not primarily environmentally motivated. It is aimed at influencing individuals' eating habits and is officially motivated by concerns about human health and the desire to bring down the costs of health care.

Activity 6.2   Dietary guidelines: reference values and uniform dietary recommendations

In the USA, there are two types of dietary guidelines aimed at the general public (Table 6.2). The first is a set of dietary standards, known as *reference values*, for the amounts of essential nutrients (e.g. protein; see Box 6.3) and dietary energy that should be present in the human diet and that should meet the needs of any healthy person. The second is a type of dietary guidelines, namely *uniform dietary recommendations*, the aim of which is to promote a healthy diet that reduces the risks of developing degenerative diseases.

Table 6.2   Summary of two sets of dietary guidelines: reference values and uniform dietary recommendations

	Reference values	**Uniform dietary recommendations**
History	USA since 1940s	USA since 1980
Definition	Reference values are amounts of the essential nutrients and dietary energy that should be present in the human diet to meet the needs of a healthy person	Uniform dietary recommendations promote healthy diet with the aim of reducing the risks of developing degenerative diseases
Relate to	Chemistry of the body and are based on the best available scientific knowledge	Foodstuffs (including the main food groups – starchy foods; dairy products; meat, poultry and fish; and vegetables and fruits) and food constituents deemed to have, depending on quantity, either positive (fibre; see Box 6.3) or negative (cholesterol, salt) impacts on human health
Aims	Variety and moderation in food consumption; prevent deficiency	Reduce the risk of chronic and degenerative diseases
Example	Protein content in an individual food	Consumer-oriented campaigns such as 'five-a-day' advice for fruit and vegetables

How have US government dietary guidelines changed over time? Consider the social, economic and research changes in this period that might have informed these changes.

Comment

Both the definition of dietary problems and ideas about how to respond to dietary changes developed over time. In the 1940s and 1950s, governments were concerned about how populations might eat well at a time of food shortages and a narrower range of food choices. In the 1980s, governments became more concerned to guide choices in times of plenty. Most people in the USA had more disposable income in the 1980s, and more women were working outside the home, with less time available, and less inclination, to cook daily using fresh ingredients. The fast food and supermarket industries developed in step with these economic and social changes. Medical and dietary research in the 1940s was focused on the dietary energy needs of a healthy body, whereas four decades later there was more focus on the negative effects of particular kinds of eating (including increasing levels of salt and fat and reducing levels of fresh fruit and vegetables in the diet).

Box 6.3   Nutrients

Fats, carbohydrates and proteins, nutrients needed in considerable amounts, are collectively referred to as *macronutrients*. In addition, there are two other nutrient categories – *minerals* (e.g. iron, sodium and potassium) and *vitamins* (chemical compounds which the human body cannot synthesise) – which help to maintain and regulate body processes. For example, sodium, a chemical element found in common salt and most food materials, is essential in many biochemical processes in the body, such as the regulation of materials entering and leaving cells, nerve transmission and maintenance of appropriate blood pressure. Minerals have a variety of functions, including, for example, that of iron in the transport of oxygen in red blood cells, and that of calcium as a component of bone. Minerals and vitamins are needed only in small quantities; hence they are referred to as *micronutrients*.

While the body has a minimum level of need for all these requirements, for some there are upper limits beyond which the material may be toxic or have other deleterious effects. For example, high intakes of a form of fats called saturated fats, and the fat-related compound cholesterol, in particular, have been associated with various health issues. High salt consumption is associated with high blood pressure and heart disease.

One other component of diet is *dietary fibre*. Dietary fibre comprises complex carbohydrates (polysaccharides), such as cellulose and other materials that provide the strengthening tissues in plant materials, which act as a bulking and lubricating agent for food passing through the digestive tract, and help to keep it in a healthy condition (Schröder, 2003).

Although there is scientific consensus on the five nutrient categories (three macro- and two micronutrients) of diet (Box 6.3), agreeing practical advice on which foods to eat and in what quantities is much less straightforward and is laden with uncertainties. Given the overriding importance of dietary energy, a first step in assessing food needs is to know how much energy is being dissipated by the subject. This will depend on several things, including body size, activity level and outside temperature.

Another area of official guidance concerns fish consumption. Consumers in the UK are encouraged to eat two portions of fish a week. Fish is a source of protein, vitamins and minerals. One of the two portions should be oily fish which is high in omega-3 fats and which has been found to help to prevent heart disease. While recommendations on food consumption motivated by health concerns are usually environmentally beneficial (reduced consumption of unhealthy food reduces environmental impacts), in this specific case, public policy advice on healthy human diet may impede the efforts to protect marine biodiversity and sustainable fish stocks. This illustrates that the different values (human health and environmental conservation) in the responsibility apex of Belasco's identity–convenience–responsibility triangle may, in certain cases, conflict with each other.

Dietary guidelines are a source of fierce contestation between, on the one hand, those advocating goals of public health and, on the other, food companies defending their profits. While advice to consume more of certain food products (e.g. five portions of fruits and vegetables a day) to reduce risks from diseases and prevent nutrient deficiencies generates little opposition, as companies can use it to market their products, the same does not apply to advice to reduce the intake of foods containing sugars, saturated fat, salt and cholesterol. Exploiting scientific uncertainties about the risk of eating certain foods, many food companies have in the past opposed advice for the reduced intake of these food groups. Falbe and Nestle (2010) described how each step (research reviews, hearings, collection of testimonies and report writing) of the periodical revision of the Dietary Guidelines for Americans (the US variant of uniform dietary recommendations) is subject to intense lobbying by food companies and trade associations. The companies nominate members of the advisory committee, submit research reviews, testify at hearings and promote the health benefits of their products (Box 6.4).

> ## Box 6.4   Diet, health and business interests
>
> One outcome of the 2005 revision of the Dietary Guidelines for Americans (the Guidelines are revised every five years) was the increase of the longstanding recommendation of two daily dairy servings to three (i.e. a 50 per cent increase). The change was justified on the grounds that potassium in dairy products would help to counter the effects of high-sodium diets on blood pressure. However, while dairy foods are good sources of potassium, they also are high in sodium and saturated fats. Vegetables and fruits are better sources of potassium and are low in sodium. The negative effects of increased intake of one mineral – sodium – were addressed by increased intake of another mineral – potassium (and of an entire food category – dairy produce), rather than by reducing the recommended intake of foods containing sodium. An investigative report by the *Wall Street Journal* attributed this decision to lobbying by the National Dairy Council and to the influence of dairy trade groups on several members of the advisory committee.
>
> Source: Falbe and Nestle, 2010

Dietary guidelines also have environmental consequences, although these consequences are rarely made explicit. For example, in the USA the food industry and the Department of Agriculture have consistently promoted diets that emphasise consumption of foods from animal sources (Lang and Heasman, 2005), as meat and dairy products are highly profitable. Animal farming leads to greater depletion of environmental resources than growing plants, and thus any increase in recommended dietary intakes of animal products will have detrimental environmental effects.

Activity 6.3   Dietary advice: what sticks?

Recall one or two examples of dietary advice that you have heard in the last few years. How did you receive them (e.g. from a friend or colleague, through the media, in a leaflet)? Did the advice contradict other advice or messages you regularly receive? Have you acted on it? Does dietary advice ever contradict what you know about environmental issues?

Comment

The author of this chapter gave the following response to this activity. It suggests that not just the content, but also the form and carrier of health-related diet messages can influence the way individuals respond to them:

'Although I think of myself as someone who takes care of himself I'm pretty resistant to being told what to do by "big brother"-type messages from government. So, when the Chief Medical Officer or whatever they're called tells me how many units of alcohol to take (and that advice is lower than the amount I generally consume), I don't take too much notice. I'm much better at hearing about the things I already do! I'm mad for fresh fruit and eat plenty of vegetables, so glow with smug self-satisfaction when a TV chef makes a jokey reference to having your five-a-day. The only lingering doubt in my mind then is that I know that my fresh soft fruit in winter is coming from, say, Africa, and my supermarket apples arrive in a British summer on the slow boat from New Zealand – with a pretty big environmental impact (though not much cost difference) compared with seasonal stuff. But supermarkets make it all too easy for me as an individual to make food selection choices that carry high environmental impacts.'

5   Beyond individual action

In the previous section you saw that, although diets are influenced by a number of factors, most of the guidelines are aimed at altering individual behaviour. By modifying their diet, individual consumers can make a change that is either positive or negative to both their health and the environment. For example, a shift from an affluent, meat-rich diet to a vegetarian diet might lead to a significant decrease in an individual's ecological 'foodprint'. Similarly, drinking tap water (where it is safe for human consumption) instead of tea, coffee, beer, wine and soft drinks significantly reduces pressure on natural resources needed for the production, processing and distribution of these drinks.

Environmentally beneficial changes in diet at the individual level might be motivated by a number of reasons which would come under the responsibility apex of Belasco's triangle. These include health concerns (related to Maslow's second-order needs) and values-related reasons such as animal welfare and environmentalism (related to Maslow's fourth-order needs). Individuals might arrive at the decision to make the changes motivated by this set of reasons independently of the advice provided by governments and other institutions. This kind of change is precisely where most governments put their efforts.

ABC model
A model of social change which holds that people's attitudes and values (A) drive the kinds of behaviour (B) that individuals choose (C) to adopt.

The sociologist Elizabeth Shove (Shove, 2010) coined the term **ABC model** which, she argued, was the basis of today's consumption-related environmental policy (e.g. around individual diet, energy or transport decisions) in countries of the global North. 'A' stands for attitude, 'B' for behaviour and 'C' for choice. Adapting the model to food, it is values and attitudes (the A), which drive the diet-related behaviour (the B) that individuals choose (the C) to adopt. In much environmental policy, Shove (2010) argued, the concept of choice was absolutely central.

Despite its popularity with policy makers and large sections of the research community alike, the ABC model of social change is problematic on a number of grounds. The first, and perhaps the most obvious, difficulty concerns its effectiveness. Taking the example of advice aimed at reducing the rates of obesity in affluent societies, the model clearly fails to deliver because the rates keep increasing. Critics have suggested that placing the responsibility for change on individuals may not produce the desired change, but from the government's point of view it is a convenient way of demonstrating activity while avoiding responsibility.

As Shove (2010, p. 1274), referring to climate change policy, put it: 'ABC obscures the extent to which governments sustain unsustainable economic institutions and ways of life, and the extent to which they have a hand on structuring options and possibilities.' Another problem is the **value–action gap** (Blake, 1999) which denotes the limited extent to which intention leads to action; in other words, people who notionally subscribe to environmental values do not always act accordingly. This raises the fundamental question about the extent to which values drive actions and forces us to ask whether value change is a necessary precursor to social change and, if so, whether it is sufficient to guarantee change or just one necessary condition for change.

According to Shove (2010, p. 1277), the achievements the ABC model can deliver, relying on individual choice, are relatively modest: it can encourage green purchasing, reduction of some forms of waste (e.g. by switching off lights that are not needed, or by recycling), technological efficiency (adoption of green technology such as efficient appliances) and occasional restraint (such as consuming a low-impact diet) – behaviours which, rather than achieving significantly reduced environmental impacts, reinforce the status quo. Moreover, a sense of fatalism and helplessness in the face of environmental risks often leads even environmentally concerned people to conclude that individual actions on global environmental issues are both inadequate and ineffective.

Value–action gap
The behavioural gap that occurs when an actor's values and beliefs do not correspond to their agency.

Activity 6.4   Can ABC approaches close value–action gaps?

Shove is very critical of individualised ABC approaches in relation to sustainability. But can you think of any example of an area of consumption where the ABC approach has been effective in bridging the gap between values and actions?

Comment

One of the editors of this block gave the example of the rapid spread of Fairtrade labelling on supermarket shelves: 'When I was at school it was a phrase that just a few church groups would have been aware of. In the space of less than 20 years, some of the biggest chocolate, coffee and tea consumer brands on the planet felt it was essential to be badged as Fairtrade, with lots of positive results for growers.' Another pointed to the growth of organic food as a sector of the market over the same period. It is interesting that although these examples can both be understood as following the 'ABC' model, governments have barely been involved in the growth of these areas of consumption.

Despite evidence of growth in some environmentally or socially sustainable sectors of food production in recent years, most trends are going in a more environmentally destructive direction. This leaves us with the question: if individual action is generally inadequate, what other ways of responding to environmental concerns are needed? Returning to the problem of obesity, we find that escalation in concern over obesity has been accompanied by a shift away from explanations focusing on individual failings or predispositions to obesity, towards a concern with the way that overall conditions of life within a place or nation promote unfitness, poor nutrition and excessive weight gain.

A UK government report *Tackling Obesities* (Government Office for Science, 2007) calls these conditions of life an 'obesogenic environment': 'The term embraces the entire range of social, cultural and infrastructural conditions that influence an individual's ability to adopt a healthy lifestyle' (Government Office for Science, 2007, p. 52), including the way people prepare food and what they eat, how they get around and how they work.

It may be assumed that more affluent people would be more obese, as they can afford to buy more food, drive and do physically less demanding work. Yet, it is often poorer segments of society and people with lower social status who suffer disproportionately from obesity. One explanation for this is that poorer people work longer hours and have less time for exercise. Human geographer David Harvey theorises this in a more sophisticated way, arguing that contemporary capitalism is created through the 'productive destruction' of the human body (Harvey, 2008). For Harvey, capitalist conditions serve to exhaust and damage bodies through factors such as obesity, while at the same time valuing these bodies only through their ability to work. This is what he means by productive destruction. Capitalism also values the needs of capital, of companies who sell unhealthy food to make a profit, over the health needs of consumers. These foods are often mass-produced cheaply, using poor ingredients and using fat, sweeteners and salt to enhance taste. They thus encourage obesity.

Harvey's arguments are supported by evidence: inequality, which often rises in capitalist societies, leads to increased obesity. The fact that the rates of obesity are vastly diverse between societies with a similar level of wealth (Figure 6.7) but with different levels of income inequality – for example, the USA (GDP per capita in 2010: 47,000 US$) and Sweden (49,000 US$) – suggests that obesity is not simply a function of affluence. Obesity is closely correlated with income inequality in society (Wilkinson and Pickett, 2010), itself increasingly seen in capitalist societies. While correlation is not an explanation, this finding nonetheless suggests that obesity is not purely a matter of individual choices and preferences, but that its causes are more complex and interactive; in other words, that it also has a wider structural dimension. It is underlain by ways of life and by infrastructures of food production and consumption which are very hard for individuals to alter.

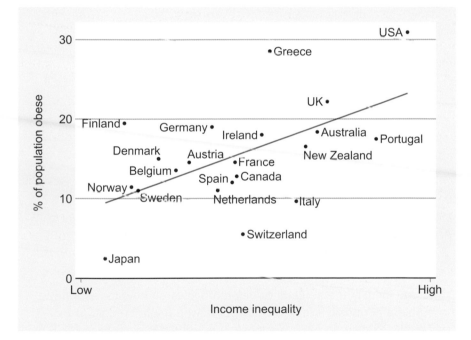

Figure 6.7   More adults are obese in more unequal societies (based on Wilkinson and Pickett, 2010, p. 92, Figure 7.1)

Although this story of the dynamics of capital is important, so too is a recognition of the more intimate emotional and experiential aspects of lives people live under conditions not of their own choosing. According to professor of English Lauren Berlant, certain kinds of eating and drinking are a response to an exhausting and stressful environment

(Berlant, 2007). Shared consumption of quickly gratifying foodstuffs offers a way to conviviality and comfort which holds a special appeal for those who have lost any hope of a better long-term future. Obesity, therefore, cannot be understood or addressed at an individual level alone. Social, cultural and economic analyses, of the kind pursued by Harvey or Berlant, help to offer a much richer explanation of the complexities of the increase in obesity rates.

Activity 6.5   Obesity, responsibility, agency

Read the following extract from the UK government report *Tackling Obesities* alongside the text in Section 5 above, and answer the questions below.

> Solutions to address the obesogenic environment such as changes in transport infrastructure and urban design can be more difficult and costly than targeting intervention at the group, family or individual. However, they are more likely to affect multiple pathways within the obesity system in a sustainable way. In the short term, creating demand for such change may rely on aligning the benefits with those arising from broader social and economic goals such as reducing energy consumption, pollution, direct and indirect health costs, traffic congestion and crime rates. In the long term, strengthening action against obesity may not only reduce health and disability costs but also produce a generally healthier and more environmentally sustainable society.
>
> (Government Office for Science, 2007, p. 11)

Could you identify the sources of different views on how to respond to the problem of obesity? In each viewpoint, who might be said to be responsible? How can each responsible agent act?

Comment

Here is the list that the author of this chapter came up with:

- Public policies often hold individuals responsible. Individuals are asked to exercise, eat sensibly and to follow dietary guidelines.
- David Harvey, writing on capitalism, blames unequal societies and the economic processes through which these inequalities are created. His analysis can be applied to the profit-seeking activities of food

companies that make, advertise and sell foods that produce obesity. This analysis places the onus on governments to change the way in which companies function within the food system. Lauren Berlant writes about how everyday feelings are also important in influencing how much people eat. She adds dimensions relating to values and emotions to Harvey's arguments.

* The UK government identifies practical policies to reduce obesity. The report above suggests that those involved in designing urban environments and transport infrastructures, and, by extension, those who assign budgets for urban and environmental planning and policies; experts who influence how money is spent on infrastructures; transport-related industries, and many others also, all play a part in reducing obesity. It also links reduction of obesity with wider environmental issues.

This chapter has shown how a multitude of actors are involved in producing, preventing and regulating obesogenic environments. However, when governments or the media consider how to respond to such an issue, the individual is often targeted as the primary cause of obesity. It is no surprise, then, that communication to the individual about consumption choices is widely considered to be the primary route to a solution. This is a far easier route than challenging and changing the social, political and economic relations that enable unhealthy and environmentally damaging food to be produced and consumed so routinely.

Conceptualising environmental and health problems related to obesity as an aggregate result of behaviour and choices made by individuals who need to be better informed and educated depoliticises these issues. It avoids confrontation with the interests of powerful food companies and their political allies. However, it is not just the economic power of food and agricultural interests that has directed government actions. It is also the case that most Western governments want to be seen to protect freedom of choice, and believe in the effectiveness of free markets in delivering economic growth. However, the chapter has shown that obesity cannot simply be addressed on the scale of individual bodies or individual places. Both the responsibility and the ability to act are distributed across a number of people, attitudes, behaviours, organisations and infrastructures. Among other things, obesity needs to be understood as an example of market failure, and also a failure of the state to regulate successfully a sector of the economy that is resulting in significant health problems. The discussion of the UK government's report on obesogenic environments showed that sophisticated understandings and responses to these issues are discussed within government. However, change will only be possible if the more complex interrelationships and more widely distributed responsibilities outlined in that report are recognised.

6 Summary

The discussion of the social, cultural, economic and nutritional aspects of diet in this chapter has given you further opportunity to reflect on the Block 5 question, *How can we make a difference?* As the chapter has shown, there is a degree of compatibility between the goals of actors who seek to alleviate the environmental impacts of food production and consumption and the goals of the public health community. That means that there is an affinity between efforts – motivated by self-interest – to improve one's health or reduce risks of chronic diseases and the goal of reducing the impact of food consumption on the environment. Theoretically, at least, this offers an opportunity for environmental gains. You don't have to be a committed environmentalist, but if you care for your health and seek to modify your eating habits along the main principles of a healthy diet (e.g. eating less or reducing the intake of unhealthy food groups, such as meat or soft drinks), even without altering the contemporary food production and supply system, your behavioural change could have positive environmental implications.

However, when this approach – advice to reduce intake of certain types of food – is extended to the realm of public policy, some food companies, exploiting scientific uncertainty, have been known to fiercely oppose it. At the same time, the individualising of the problem by advising consumers to eat more fruit and vegetables and exercise more shifts responsibility for health and the environmental consequences of food production and consumption to individual consumers. Hence, attention is drawn away from investigation of the structural causes of environmentally unsustainable food systems that produce food detrimental to human health. While this approach offers some scope for change, Section 5 of this chapter showed that the effectiveness of this model – the ABC model of behavioural change – has severe limits. It fails to address the cultural, social, structural and infrastructural problems that have led to obesity, and its attendant environmental effects.

References

Belasco, W. (2008) *Food: The Key Concepts*, Oxford and New York, Berg.

Berlant, L. (2007) 'Slow death (sovereignty, obesity, lateral agency)', *Critical Inquiry*, vol. 33, no. 4 (Summer), pp. 754–80.

Blake, J. (1999) 'Overcoming the "value–action gap" in environmental policy: tensions between national policy and local experience', *Local Environment: The International Journal of Justice and Sustainability*, vol. 4, no. 3, pp. 257–78.

Carpenter, L. (2011) 'Four families living in one London square, but separated by class and income. How is that divide reflected in their diet?', *Observer Food Monthly*, no. 118, 13 March, pp. 20–27.

CTA (2011) 'The water we eat – tackling scarcity in ACP countries', CTA Policy Brief No. 2, June, Brussels, CTA [online], http://brusselsbriefings.files.wordpress.com/2011/07/policy_brief_water_en.pdf (Accessed 9 November 2012).

Evans, L. (2012) 'Obesity in England: why is it increasing?', *The Guardian*, 23 February [online], http://www.guardian.co.uk/news/datablog/2012/feb/23/obesity-problem-increasing (Accessed 6 November 2012).

Falbe, J. L. and Nestle, M. (2010) 'The politics of government dietary advice', in Germov, J. and Williams, L. (eds) *A Sociology of Food and Nutrition*, Oxford, Oxford University Press.

Gerbens-Leenes, P. W. and Nonhebel, S. (2002) 'Consumption patterns and their effects on land required for food', *Ecological Economics*, vol. 42, no. 1, pp. 185–99.

Government Office for Science (2007) *Tackling Obesities: Future Choices Project* [online], http://www.bis.gov.uk/assets/bispartners/foresight/docs/obesity/obesity_final_part1.pdf (Accessed 8 November 2012).

Guthman, J. (2011) *Weighing In: Obesity, Food Justice and the Limits of Capitalism*, Berkeley, CA, and London, University of California Press.

Harvey, D. (2008) 'The right to the city', *New Left Review*, vol. 53, pp. 23–40.

Hayward, T. (2011) 'How a 10-year revolution has put food at the heart of our national conversation', *The Observer*, 16 October, p. 32.

Lang, T. and Heasman, M. (2005) *Food Wars: The Global Battle for Mouths, Minds and Markets*, London, Earthscan.

Montague, C. T. and O'Rahilly, S. (2000) 'The perils of portliness: causes and consequences of visceral adiposity', *Diabetes*, vol. 49, pp. 883–8.

Ross, B. (2005) 'Fact or fiction? Weighing the obesity epidemic', in Gard, M. and Wright, J. (eds) *The Obesity Epidemic: Science, Morality, and Ideology*, London, Routledge.

Schröder, M. J. A. (2003) *Food Quality and Consumer Value: Delivering Food That Satisfies*, Berlin and New York, Springer.

Shove, E. (2010) 'Beyond the ABC: climate change policy and theories of social change', *Environment and Planning A*, vol. 42, no. 6, pp. 1273–85.

Smil, V. (2004) 'Improving efficiency and reducing waste in our food system', *Environmental Sciences*, vol. 1, no. 1, pp. 17–26.

Wilkinson, R. and Pickett, K. (2010) *The Spirit Level: Why Equality is Better for Everyone*, London, Penguin.

Chapter 7   Beyond the ABC model: from biotechnology to 'grow your own'

Petr Jehlička

Contents

1   Introduction

In the previous two chapters you explored why food has become an environmental issue and how making individual changes in consumption might form part of the response to this issue. Chapter 6 showed the limitations of attempts to reduce the social and environmental impacts of food consumption through changing individual attitudes, behaviours and choices. The chapter also showed that systems for production and distribution form part of the basic infrastructure of food provision and that one reason why behavioural change is inadequate is that agricultural systems, as well as those of production, distribution and marketing, ultimately shape how and what people consume. Behaviour and choice around food are part of social practices, and are therefore circumscribed in many ways.

This chapter suggests that moving away from the ABC model of social change might offer better scope for understanding how to respond to the problems of food production, distribution, consumption and waste. The two approaches to sustainable food provision that the chapter explores are new technologies (in this case, genetic modification), and growing your own food (or food self-provisioning).

The previous two chapters demonstrated how modifying food production systems has to be part of the array of responses to environmental issues, and altering how food is grown and the relationship between how it is grown and how it is used are both important responses to these issues. The example of biotechnology will be used to address the extent to which scientific innovation can generate more productive, and more environmentally friendly, agricultural systems. The chapter considers the type of biotechnology which has attracted the most attention – genetic modification (GM) – and the polarised nature of the debates on GM. The second response to sustainable food provision discussed in the chapter generates the shortest possible food supply chain – food self-provisioning (FSP). This is a social practice that draws on more traditional knowledges. This chapter will demonstrate that, despite its outward appearance as a 'trivial', individualised and inner-directed hobby, FSP directly relates to the tending and nurturing of values that are of great significance to any discussion of how societies in the global North might become more sustainable (Jehlička and Smith, 2012b). The consideration of FSP in the chapter expands on the social science concept of social practices as an alternative to the ABC approach, and views the sharing of the products of FSP as one kind of social practice that can support moves towards sustainability.

The chapter does not seek to argue that either of these responses is better than the other. It does not suggest that they are mutually exclusive, nor that one or both should be pursued. Rather, it seeks to illustrate and debate two responses to food and environmental issues that are already being practised. These responses have very different relationships to science, technology, the economy and society, and considering them side by side in this chapter makes clear that humanity's future responses to food and environment will draw on diverse strategies, including some that are highly innovative and others that draw on longstanding social practices. The chapter also shows that responses are geographically diverse, with social, cultural, political and technological contexts all shaping choices and strategies.

2   Genetic modification: a response by technology and industry

Biotechnology involves the application of biological science to the technical manipulation and use of living things for human ends. Although some technological knowledge, such as choosing and breeding plants to increase crop yields, has been part of the long history of agriculture, in this chapter the term biotechnology refers to modern genetic manipulation or to the most recent state-of-the-art technological innovations (Gregory et al., 2009).

Genetic technology, a specialist field of biotechnology, takes place where a gene or genes from one organism is inserted into the cell of another organism, thus creating a **genetically modified organism (GMO)**. Plants were first genetically modified in 1983. Among the major crops that have been genetically modified are maize, oil seed rape, tomatoes and potatoes. The intention of genetic engineering is that the GMOs will exhibit certain properties, or traits, seen as desirable. For example, genetically modified crops can be enhanced with additional nutrients or made resistant to certain types of pests, thus increasing crop yield rates.

GM crops and food have generated highly polarised debates and controversies since the first field trials in the mid 1980s. Advocates of GM food (and increasingly also GM animal feed) present the 'agricultural bio revolution', the input of biological knowledge into agricultural practices, as the latest anti-scarcity (i.e. anti-hunger) response. Recall nineteenth-century free trade as an anti-scarcity response mentioned in Chapter 5, Section 2. When first discussed in public debates, GM crops were often presented by their proponents as a route to delivering more calories to the world's poor. This argument has been noted for its Malthusian character; that is, its assumption that food shortage is based on inadequate food production and that the response to food insecurity must, therefore, be to increase food production (Nally, 2011). The leading GM company Monsanto (for examples of its products, see Table 7.1) adopted this line in its 2000 advertising campaign:

> Worrying about starving generations won't feed them. Food biotechnology will. The World's population is growing rapidly, adding the equivalent of a China to the globe every ten years. To feed these billion more mouths, we can try extending our farming

Biotechnology
The application of biological science to the technical manipulation and use of living things for human ends.

Genetically modified organism (GMO)
An organism engineered using a technique that transfers the genes from one organism to another, either of the same, or a different, unrelated species.

land or squeezing greater harvests out of existing cultivation ... Fertilizer, insecticide, and herbicide use will increase globally. At Monsanto, we now believe food biotechnology is a better way forward.

Monsanto, quoted in Shiva, 2000, p. 11

Box 7.1   Global regulation of GMOs

Two major categories of issues make GMOs a contested issue of global politics: safety and risk (protection of biodiversity), and free trade. In terms of international law, the former category is addressed by:

- the Cartagena Protocol on Biosafety under the Convention on Biodiversity
- the European Union's Directives on deliberate release, labelling and traceability of GMOs.

International law in the free trade category includes:

- the Codex Alimentarius
- the World Trade Organization agreements that rely on the Codex: the Technical Barriers to Trade Agreement and the Sanitary and Phytosanitary Agreement.

The two sets of regulation provide the legal framework for two GMO regulatory regimes: the regime emphasising the precautionary principle (introduced in international law in the 1992 Rio Declaration and restated in the Cartagena Protocol; see Book 1, Chapter 2, Section 4), which focuses on the safety/risk/sustainability nexus, and the regime exemplified by the Codex Alimentarius, which is aimed at the promotion of free trade and the harmonisation of international standards based on sound science. The main champion of the safety/risk/sustainability regime is the European Union and the main proponent of the free trade regime is the USA.

Source: based on Toft, 2012

A powerful alliance of GM food companies, governments and international organisations (e.g. the United Nations Development Programme (UNDP) and the World Health Organization (WHO)), as well as of many scientists and farmers supporting GM food, argue that GM food is a 'weapon in the battle against a future food crisis and in helping to feed the exponentially growing world population' (Toft, 2012, p. 224). Without this new green revolution (the original green revolution in the 1960s was a 'package' promoting new higher-yielding crops combined with the application of agricultural chemicals in the global South) led by genetically modified crops, they claimed, it would be impossible to feed the world. These highly emotive arguments were presented to balance widely held objections that were rooted in two different sets of concerns: safety/risk issues around the introduction of a novel technology, and issues around trade and protectionism (Box 7.1).

The arguments of opponents (large sections of the public and the media, NGOs, green parties and some academic researchers) have been more diverse. Initially, the focus of the GM food critique was on:

- issues of risk to health and safety and on arguments related to particular values – the supposedly unnatural qualities of GM food ('Frankenstein food' as British tabloid newspapers labelled GM food in the 1990s)

- the uncertainty surrounding the environmental impacts of GM crops

- the possibility of non-GM food contamination by GM foods.

A more system-level critique relates to concerns about GM food facilitating increased corporate control over the food system and to the denial of consumer choice. This is expanded on later in this section. But first we consider the technological dimension of GM food and the traits for which GM crops have been developed (Table 7.1).

Table 7.1   Selected traits of GM crops

Introduced traits	Description	Examples
Insect resistance	Crops protected from some forms of insect destruction through the introduction of a gene from *Bacillus thuringiensis* (Bt), leading to the production of insecticidal proteins	Monsanto's Bt corn (protected from corn borers), Monsanto's Bt cotton (protected from cutworms and bollworms)
Herbicide tolerance (HT)	Crop made tolerant to specific herbicides through the overproduction of specific enzymes that interact with the herbicide. HT allows for weed control and soil conservation through no-till weed control	Monsanto's Roundup soybean is tolerant to glyphosate, a wide-spectrum, low-toxicity herbicide
'Stacked traits' (multiple traits)	Stacked traits mean that these crops combine insect resistance and herbicide tolerance	Monsanto's Yieldgard VT corn is resistant to corn borers, cutworms and other insects, and also herbicide tolerant
Nutritional enhancement; 'biofortification'	Enhancement of micronutrients (vitamins, minerals). Also called 'functional food'	Golden rice 1 developed as proof of principle to combat vitamin A deficiency
Virus resistance	Protects against specific plant viruses	Rainbow cultivar of papaya protects against the papaya ring-spot virus
Fungal resistance	Protection against specific fungal pathogens	BASF's anti-blight GM potato (under field trials)
Improved shipping and storage	Altered ripening	Calgene's Flavr-Savr tomato (first marketed GM crop in the USA; no longer marketed)
Pharmaceutical production	Plants produce recombinant proteins for medical purposes	Ventria's recombinant human lactoferrin and lysozyme for rehydration therapy in treatment of childhood diarrhoea
Environmentally enhanced crops	Traits that allow plants to cope with climate change and environmental instability (e.g. limited water or fertiliser supply), for production of biofuel and food	Low nitrogen fertiliser – using rice varieties for carbon offset (under development; Arcadia Biosciences with the Chinese government)
Industrial chemicals	Plants to produce industrially important chemicals	GM corn and GM sugar cane for biofuels, GM soybean oil for biodiesel

Introduced traits	Description	Examples
Bioremediation	Plants used to extract compounds such as toxic heavy metals or organic compounds (e.g. PCBs) from polluted soil through hyperaccumulation	Under development; unlikely to be food plants

Source: adapted from Morin, 2008, Table 1

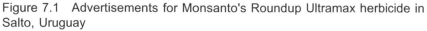

Figure 7.1 Advertisements for Monsanto's Roundup Ultramax herbicide in Salto, Uruguay

The social geographer David Nally offered a radical critique of the promotion of GM food technology as a comprehensive solution to food shortages (Nally, 2011). In his view, 'these cornucopian fantasies mask the fact that industrial biotechnologies are furthering the commodification of the food system' without addressing equitable access to food for marginalised people globally (Nally, 2011, p. 46). These processes transform human, animal and biological systems to suit private interests and increase further the power of agribusiness corporations: 'The end game of this logic is the corporate control of the means of production and the gradual elimination of non-market access to food' (Nally, 2011, p. 46). The prime example of this is corporate control of seed production and reproduction. Corporations now convert scientific innovations into commodities through patent protection and charge an 'innovation fee' for their use. GM crop companies produce seeds that are paired with particular herbicides. For example, Monsanto's Roundup soybean is genetically engineered to resist Monsanto's wide-spectrum herbicide (Figure 7.1). Farmers growing GM crops must buy their seeds from companies and are not allowed to plant seeds they gather (Morin, 2008). Corporations are developing surveillance systems aimed at detecting unauthorised use of patented plants, forcing farmers to sign contracts allowing random farm inspections and encouraging neighbouring farmers to report any breaches of their patents (Nally, 2011).

Box 7.2   GM crops: the sustainability arguments in favour

Crops that are genetically modified to be resistant to certain pests can deliver significant environmental benefits, according to a study spanning two decades (1990–2011). The main finding of the large-scale study led by Professor Kongming Wu from the Chinese Academy of Agricultural Sciences was that the benefits extended to non-GM crops in neighbouring fields (Lu et al., 2012). Since its introduction in 1997, the use of pesticides on China's Bt cotton plantations (95 per cent of China's cotton plantations) has halved. At the same time, natural insect predators such as ladybirds, spiders and lacewings have doubled. These natural predators killed pests beyond the reach of the insecticide in Bt cotton (which was designed to kill cotton bollworm), not only in cotton fields, but also in neighbouring non-GM fields of corn, soybean and peanut. Scientists had believed that as Bt cotton fields did not need spraying, pests not targeted by the insecticide in Bt cotton would multiply, ultimately resulting in a lot more pesticide spraying. This did not happen for the main pest – aphid – whose population decreased by two-thirds after Bt cotton was introduced. Natural predators doubled and the population of aphid fell. However, Professor Wu's previous research showed that since Bt cotton has been introduced, one pest, the mired bug, has increased. As a result, pesticide use has not dropped further than 50 per cent.

Sources: based on Lu et al., 2012; Carrington, 2012

Activity 7.1   Potential environmental benefits of GM crops

Using the information in Table 7.1 and Box 7.2, identify some potential environmental benefits associated with GM crops.

Comment

Among the potential environmental benefits of GM crops are weed control and soil conservation through no-till weed control of herbicide tolerant crops (the crops still need to be sprayed with herbicides, but to a lesser extent) and lower amounts of pesticide spraying of crops which produce insecticide proteins (as Box 7.2 shows, an added benefit might be the increase in natural predators killing other pests – even in neighbouring, non-GM crop fields). Plants needing lower volumes of irrigation water and/or fertilisers and plants capable of decontamination of soils of heavy metals or organic compounds are currently under development. The former would hold the potential to help address climate change (by reducing carbon dioxide emissions) and make a contribution to enhancing the ecosystem services provided by agriculture.

Activity 7.2   Evaluating GMOs

Look again at Table 7.1. First, based on the information presented in the table, give two general arguments in favour of GM technology in relation to the benefits to the world's poor. Second, bearing in mind what you learnt in Chapters 5 and 6, and your study of the module more widely, consider how you would interpret the information in the table using the module concepts of values, power and agency; risk and uncertainty; and space and time. Note that the original table was published in an academic journal called *Analytical and Bioanalytical Chemistry* and that the author of the article, Xenia Morin, is a biochemist by training.

Comment

The way the information in Table 7.1 is presented invokes the value of technological progress and the belief in technology as an agency driving social change. It seeks to show how GM technology could:

- feed the world's poor and hungry, provide them with essential minerals and vitamins and cure their diseases
- protect them from risks such as climate change through crops producing biofuels and crops requiring lower amounts of fertilisers or water.

Interpreting these arguments in the light of the module concepts, it is possible to draw out the following points:

The hunger argument ignores the fact that the problem of many hungry people is not that there is not enough food but that it does not reach them (Chapter 5). The argument neglects institutions, justice and politics and plays down the importance of risk and uncertainty caused by economic factors such as speculation. While many of the goals and ambitions outlined in Table 7.1 are individually achievable, it is unlikely that all of them could be achieved simultaneously. Some of them are incompatible. For example, land used for growing GM crops to produce biofuels will not be available for the production of GM food, curative or biofortification plants. Nally (2011) argued that the effect of addressing hunger by GM food is unlikely to be the end of hunger, but its displacement over space and time. While biofuels would reduce dependency on oil and reduce risks of climate change, there is the danger that many people will go hungry as a result of increased food prices.

It seems that, within the policy and academic communities, a more middle-ground assessment of the potential of GM crops to provide a response to the problems of hunger and environmental degradation has recently begun to take hold: 'GM crops are neither all good nor all bad and GM is not going to feed the world overnight. But it is a very powerful tool and should be kept in the tool box' (Professor of Ecology Guy Poppy, quoted in Carrington, 2012). Jan Boersema and Andrew Blowers (2011, pp. 244–5), reflecting on the two decades of experience of GM crops, concluded: 'the disasters that were foretold by the environmentalists have not happened, but the same applies to the golden mountain – to solve the hunger … No disasters and no golden mountains – that is also what might be expected of the future.' However, the long-term effects of GMOs are unknown, so the future risks posed by this technology are still uncertain.

GM seed is now widely used around the world, and under widely differing governance regimes. Within the USA and China, GM seed has become a staple of agricultural production of cotton and corn, with a supportive regulatory environment. Within the European Union, the popular mood and a more precautionary regulatory environment have seen a far more cautious approach. What is certain is that the potential social, economic and environmental benefits and risks of GM technologies need to be carefully weighed, and this will require an ongoing research effort, and informed and thoughtful public and political debate.

3   Food self-provisioning (FSP): a homegrown route to more sustainable food

The introduction of GM technologies required major research investments, and government assessment and regulations. In this section we explore self-grown food, or food self-provisioning (FSP). FSP represents a very different kind of relationship between humans, food and environment from GM. It is one that requires no research effort, sees almost no governmental intervention and varies widely in the level and style of its adoption around the world. In this and the following two sections we explore everyday practices of household food production and sharing. These sections consider the ways in which FSP is environmentally and socially sustainable. Research has shown how these practices foster local resilience by strengthening social networks of cooperation spanning extended families, friends, neighbours and co-workers. This mode of food provision is also effective in terms of resource and energy conservation and waste reduction. Moreover, it gives practitioners control over an environmentally friendly form of food production and consumption that has no need for technical experts, government agents or businesses.

Activity 7.3   Alternative vision of food provisioning

Read carefully the following extract from *Grow Your Own* magazine. It was taken from a speech by the policy director of the New Economics Foundation, an organisation which advocates alternative economic models. List the main sustainability-related features of the model of food provisioning promoted in the extract.

> The UK has huge domestic potential to secure itself against impending change [decreasing food reserves], but we can always do more! I suggest that work places offer staff time off to work on gardens, allotments or productive community growing schemes. This would tick all our boxes, and the psychological and physical health benefits are also well-proven. ... How about planting fruit trees on the streets of our own towns and cities, and allowing anyone to harvest the produce? Fruit trees make a town look more beautiful and they might remind a younger generation where food comes from –

they might also please the bees, on whom we rely for all that food. Why not create somewhere at the heart of our local communities where small producers can sell and exchange food, swap knowledge, learn more about growing, cook (and serve it) – even share tools? Our high streets are pockmarked with empty properties and some of these could be turned into new, micro food hubs, where all this could happen – putting good food at the heart of the community.

(Simms, 2011, p. 98)

Comment

One member of the module team offered the following response to this activity:

'The features of the model that I identified would include fresh healthy produce; an extremely short food chain – or food localism – with significantly reduced environmental impacts; limited packaging; organic or semi-organic mode of production; the strengthening of social bonds through cooperation; fostering links with local community via sharing tools and produce; and the non-monetary and non-market character of this activity. The article promotes an enthusiasm for and a positive image of the food self-provisioning model and implicitly relates FSP to environmental (resource and energy conservation) and social (trust, social bonds and cooperation) sustainability.'

FSP is a part of a larger economic category usually labelled the **informal economy**, which also includes hidden paid work and unpaid but productive work. To Teitelbaum and Beckley (2006), the defining characteristic of an informal economy is activity that it is not regulated and recorded by the government, and involves activities ranging from criminal behaviour to barter, gifts and self-provisioning. In this chapter we are concerned with lawful informal economic activities, such as growing and foraging food and sharing it with others.

Informal economy
Economic activity not regulated and recorded by the government, including activities from criminal behaviour to barter, gifts and self-provisioning.

The question of what kinds of 'food production and distribution optimizes human well-being at what scale (local, regional, national) and over what time period (seasonal, annual, multiple years) depends crucially on how people value the various attributes of food, including their differing views on social and environmental impacts of agricultural production' (Tomich et al., 2011, p. 210). Social researchers point to how these values are 'enacted' in the process of growing food.

'Household food production' is one of the terms used to describe non-commercial food production. A popular term in the UK (and in some other English-speaking countries) is 'grow your own' (the title, as you saw in Activity 7.3, of a British magazine). Following Teitelbaum and Beckley (2006), this section defines **food self-provisioning** as a non-market, non-commercial activity aimed at production of food within a household, in which people engage primarily for the satisfaction of needs beyond the narrowly economic. In affluent societies, FSP is a way of obtaining food that is complementary to using shops or markets, rather than a means of survival. FSP includes growing fruit and vegetables, raising animals and poultry for domestic consumption of meat and eggs, foraging or wildcrafting (gathering wild plants, fruits and berries from their natural environment) and preserving food for domestic consumption or non-market distribution to other people (sharing). These legal activities take place not only beyond the market but also beyond government regulation, although some elements of FSP might be subject to regulation, such as veterinary control of pigs and rabbits. In that sense, it is a form of sustainability in action (Jehlička and Smith, 2012a, p. 57). You will learn more on the sustainability dimension of FSP in Section 5 below.

Now look at Figure 7.2, which gives you some basic indicators about the extent of FSP in Europe and its contribution to the nutrition needs of these populations. The left-hand graph shows the percentages of respondents who were not professional farmers and who answered 'yes' to the question: 'In the past year, has your household helped meet its need for food by growing vegetables or fruits or keeping poultry or livestock?' The right-hand graph shows the percentages of respondents who were not professional farmers and who stated their FSP met greater than 50 per cent of their households' needs. (Note that the symbol > should be read as 'greater than'. A confidence interval describes the amount of uncertainty associated with a sample survey of a population.)

Food self-provisioning
A non-commercial activity aimed at production of food within a household, in which people engage primarily for the satisfaction of needs beyond the narrowly economic.

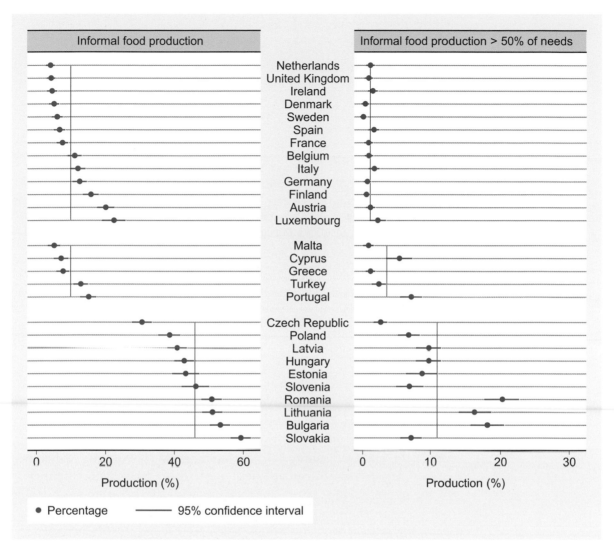

Figure 7.2   The extent of food self-provisioning in European countries and Turkey, 2003 (Source: based on Alber and Kohler, 2008, p. 117, Figure 1)

Activity 7.4   Reading information from a graph

Use the two graphs in Figure 7.2 to answer the following questions:

1   What percentages of Luxembourgers and Bulgarians meet more than 50 per cent of their nutrition needs in their households through FSP?

2   Are the UK and Italy above or below the average percentage of the population involved in FSP within the group of the most affluent countries (Netherlands–Luxembourg)?

Comment

1   Approximately 3 per cent Luxembourgers and 18 per cent of Bulgarians.

2   The average percentages of population involved in FSP for the three groups of countries are represented by vertical lines. The average for the 'top' group of the most affluent European countries is approximately 10 per cent (as represented by the black average line that runs through the plots for this group of countries). The dot showing the UK's percentage is to the left (located at approximately 5 per cent) of the average line, which means that the proportion of the UK population growing their own food is below the average of this group of countries. The dot for Italy is to the right of the average line. The percentage of Italians growing their own food (approximately 13 per cent) is above the average of this group of countries.

The answer to the first question can be found on the right-hand graph, and to the second on the left-hand graph.

Informal economic practices such as FSP are usually perceived in a positive way. However, Michael Samers (2005) cautions against over-romanticisation of such practices and informal economics in general. He questions whether it should be considered a form of resistance to formal market relations. For example, FSP might require long hours of very hard work with unpredictable results owing to weather conditions or pest infestations. In certain social contexts – especially in countries of the global South – informal food production and consumption might not be a matter of choice and enjoyment, but of economic necessity. Also, the roles of women in households are changing, with increased opportunities of work and affluence. While FSP has clear environmental benefits, it carries with it risks and uncertainties for those who rely on it for a secure supply of food. While not discounting the possible negative aspects of FSP, the focus here is on the nature of its contribution to more sustainable food systems.

The extract you looked at for Activity 7.3 by the policy director of the New Economics Foundation projected a very positive and 'progressive' image of both FSP and of sharing. Some Western media have glamorised 'growing your own' as a status-enhancing activity suitable for the social elite and celebrities (Figure 7.3). Yet, in many accounts (the media, academia or policy advice), FSP is presented in a less positive light. How the phenomenon of FSP is interpreted is context-specific. In the former socialist European countries (see Figure 7.2), FSP is sometimes seen as an indicator of their traditional, non-modern character, a phenomenon left over from their socialist or even pre-socialist past that slows current economic development. For example, in a document on Czech agricultural and countryside policies, European Union (EU) policy consultants working for the Czech government characterised FSP in the Czech Republic in the following words:

> Ineffective self-provisioning habits (eggs, poultry, potatoes, vegetables, fruit) hang over from the past, which contributes to the relatively low purchasing power of the countryside ...

> Food self-provisioning, which provides households involved in this activity with a basic livelihood, can sometimes contribute to decline and exclusion.

> (Ministerstvo pro místní rozvoj a Ministerstvo zemědělství, 2000, pp. 18 and 43)

(a)   (b)

Figure 7.3   (a) Michelle Obama, wife of President Barack Obama, in the garden of the White House, Washington DC; (b) Sarah Brown, wife of former British Prime Minister Gordon Brown, in the garden of 10 Downing Street, London

In contrast, FSP in western European and North American households is interpreted more positively: as a fashionable lifestyle activity, a hobby of affluent sections of society, or a self-improvement activity with positive educational, health and dietary benefits (Jehlička and Smith, 2011). These very different ways of viewing FSP provide a reminder that how human activities are valued is strongly influenced by where and when they are happening. In other words, they are temporally and spatially distinct. The negative account of FSP in former socialist societies in the official Czech government document confirms Nally's (2011) point about the promotion of agrarian capitalism (i.e. farming systems based around financial exchanges motivated by profit) in the world's 'peripheral' regions, and how this results in the commodification of their food systems. The prerequisite for the attainment of this goal is the derision of indigenous modes of food provision as backward and in need of modernisation and improvement. This line of thinking imagines a kind of temporal pathway of development in farming and agriculture (along with the rest of the economy), along which societies gradually 'advance' from 'underdeveloped' to 'developed'. Some of the hidden assumptions in this way of thinking have been the source of vigorous criticism by authors such as Nally (2011).

4   Sharing, sustainability and food

The idea of sharing has been mentioned earlier in the module. This section will extend this to point to other forms of human interaction that transcend self-interest, such as generosity and hospitality.

Table 7.2   Ways of thinking about consumption: commodity exchange, gift giving and sharing

	Commodity exchange	Gift giving	Sharing
Example	Buying bread in a shop for money	Birthday present	Pooling and allocation of household resources
Characteristics	Reciprocal	Non-reciprocal in appearance; reciprocal exchange in practice	Non-reciprocal
	Balanced exchange		Social links to others
	No lingering obligations	Non-obligatory in appearance; obligatory in practice	De facto or de jure shared ownership or usufruct rights
	Transfer of ownership		
	Monetary	Transfer of ownership	Money irrelevant
	Non-singular	Luxury	Singular objects
	Calculation	Singularises objects	Non-ceremonial
	Inspection	Ceremonial, wrappings	Networked inclusion
	Impersonal	Lingering imbalance	Personal
	Independent	Personal; dependent	Dependent
	Trade/barter context	Gift-giving/alliance-formation context	Sharing context
	Quantitative relations between objects	Qualitative relations between people	Social reproduction
			Love, caring

> ## Explanations of terms in Table 7.2
>
> **Dependent/independent** refers to the relationship between people; if the value of objects depends on whom objects are exchanged with, they are referred to as **singular** objects.
>
> **Usufruct** is the right to use and gain from a piece of property belonging to another person, provided that the property itself remains undiminished and uninjured in any way (*Collins English Dictionary*, 1994).
>
> Source: adapted from Belk, 2010, Table 1, p. 721

Early twentieth-century thinkers such as the anthropologists Marcel Mauss (Mauss, 1925 [1967]) and Bronisław Malinowski (Malinowski, 1926) equated sharing with forms of either gift giving or commodity exchange (barter). Recent debates have centred on the differences between sharing and gifts, on the one hand, and commodity exchange, on the other (Table 7.2). There is a growing consensus today that one of the key differences between sharing and gift giving is that the former is non-reciprocal (Price, 1975; Belk, 2010). For example, with gift giving around birthdays there is an expectation, often unspoken, that if A gives B a gift for B's birthday then B will, in turn, give a gift for A's birthday. In other words, there is reciprocity. Sharing, however, is seen as non-reciprocal; that is, one gives without the expectation of receiving something back in return.

The distinctions between commodity exchange, gift giving and sharing are summarised in Table 7.2. Characteristics of the three interactions should be read as descriptors of the three prototypes, not as definitional criteria. If a specific behaviour does not correspond with one or several characteristics, it does not necessarily mean that the behaviour does not belong to that category. The three categories of commodity exchange, gift giving and sharing should not be seen as separate from each other – there are overlaps among them.

Activity 7.5   Categorising consumption: the ABC model and homegrown food distribution

Which category or categories in Table 7.2 might the ABC model, discussed in the previous chapter, and the distribution of homegrown food (Figure 7.7), fall into?

Comment

The ABC model relies on commodity exchange, in that it assumes that people will be encouraged to change their purchasing behaviour. The distribution of homegrown food falls in the category of sharing, although there might also be an element of gift giving.

5 Social practices that deliver 'sustainable development in action'

Although FSP in former socialist European societies might not be motivated primarily by environmental reasons, it does, as Activity 7.3 suggests, result in environmental and social benefits. Unlike all the local and national policy documents in western European countries that try to sketch out what sustainability might be like and how it might be achieved, FSP in previously socialist countries could be said to be an example of sustainable development actually being implemented (Jehlička and Smith, 2012a).

While there is a seasonal rhythm to growing and supplying fruit and vegetables, which determines peaks and lows of availability, FSP is an activity conducted on a routine and fairly frequent basis for a significant period of the year. It is helpful, therefore, to understand FSP in terms of social practices, a concept that highlights the everyday and the routine. FSP can be considered a social practice that can be a valuable part of a transition towards a more sustainable future.

What contributes to the emergence of a social practice? Two broad reasons may be identified. The first concerns changes in the world about us, in the broader social structures in which people lead their lives. Shove and Walker (2010) argue that innovations – in the form of new technologies, systems of supply and infrastructures – can shape new social practices. For example, and as you saw in Chapter 3 of this book, infrastructural change through the introduction of low carbon energy technologies can generate new social practices that reduce the carbon footprints of individuals. (Similarly, new technologies can generate new social practices that undermine sustainability, such as the increasing use of air conditioning in some countries.)

However, the agency of an individual person is never solely dependent on structural changes. This leads to the second reason why new social practices may emerge. A person may change their agency through a change in values or beliefs or out of conscience. Social practices are therefore shaped at both structural and individual levels (Figure 7.4). If an individual changes their behaviour, they may set a precedent that others then follow. If we are to understand how we can make a difference, it is important to understand how the social practices that can contribute to a more sustainable future emerge, persist and disappear (Shove, 2010). To consider this, we explore, later in this section, the reasons why people get involved in FSP.

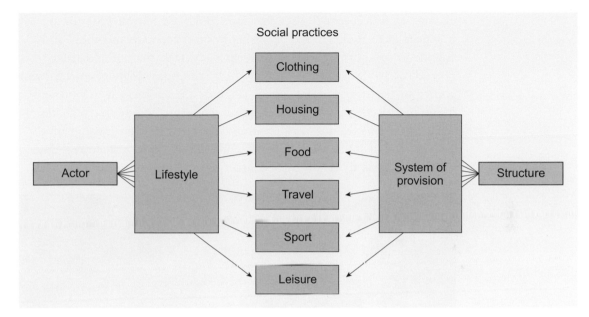

Figure 7.4   The social practices model (Source: based on Spaargaren, 2003, p. 689, Figure 1)

Seyfang et al. (2010) characterised the nature of social practices as follows:

- Social practices include various types of knowledge, skills, understandings and forms of emotional attachment and are performed repeatedly, thus becoming embedded and embodied within practitioners.

- Social practices involve the integration of human, non-human, social and technical elements.

- Social practices are the key unit of analysis, not the individuals or social structures.

In the remainder of this section, FSP and sharing are explored as a set of social practices with low environmental impacts, which foster social bonds and which are compatible with, and have considerable potential for transition to, sustainability. Among other things the rest of the section considers the values that underlie these social practices.

One research project carried out in Slovakia showed that FSP and sharing were motivated by a mixture of values, such as altruism and self-interest. These practices embodied egalitarianism and some deeply rooted moral norms, including the stigmatisation of self-centredness and the promotion of mutual help and sharing (Acheson, 2007). As such, the values and perceptions of those involved in FSP are not easy to classify. In a different project that also looked at Slovak FSP, these practices were found to foster strong ties between kin members and friends by establishing mutuality, reciprocity, task sharing and trust (Torsello, 2005). Czegledy's (2002) Hungarian study highlighted FSP as a source of pleasure and enjoyment (Figure 7.5). Homegrown food and home-produced drinks (including wine and fruit brandy) were shared with guests and friends. This sharing celebrated the relationship of hospitality, but it also served as an opportunity to appreciate the time, effort and skills invested in food growing and preparation.

Figure 7.5   Farmhouse garden in Bugac, Hungary

Czech household food production (Figure 7.6) is primarily a voluntary activity imbued with deep social and cultural meanings and associated with feelings of exuberance, joy and a sense of achievement rather than a sense of obligation (Jehlička and Smith, 2012a). It is an example of E. P. Thompson's notion of 'moral economy' in practice (see Chapter 5, Section 3.2). Financial saving was only the third or fourth most important reason given for their activities by Czech food self-provisioners. The main reasons given for FSP were production of fresh and healthy food, and food growing being a hobby:

We can buy food with chemicals in shops. The point of growing food at home is to do it without chemicals (Interview, Stěžery, 29 March 2005).

The non-alcoholic cider we make from our apples is without added sugar. It is something different to the cider bought in shops. Ours is naturally sweet (Interview, Pardubice, 30 March 2005).

(Jehlička and Smith, 2011, p. 367)

Figure 7.6   Czech food self-provisioners at work

These two quotations demonstrate that people producing food deeply value the natural state of their homegrown food, and their capacity to control its production. In 2007, consumption of self-provisioned food accounted for 34 per cent of the overall consumption of fresh fruit in

Czech households (restaurants and canteens are excluded from this statistic), 32 per cent of eggs, 27 per cent of potatoes and 22 per cent of vegetables (Štiková et al., 2009). In terms of volume (tonnes) of produced fruits, with the exception of apples and sour cherries, Czech households produced over 80 per cent of the national production of all fruit commodities (imports are not included; Czech Statistical Office, 2007). These FSP households also account for 30 per cent of the total area used for growing vegetables in the country, with commercial farms accounting for 70 per cent (Czech Statistical Office, 2007).

It is economically secure rather than insecure Czech households who are predominantly growing their own food. For instance, 48 per cent of respondents who indicated in 2010 that the living standard of their households was 'good' were self-provisioning, whereas the percentage of respondents from households whose living standard was 'neither good, nor bad', and from households with a 'bad' living standard, were 43 and 33 per cent respectively. FSP was a highly inclusive practice socially, as it was very evenly spread, not only across income groups but also across educational and occupational groups (Jehlička and Smith, 2012a). The percentage of the population with the lowest and highest (university degree) educational levels who were growing some of their food was identical – 35 per cent. These findings show that practices such as FSP, which are not motivated primarily by environmental values, can appeal to a wider social spectrum, rather than being confined to middle classes as is found to be predominantly the case with, for example, current environment-related FSP activities in western Europe and North America.

In terms of environmental sustainability, sharing of self-provisioned food in the Czech Republic served as a way of distributing surplus production which might otherwise go to waste. This involved exchanges between family and friendship networks in large cities as much as rural areas. In 2010, 60 per cent of food growers shared their harvest with others (Jehlička and Smith, 2012a). Building solidarity and strengthening social bonds through food sharing is not restricted to extended families, as neighbours, friends and co-workers are frequent recipients of food. People have a range of motivations for sharing their food (Figure 7.7).

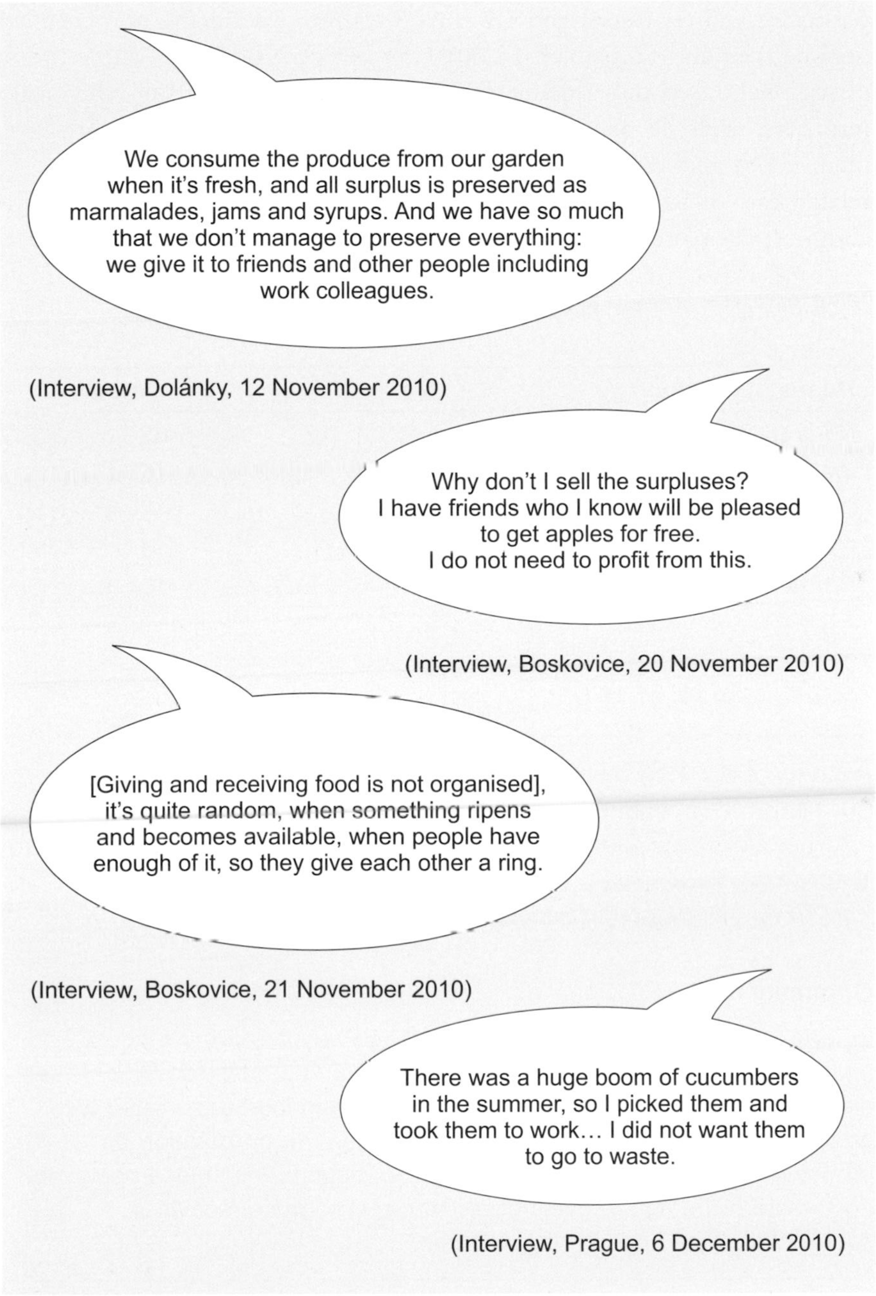

> We consume the produce from our garden when it's fresh, and all surplus is preserved as marmalades, jams and syrups. And we have so much that we don't manage to preserve everything: we give it to friends and other people including work colleagues.

(Interview, Dolánky, 12 November 2010)

> Why don't I sell the surpluses? I have friends who I know will be pleased to get apples for free. I do not need to profit from this.

(Interview, Boskovice, 20 November 2010)

> [Giving and receiving food is not organised], it's quite random, when something ripens and becomes available, when people have enough of it, so they give each other a ring.

(Interview, Boskovice, 21 November 2010)

> There was a huge boom of cucumbers in the summer, so I picked them and took them to work… I did not want them to go to waste.

(Interview, Prague, 6 December 2010)

Figure 7.7   Why do people share their home food produce? Some responses from the Czech Republic in 2010

Food sharing is an effective method of waste minimisation, with environmental benefits that are potentially wider than those associated with organic food. Many growers do not use industrially produced pesticides and fertilisers, and are thus effectively producing non-certified organic fruit and vegetables. In 2010, 54 per cent of Czech self-provisioners used only organic fertilisers, 15 per cent used no chemical fertilisers, while 48 per cent used no, or only natural and manual, methods of pest control (Jehlička and Smith, 2012a). The transport-related carbon footprint of homegrown food is minimal compared with commercial organic food, as Table 7.3 shows.

Table 7.3   Transport to and from the plot (Czech food self-provisioners, 2010)

Means of transport	Percentage
None (plot by house where growers live)	65
Walk	10
Cycle	4
Public transport	6
Private car or motorbike	15

Source: Jehlička and Smith, 2012a

Activity 7.6   FSP – an environmentally and socially sustainable practice

Drawing on Sections 3, 4 and 5 of this chapter, summarise the main ways in which FSP in the Czech Republic might represent an environmentally and socially sustainable practice.

Comment

In terms of environmental sustainability, FSP involves very modest amounts (if any) of fossil fuel-based fertilisers and pesticides. There is also very little (if any) fossil fuel used in the transport associated with growing and gathering FSP-derived products. The preparation and processing of FSP products also tends to result in much less packaging and waste, with higher levels of reuse (or, in terms of social sustainability, the sharing of resources).

Box 7.3   Household food preservation

Sharing fresh fruit and vegetables is a form of sustainable resource management as it minimises waste and losses during the vegetation season by spreading the benefits of homegrown food more widely beyond the growers' households. Food preservation is another practice that further enhances the sustainability potential of FSP food, although it varies depending on energy and material inputs associated with individual preservation and storing techniques. Drying, salting, pickling, smoking, fermenting, canning, freezing and dehydrating are techniques used to extend the usability of food in time beyond the immediate post-harvest period (Figure 7.8). Household food preservation 'presents an opportunity to move alternative food practices away from an individualistic consumer-oriented politics to a politics based upon relationships to self, others, and the earth, enabling activists to connect more deeply to the goals of food movements' (Click and Ridberg, 2009, p. 316).

Figure 7.8   Preservation of home grown vegetables in pickle jars in Hungary

6   Summary

This chapter provided another opportunity to consider the block question *How can we make a difference?* The chapter looked at two ways of responding to this question which could hardly be more different: GM food and FSP. Despite their differences, they share one feature: both transcend the ABC model of social change driven by individual behaviour. As a response to the issue of food, GM food is driven by corporate interests and scientific innovation and can help mitigate some environmental impacts of industrialised agriculture while increasing harvests. Industry has the capacity to deliver new technology rapidly and on a large scale, and research undertaken over a long timescale points to some environmental benefits of the technology. At the same time, however, GM technology generates new ecological risks and uncertainties. It also holds the potential to represent another step towards the commodification of food and greater corporate control over the food system.

In contrast, in the practices of FSP and sharing, non-commoditised food is produced, distributed and consumed outside formal market relations. The motivations for participants include generosity, a desire to please recipients, pride of achievement and waste limitation. The values underpinning this practice include altruism, stigmatisation of selfishness and the extolling of mutual help and cooperation. In addition, since FSP constitutes an extremely localised – or shortened – food supply chain, the environmental benefits of FSP are likely to be at least equal to those associated with market-based alternative food networks, which we consider in the next chapter. In addition to the resource conservation inherent to all forms of sharing, FSP as a social practice has the potential to build social values that are an alternative to the dominance of materialism, market forces and individualism.

References

Acheson, J. (2007) 'Household exchange networks in post-socialist Slovakia', *Human Organization*, vol. 66, no. 4, pp. 405–13.

Alber, J. and Kohler, U. (2008) 'Informal food production in the enlarged European Union', *Social Indicators Research*, vol. 89, no. 1, pp. 113–27.

Belk, R. (2010) 'Sharing', *Journal of Consumer Research*, vol. 36, no. 5, pp. 715–34.

Boersema, J. and Blowers, A. (2011) 'Changing our eating habits by playing the cultural trump card', *Journal of Integrative Environmental Sciences*, vol. 8, no. 4, pp. 243–52.

Carrington, D. (2012) 'GM crops good for environment, study finds', *The Guardian*, 14 June [online], http://www.guardian.co.uk/environment/2012/jun/13/gm-crops-environment-study (Accessed 14 November 2012).

Click, M. A. and Ridberg, R. (2010) 'Saving food: food preservation as alternative food activism', *Environmental Communication: A Journal of Nature and Culture*, vol. 4, no. 3, pp. 301–17.

Czech Statistical Office (2007) *Zemědělská produkce domácností v roce 2006* [online], http://www.czso.cz/csu/2007edicniplan.nsf/t/7C002F5667/$File/213207a02.pdf (Accessed 14 November 2012).

Czegledy, A. (2002) 'Urban peasants in a post-socialist world: small-scale agriculturalists in Hungary', in Leonard, P. and Kaneff, D. (eds) *Post-Socialist Peasant? Rural and Urban Constructions of Identity in Eastern Europe, East Asia and the Former Soviet Union*, Basingstoke and New York, Palgrave.

Gregory, D., Johnston, R., Pratt, G., Watts, M. J. and Whatmore, S. (2009) *The Dictionary of Human Geography*, Chichester, Wiley-Blackwell.

Jehlička, P. and Smith, J. (2011) 'An unsustainable state: contrasting food practices and state policies in the Czech Republic', *Geoforum*, vol. 42, no. 3, pp. 362–72.

Jehlička, P. and Smith, J. (2012a) 'Shelf life: post-socialism, food and politics of sustainable consumption', in Butcher, M., Clark, N., Smith, J. and Tyszczuk, R. (eds) *Atlas: Geography, Architecture and Change in an Interdependent World*, London, Black Dog Publishing.

Jehlička, P. and Smith, J. (2012b) '"Sustainability and the urban peasant": rethinking the cultural politics of food self-provisioning in the Czech Republic', in Zahrádka, P. and Sedláková, R. (eds) *New Perspectives on Consumer Culture, Theory and Research*, Newcastle upon Tyne, Cambridge Scholars Publishing, pp. 78–96.

Lu, Y., Wu, K., Jiang, Y., Guo, Y. and Desneux, N. (2012) 'Widespread adoption of Bt cotton and insecticide decrease promotes biocontrol services', *Nature*, vol. 487, no. 7407, pp. 362–5, 19 July [online], http://www.nature.com.

libezproxy.open.ac.uk/nature/journal/v487/n7407/full/nature11153.html (Accessed 14 November 2012).

Malinowski, B. (1926) *Crime and Custom in a Savage Society*, London, Routledge & Kegan Paul.

Mauss, M. (1925 [1967]) *The Gift: Forms and Functions of Exchange in Archaic Societies*, New York, Norton.

Ministerstvo pro místní rozvoj a Ministerstvo zemědělství (2001) 'Plán SAPARD: Plán rozvoje zemědělství a venkova České republiky na období 2000–2006', *eAGRI*, 24 June [online], http://eagri.cz/public/web/mze/dotace/ dobihajici-a-ukoncene-dotace/sapard/programove-a-jine-dokumenty/plan-sapard.html (Accessed 12 November 2012).

Morin, X. K. (2008) 'Genetically modified food from crops: progress, pawns and possibilities', *Analytical and Bioanalytical Chemistry*, vol. 392, no. 3, pp. 333–40.

Nally, D. (2011) 'The biopolitics of food provisioning', *Transactions of the Institute of British Geographers*, vol. 36, no. 1, pp. 37–53.

Price, J. A. (1975) 'Sharing: the integration of intimate economics', *Anthropologica*, vol. 17, no. 1, pp. 3–27.

Samers, M. (2005) 'The myopia of "diverse economies", or a critique of the "informal economy"', *Antipode*, vol. 37, no. 5, pp. 875–86.

Seyfang, G., Haxeltine, A., Hargreaves, T. and Longhurst, N. (2010) 'Energy and communities in transition – towards a new research agenda on agency and civil society in sustainability transitions', *CSERGE* [online], http://www.cserge.ac.uk/sites/default/files/edm_2010_13.pdf (Accessed 14 November 2012).

Shiva, V. (2000) *Stolen Harvest: The Hijacking of the Global Food Supply*, Cambridge, MA, South End Press.

Shove, E. (2010) 'Social theory and climate change: questions often, sometimes and not yet asked', *Theory, Culture & Society*, vol. 27, nos. 2–3, pp. 277–88.

Shove, E. and Walker, G. (2010) 'Governing transitions in the sustainability of everyday life', *Research Policy*, vol. 39, no. 4, pp. 471–6.

Simms, A. (2011) 'Is GM the answer?', *Grow Your Own*, February, p. 98.

Spaargaren, G. (2003) 'Sustainable consumption: a theoretical and environmental policy perspective', *Society and Natural Resources: An International Journal*, vol. 16, no. 8, pp. 687–701.

Štiková, O., Sekavová, H. and Mrhálková, I. (2009) *Vliv Socioekonomických Faktorů na Spotřebu Potravin*, Praha, Ústav zemědělské ekonomiky a informací.

Teitelbaum, S. and Beckley, T. (2006) 'Harvested, hunted and home grown: the prevalence of self-provisioning in rural Canada', *Journal of Rural and Community Development*, no. 1, pp. 114–30.

Toft, K. H. (2012) 'GMOs and global justice: applying global justice theory to the case of genetically modified crops and food', *Journal of Agricultural and Environmental Ethics*, vol. 25, no. 2, pp. 223–37.

Tomich, T. P., Brodt, S., Ferris, H., Galt, R., Horwath, W. R., Kebreab, E., Leveau, J. H. J., Liptzin, D., Lubell, M., Merel, P., Michelmore, R., Rosenstock, T., Scow, K., Six, J., Williams, N. and Yan, L. (2011) 'Agroecology: a review from a global-change perspective', *Annual Review of Environment and Resources*, vol. 36, pp. 193–222.

Torsello, D. (2005) 'Neviditeľné základy dôvery. Domáca produkcia, práca a výmena na slovenskej dedine', *Slovenský národopis*, vol. 53, no. 1, pp. 5–18.

Chapter 8   Growth markets? Market-based alternatives, certification and ethical consumption

Wendy Maples

Contents

1   Introduction

In the last three chapters, you have read about a range of actions, such as changing diet and food self-provisioning. You have considered ways in which changing what we eat, how food is grown and how it is consumed can make a difference to humans' impact on the environment. You have also explored how values and power both constrict and enable agency. These chapters have demonstrated that food is a subject of deep contestation, and that the decisions people make about food are often fraught owing to uncertainties and anxieties over risks. After all, next to water, food is at the base of Maslow's hierarchy of needs: it is essential to survival. However, you will have grasped that food is much more than just sustenance. It is at one and the same time nourishment, a drain on natural resources such as water or minerals, a global commodity, and a way to show love and affection. Food, in the most visceral of ways, helps to define humanity. Food links us as members of a family, to friends, to farming communities, and it can link producers and consumers across the globe.

Chapter 7 explored genetically modified crops and food self-provisioning. As Jehlička notes, two more different approaches to the provisioning of food are difficult to imagine. It also focused on the significant role that sharing can play in some food systems. Chapter 8 explores ways in which the principles and benefits of sharing can be scaled up, particularly by making use of different features of how markets, both local and global, function. In doing so, it develops the notion that sharing is a manifestation of caring. It examines the reasons why producers and consumers choose to trade at farmers' markets, and the economic and environmental potential of other producer networks. It also considers private certification and labelling, the development of the fair trade movement, and the extent to which ethical production and consumption might be scaled up.

2   Food cooperation: farmers' markets, international policy and networking

As you saw in Chapter 7, food self-provisioning is both part of traditional food provisioning practices and an increasingly popular activity. Indeed, waiting lists in England for municipal food-growing plots, or allotments, are notoriously long, with keen potential self-provisioners in some areas waiting more than a decade for council-allocated space (*Viva Lewes*, 2012). Although there are some movements for micro-provisioning, including small-space apartment agriculture such as hydroponic window farms (*Good*, 2010), that attempt to address many urbanites' lack of soil access, the over 50 per cent of the global population who now live in urban areas generally remain dependent on others for the production of their food.

In many nations in the global North, in the period following the end of post-Second World War rationing, the main source of food for most consumers became the supermarket. In recent years, what has come to be thought of as conventional food production, distribution and consumption has, however, been challenged. Concern over the future decline in the availability of fossil fuels and its impact on the price of food, for instance, has led to a demand to shorten the distance between producers and consumers of food. Authors such as Granvik call this attempt to adapt to more sustainable food practices that reduce the distance between production, processing and consumption 'localisation' (Granvik, 2012). Others call it 'relocalisation', recognising that it is a return to a previously dominant food system.

2.1   Farmers' markets

Farmers' market
A market where most or all of the stallholders are farmers or farm employees who sell their produce directly to consumers.

Farmers' markets have emerged as one alternative to large-scale global food production and distribution, and to consumption tied to delocalised systems. Farmers' markets have some key distinguishing characteristics. A farmers' market may have as many as 150 stalls, selling local produce, flowers and some processed foods, such as breads, pastries, yogurts or home-made sandwiches (Figure 8.1a). However, many are much smaller affairs, with perhaps only 20 stallholders or fewer. They may be held weekly, monthly or only during the peak of the fruit and vegetable growing season (Figure 8.1b).

(a) (h)

Figure 8.1   (a) Farmers' market, Santa Monica, California; (b) Dutch council-owned small farm and market, the Statsboerderij Caetshage

Markets for farm produce used to dominate trade before the growth in global flows of food during the first half of the twentieth century and, later, the rise of the supermarket. International trade and supermarkets have led to the marginalisation of more localised markets as a source of food for consumers. However, in western Europe and the USA, farmers' markets re-emerged between the late 1970s and the 1990s as part of a wider food movement that sought to redress the crisis of trust in food by urban dwellers (Brown, 2001). Indeed, in recent decades, certain sectors of the food and agriculture industries have been faced with a collapse of trust by some consumer sectors. This was signalled, or perhaps has been triggered, by developments such as GM food scares or uncertainties about the environmental impacts of large-scale food production by multinational corporations. As a result, some consumers have rejected 'placeless and faceless' foods: for some consumers, locally grown, fresh food, sold by familiar faces at the farmers' markets, is a preferable alternative.

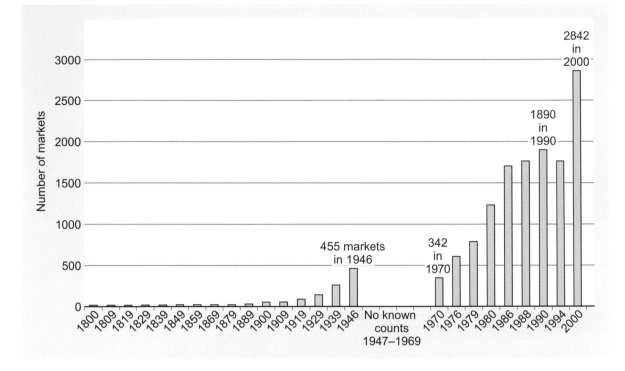

Figure 8.2   In 2000 there were over 2800 farmers' markets registered in the USA (Source: Brown, 2001, p. 667)

Farmers' markets are distinct from street stalls and permanent market structures. The two main distinguishing features of farmers' markets are the predominance of producer-stallholders and the coexistence in the same time/space of producers and consumers (Pyle, 1971, cited in Brown, 2001). These features have been considered important by both producers and consumers (Figure 8.3).

In a study of shoppers in Ontario, Canada, three aspects of farmers' markets were considered important to consumers. According to Connell et al. (2008, p. 180), farmers' markets offered food that was '"in season (fresh)" (associated with quality and freshness), "grown or produced locally" (associated with local embeddedness), and "grown or produced by someone known" (associated with social embeddedness)'.

Figure 8.3 Stallholders interacting with customers at a Santa Monica farmers' market

Relocalisation
Term used to describe local spaces where producers and consumers are co-present, as in earlier times.

Farmers' markets are underpinned by the principle of localism. But what is meant by 'localism'? Localism involves both short food supply chains and an identification of groups of people and their products with a geographically defined place. Kneafsey et al. (2008, p. 48) see farmers' markets as an expression of **relocalisation** where 'the embodied co-presence of producers and consumers is crucial'. As suggested above, the use of the term relocalisation rather than localisation recognises that in earlier times, or in other places in the present, producers and consumers were or are often located near to one another. However, for societies in the global North, such as the USA and the UK, this was lost in an era when, following market or state logics that pursued efficiencies of scale, food travels long distances to get from the producer to the consumer.

Provenance
The geographical origin of commodities.

Related to localism is the notion of produce **provenance**. Produce provenance indicates the geographical origin of food. Such is the cultural and economic importance of provenance that certain local, traditional artisan produce, for example, Parmigiano Reggiano, are protected by international agreement (Guthman, 2007). The French term **terroir** is similar to the idea of provenance, but goes further. It suggests that a product's geographical origin, including soil structure, rainfall, water mineralisation, and geography in general, gives it a special quality or value. It also establishes authenticity through traditional methods and processes and, increasingly, through formal legal processes of certification and protection. Perhaps the most famous example of *terroir* protection was established in the international treaties of Madrid (1891) and Versailles (1919), which ensured that the Champagne region's vintners retained exclusive rights to label their sparkling wine 'Champagne' (Figure 8.4).

Terroir
The combined effects of a given location – climate, soil structure and rainfall – on a given product.

More prosaically, however, local produce may simply be whatever will grow at a given time of year in the local soil.

Figure 8.4 Champagne: perhaps the most celebrated example of the French concept of *terroir* and the general notion of provenance

Activity 8.1 Farmers' markets: nostalgia or the future of food?

This section has presented farmers' markets as an alternative to industrialised food production. It has also introduced the idea of relocalisation, suggesting that a close relationship between producers and consumers isn't exactly new.

What do you think of farmers' markets? Are they the future of food – or the past (Figure 8.5)?

Comment

One of the editors of this book responded to this activity with the following comment:

'I head for the farmers' market in my town every week. It's a chance to get some sense of how shopping might have been for my grandmother. Since the closure of local butchers, bakers and grocers back in my home town, and in the place I live now, it's a chance to connect with the source of my food, and people that process it. So I go to 'the chicken and eggs guy', 'the bread guy', 'the bacon woman' and the veg stall, and often I'm thinking about how this all takes me back. But the truth is this is a new thing: our farmers' market has only been running since around 2006. Stallholders have websites as another way of marketing their stuff; several of them are doing this as a second career, having walked out of office jobs after paying off mortgages. This isn't about recreating the past, but personally I don't see how it could possibly be the future of all food. But for me and the stallholders it's a very important niche.'

Where and when you were born and where you live now will make a significant difference to how you respond to Activity 8.1. As with food supply chains, the experience of farmers' markets is very much time and place specific. However, farmers' markets do mark a break with historical forms of food (self-)provisioning, and they may be an alternative to the globalised food industry.

However, the localisation agenda also raises the question: what counts as local? Farmers' markets in London may draw producers from 100 miles (160 kilometres) away; the local farmers' market in Lewes, South East England has a general limit of 30 miles (48 kilometres) (Common Cause, n. d.). The Santa Monica farmers' market in Southern California has been criticised for drawing producers from Central California, with some farmers making round trips of nearly 500 kilometres for a single day's market (Anonymous, 2012). Nevertheless, the average food miles, even for the Santa Monica market, remain significantly less than that for the majority of produce in supermarkets. For consumers wishing to reduce their food miles and support local producers, the farmers' market may be a good market-based alternative.

Figure 8.5   Farmers' markets may play on nostalgic associations with formerly dominant food systems, including 'market days', such as this one in Tregaron, Wales

Social embeddedness, a term associated with Hungarian social theorist Karl Polanyi (for example, Polanyi, 1994), expresses the importance of social interaction in a given exchange. The strong social dimension of farmers' markets that arises out of the exchange experienced by both producers and consumers is demonstrated in a study by James Kirwan. Kirwan (2004) interviewed consumers at farmers' markets in different locations in the UK. He found that buying produce at farmers' markets was experienced by consumers as more than just a monetary exchange. Shoppers 'wanted to personally reward the effort producers had made to provide them with "high quality" food' (Kirwan, 2004, p. 404). According to one interviewee:

> I like this thing of trust, I really like the thing of looking at that person and feeling that they have worked hard and it's an exchange … me saying thank you very much … for taking the time to look after the way you have produced the food that is going to nourish me.
>
> (Anonymous, cited in Kirwan, 2004, p. 404)

By contrast, a feeling of disconnection and depersonalisation between consumers and producers is prevalent in many countries of the global North, particularly among supermarket shoppers.

Farmers may feel similarly positively about selling their produce at farmers' markets, again by contrast with the wholesale markets or through supermarket buyers. Kirwan notes that, at the farmers' markets, producers enjoyed the interaction with consumers and took pride in describing and selling their produce. One London farmers' market producer interviewed by Kirwan says:

> I like selling to people … It gives you a worthwhile feeling when people come back and say how much they enjoyed what they bought from you last time, and can they have some more. So yes from the psychological point of view it's gone from feeling like, would anybody actually notice if I disappeared from the wholesale markets …You end up feeling why the hell am I actually bothering at all. If they don't get it from me, they'll get it from Spain or wherever. You do feel worthy, valued [at the farmers' market].
>
> (Kirwan, 2004, p. 404)

The social embeddedness that Connell et al. (2008) and Kirwan (2004) observed constitutes a means by which individuals partake in different social events, such that those events, and the actions within them, become an expression of individual identity. Group affiliation and identity may also ensue, to the extent that going to the local farmers' market becomes a ritualised social action and a collective habit or, as Seyfang et al. (2010) see it, a shared set of social practices.

However, farmers' markets may also have disadvantages. Farmers' markets still represent a commodification of food which, according to David Nally, undermines traditional agrarian practices (Nally, 2011). Not all consumers will find their local farmers' market convenient; access can be difficult if there is limited car parking or public transport near the market. Sometimes there may be a limited choice of produce, meaning some consumers will make two shopping trips, one to the farmers' market and one to the supermarket. Farmers' markets may be infrequent and only open at certain hours – a disadvantage for those accustomed to shopping whenever they choose.

Furthermore, the localisation on which farmers' markets are based may not be all it appears to be. In fact, it is not always clear that local produce has a lower carbon footprint. A comparative study of cut roses brought to the UK showed that roses from Kenya had created lower carbon emissions than those from the Netherlands (Figure 8.6). This is because the emissions caused by transportation from Kenya were offset by the fact that Kenyan roses were grown in greenhouses run by geothermal energy, while the Dutch greenhouses were powered by fossil fuels (Williams, 2007). Although large-scale Dutch horticulture is not going to feature in farmers' markets, the results of Williams' study may be relevant to any local greenhouse or heated-polytunnel produce that appears on a stall at a farmers' market. Indeed, Williams' study notes that the Dutch horticultural system CO_2 impact is similar to that for British tomato growing. This shows that food miles calculations might be inadequate for understanding the environmental impact of food. In the example of the cut flowers, the carbon footprint calculation needed to consider the carbon emissions resulting from production and processing as well as transportation.

Figure 8.6 Air-freighted fruit, vegetables and flowers do not necessarily produce a larger carbon footprint than do more locally grown produce

2.2   Global policies and practices

Perhaps one of the most significant concerns about more locally based approaches to addressing environmental change is that the scale of environmental problems is such that isolated or independent local action may simply not be enough. One way to address this concern is to adopt localism in global environmental policy making. The most important scheme for furthering localisation is the United Nations initiative Local Agenda 21 (LA21). This was agreed as a global vision of locally based progress towards sustainable development for the twenty-first century at the United Nations Conference on Environment and Development in Rio de Janeiro in 1992 (UNCED, 1992).

LA21 aimed to offer a blueprint for action on environmental concerns into the twenty-first century, with local authorities required to consult with and engage local populations on environmental issues. In 2012, the meeting of the UN Commission on Sustainable Development reaffirmed its faith in Local Agenda 21 as an approach to connecting global goals to local capacity for delivery. This affirmation was summarised in the document *The Future We Want* (UNCSD, 2012).

Some international conventions have also adopted localism as one means of addressing environmental concerns. For instance, the United Nations Economic Commission for Europe's Aarhus Convention, adopted in 1998, aims to increase public rights to information, increase public participation in decision making about environmental issues, and improve access to **environmental justice** (UNECE, 1998). You were introduced to environmental justice in Book 1, Chapter 6, Box 6.3. Here the term is used to denote the exercise of agency by actors claiming equitable access to natural resources and redress for environmental damages. The Aarhus Convention recognises the importance of local people and local agendas in shaping environmental policy and practice, including that related to food, and is binding on all European parties who have ratified the convention.

Environmental justice
Claims for equitable access to natural resources and redress for environmental damages.

This support by international institutions and national governments for localisation has opened up windows of opportunity for local food producers. For instance, a study of 218 municipalities in Sweden showed that 66 per cent of Swedish municipalities were interested in helping local food producers, and 79 per cent of this group had already implemented some measures to achieve this (Granvik, 2012). Some municipalities had set up centres to which local farmers would deliver their goods in order to cut distribution costs. Municipalities also referred to LA21 as they advanced initiatives around, for example, more local procurement of food for municipal-run services such as schools and hospitals.

Another way in which local food initiatives are being scaled up is through producer networking (Figure 8.7). The remainder of this section considers three examples of networking that have moved beyond the small scale.

Figure 8.7   A soybean farm in Parana, Brazil. Producer networks can help farms such as these gain and maintain market share

One successful example of a farming network is Brazil's Federation of Family Farmers and Smallholders (FETRAF), an association of farmers who have collaborated to influence public policy in the face of risks and uncertainties in the global food trade. The Federation has lobbied the Brazilian government to set a minimum price for family farm produce and campaigned for a law that obliges municipal authorities to use significant amounts of family farm produce in their school meals programmes (Pye-Smith, 2012).

The second example is Farmer Field Schools, an initiative that was first set up in Indonesia but has now spread to 79 countries. Here, local farmers' knowledge about adaptation, biodiversity and pest management systems is shared and enhanced through research and training. Group experiments and agro-ecological analysis are used to identify the most environmentally friendly ways of farming (Davis et al., 2012).

Interestingly, research in three African countries – Kenya, Tanzania and Uganda – showed that participation in the Farmer Field Schools also led to improved crop productivity and increases in per capita agricultural income (Pye-Smith, 2012).

Figure 8.8   The European hare

The third example concerns networks that prioritise specific environmental needs. Prominent in this approach are Dutch farmers who, along with other interested parties, have joined together to form a network of environmental cooperatives. These cooperatives are not formed to buy or sell produce. Rather, they manage agricultural areas in such a way that an individual species of animal or a particular habitat is protected. A network may organise itself to address, for instance, the foraging range of a species, such as the European hare. The hare has an average home range of 34 hectares (Figure 8.8), which may cut across the boundaries of a number of neighbouring farms (Smith et al., 2004, cited in Franks, 2011). Farmers may agree to remove fencing around individual farms in order that the hare can move easily through its home range. This kind of agri-environmental scheme addresses the human impact of food production as an environmental issue beyond the scale of producer and consumer, at the level of bioregions (i.e. landscapes that are significant for the diverse fauna and flora that also occupy agricultural landscapes).

These three examples highlight some of the advantages of networking approaches in terms of abilities to put pressure on local and national governments to source locally; learn from each other in order to address environmental concerns while also improving agricultural production; and act as a forum which lobbies for and makes policy decisions that address wider environmental concerns, such as protecting biodiversity.

Networking can lead to improvements in procurement and governance of food, as well as in agricultural production and distribution. In the Brazilian case, networking enables farmers to reduce the risks and uncertainties associated with the wider global market. Working together, family farms may alter the power they have in the municipal food supply chain. For some farmers' networks, shared knowledge has resulted in improved agricultural yield. Other networks alter the way in which spaces of production are organised. Farms and their boundaries may be redrawn, and this can be done in such a way as to protect environmental interests beyond those of commercial agriculture.

Activity 8.2   Who organises localisation?

Consider one of the three examples in the preceding section – the Brazilian farmers' association that lobbies for use of local produce in school meals, the Farmer Field Schools that support knowledge sharing of environmentally sensitive farming practices, or the Dutch cooperative that focuses on supporting wild species' habitat across farmland. Can you envisage a similar initiative local to you? Drawing on your own knowledge of NGOs, farmers' groups or local government, which might be most likely to support or initiate such cooperative environmental activity? Are there other groups that might be influential in the process?

Comment

While it is not possible to imagine the range of possible responses to these questions, it is interesting to consider where power lies in terms of local food production and the environment. The author of this chapter considered these questions and was surprised to discover a local non-profit group that was working to support local farmers. The group helped farmers organise cooperative action to encourage more localised food production and consumption. This included activities such as shared marketing, participating in local farmers' markets, and providing more local produce, such as apples, to schools across the county. While the scale of the initiative is small in comparison with that of the Brazilian or Farmer Field Schools networks, the country-wide impact is potentially significant.

3   Global initiatives: certification, labelling and fair trade

Over recent years, a number of initiatives have emerged that expressly link production and consumption, and that ensure producers benefit from consumer choices. One of the main ways in which this has happened is through certification and labelling.

3.1   Labelling and certification

Labelling and certification provide another example of how concerns over food can be addressed, not just at the local level but by scaling up to a national or global level.

Assurance labels
Labels designed to offer consumers some form of assurance about a product's source or quality, often linked to certification.

Assurance labels are labels that producers print on their packaging in order to assure consumers about the qualities of a given product (Figure 8.9). The information they offer helps consumers to be informed about, for instance, perceived environmental or health benefits or risks, or the social consequences associated with a given product. The most prevalent food assurance labels in the UK are those of the Rainforest Alliance, Soil Association and Fairtrade.

Figure 8.9   Some common assurance labels

Activity 8.3   What do labels tell you?

Look at the labels in Figure 8.9. What information do they convey to you?

Comment

The labels serve as quickly recognisable symbols that help a consumer faced with a range of similar products to distinguish particular qualities of an item. This might include social and environmental standards adhered to in an item's production, as in the case of Fairtrade and Rainforest Alliance labels. Organic labelling tells a consumer there will be very low pesticide residues and positive environmental management on the farms producing the foodstuff.

But what do these labels on our foods actually indicate? Labels are commonly linked with certification. Food **certification** covers a range of practices, from health and safety measures, such as clean kitchens, to farm animal welfare, organic standards of production, or working conditions for labourers. Certification comes in three main forms: first-, second- and third-party certification (Lipschutz, 2004; cf. Raynolds et al., 2007).

First-party certification is essentially a proclamation by the producer that a product meets certain quality thresholds. First-party certification carries no independent verification of reliability or accuracy by any external regulatory body. Until the EU restriction on battery-caged hens (EU Council Directive 1999/74/EC on minimum standards for the protection of laying hens) came into force in January 2012, consumers may have been bewildered by the (first-party) claims made by some egg producers: 'farm assured' or 'farm fresh'-labelled eggs appealed to consumers' associations of 'freshness' (Connell et al., 2008, p. 180). However, while they didn't sound like they had come from battery hens reared in dark, cramped conditions, studies by organisations such as Compassion in World Farming and the RSPCA suggested that eggs labelled in these ways often had (Whatmore and Clarke, 2008; Compassion in World Farming, n. d.; RSPCA, 2010).

Second-party certification involves agreements across an industry or industries. Companies sign up to a set of agreed standards and will attest to compliance with these, often on an annual basis. Compliance earns the right to certify – and label – the company's products. It may

Certification
Certification is similar to the idea of a guarantee. An organisation, including private as well as non-profit and governmental organisations, will certify that a product meets certain quality thresholds.

First-party certification
First-party certification is synonymous with self-certification.

Second-party certification
A collective attempt, often industry-based, to agree certain standards to which individual producers then hold themselves accountable. It is sometimes used synonymously with 'professional body certification'.

be argued that second-party certification is a means by which companies simply seek to limit interference by external regulatory bodies. However, it is advantageous for industries to try collectively to regulate sharp practices, thus ensuring that the reputation of the industry at large is maintained. This form of certification may have the advantage of being cost effective for both producer and consumer, on account of not carrying the costs of the independent verification of claims.

Figure 8.10   Some products carrying the Fairtrade certified label

Third-party certification
An external body sets standards to which collectives or individual producers sign up. With third-party certification, there is often regular, external verification that standards are being met.

Third-party certification is offered by independent, disinterested organisations, including 'government agencies, nonprofit groups, for-profit companies, or organisations representing some combination of these three' (Lipschutz, 2004, p. 172). It implies a greater degree of research and bureaucratic processes that ensure compliance, and it inevitably introduces new costs to a product. These can be balanced by a higher end-price for a product, or by the product winning a greater market share. Alternatively, the stocking of third-party certified products may bring valuable reputational gains that may benefit, for example, a supermarket that wants its whole operation to be identified with a particular set of values.

Since the 1980s, campaigns on the ethical aspects of food production have led to the growth of independent ethical certification bodies and eco-labelling. In western Europe, one of the most prominent third-party certified ethical labels is the Fairtrade certification label (Figure 8.10).

3.2   Fairtrade

Fairtrade is an organisation and a movement whose aim is to reduce poverty among farmers and farm workers in countries of the global South by guaranteeing a fair price for their produce. This is called 'development through trade'. A fair price is achieved by selling products, mainly in wealthier nations, at a small premium. This premium 'travels' along what is known as a **commodity chain** (Box 8.1).

Box 8.1   Commodity chains

The term commodity chain refers to the exchanges or trades that go on as a commodity or product travels from the place where it was grown to the place where it is consumed.

In contrast to the typical buyer-driven commodity chain which may actively exploit the differences in power between small-scale producers and multinational buyers, Fairtrade's buyer-driven chain attempts to redress some of these inequalities by linking producers and consumers more closely .

It is worth noting that, when talking about international commodity markets, the phrase 'buyer-driven' does not refer just to the end-buyer in a supermarket, but also to the international commodity brokers who deal in large quantities of a specific product such as tea or sugar.

The first Fairtrade product was launched in 1988 when a single coffee brand, Max Havelaar, was sold in supermarkets in the Netherlands. According to the Fairtrade Foundation website, the coffee 'was branded "Max Havelaar", after a fictional Dutch character who opposed the exploitation of coffee pickers in Dutch colonies' (Fairtrade Foundation, 2011a). Since that time, the number of Fairtrade products has expanded significantly. In 2003, 150 Fairtrade-labelled products were available in the UK; by 2006, this had grown to 1500, and in 2012 the Fairtrade Foundation reported that over 3000 Fairtrade-labelled products were on sale. In the UK, consumer awareness of the Fairtrade mark grew from 25 per cent in 2003 to 57 per cent in 2007.

Fairtrade has a number of arms of activity. Fairtrade Labelling Organizations International (FLO) is the operational arm of the organisation and since 2004 has acted in two distinct realms. FLO International sets standards for certification and supports businesses in achieving those standards, while FLO-CERT validates certifications, ensuring that standards are met. In addition, the Foundation has a campaigning remit to increase public awareness of Fairtrade. Initiatives have included encouraging businesses to offer Fairtrade-labelled coffee and other hot drinks to staff. In 1997, activity by a small group of British Members of Parliament led to the Palace of Westminster becoming a Fairtrade workplace. Since 2000, when Garstang in Lancashire declared itself the 'World's First Fairtrade Town', Fairtrade Town status has been awarded to many towns across the world. UK towns are the most prevalent on the International Fairtrade Town map (Fairtrade Towns, 2012), with over 500 towns declared by 2012. However, countries as widespread as Canada, Costa Rica, the Czech Republic, Ghana, Italy, Japan, Luxembourg, New Zealand, Sweden, and others, have also established Fairtrade Towns.

Most important, however, is the impact Fairtrade has had on food producers. A 2009 meta-review (meaning a review that summarises the findings of all the relevant academic and policy research) of Fairtrade producer impact studies found that, while research and data were limited, most studies reported income gains and reduced economic vulnerability among Fairtrade producers. In addition, the majority of studies reported improved social conditions, not only for the producers but also for their wider communities (Nelson and Pound, 2009). In terms of environmental benefits, some producers, particularly of coffee, have shifted to organic production methods, in part to attract the higher premium guaranteed by Fairtrade for organic products. Hence, roughly half of Fairtrade coffee is produced to organic standards (and is double-certified as both organic and Fairtrade) (Raynolds et al., 2007).

According to the Fairtrade Foundation website: 'Fairtrade is about better prices, decent working conditions, local sustainability, and fair

terms of trade for farmers and workers in the developing world'
(Fairtrade Foundation, 2011b). Fairtrade makes an explicit link between
sustainable development (see Book 1, Chapter 1, Section 3) and **social
justice**. To put it another way, 'social justice is [not] ... dissociable
from ... sustainability and healthiness of production systems'
(Wilkinson, 2007, p. 229). As you saw in Chapter 6, Section 3, affluence
is linked with environmental degradation, and much of that occurs
through the externalising of environmental impacts – such as waste
products, pollutants and packaging detritus – to other, poorer, places.
However, poverty also has direct environmental impacts, even in areas
where food is apparently available.

Like farmers' markets, Fairtrade certification has the ability to alter the
behaviour of both producers and consumers. Although the two are not
brought together face to face (as in farmers' markets), consumer
preference for Fairtrade-certified goods is a demonstration of the
human relationship behind food production and consumption. With
certification such as Fairtrade, that relationship is made more visible –
more marked – than with uncertified products that move as
commodities through the international commodity markets. Purchasing
fairly traded products in the global North directly benefits farmers who
grow the products in other parts of the world. It is an example of the
concept of 'action at a distance' (Book 1, Chapter 2, Section 2.3).

Social justice
Recognising and
redressing inequalities
of power and
opportunity as well as
material inequalities,
which may include
environmental
inequalities (see also
environmental justice in
Section 2.2).

4   Redressing injustice: a politics of care

For those living in suburbs, or for the majority of people who live in cities, the people who grow much of the world's food are a long way out of sight. This may explain why it is easy to forget that they are also some of the poorest. Indeed, of the two billion poorest people in the world, most are farmers (Korthals, 2010), with an 'estimated 500–800 million resource-poor and small-holder farmers' in the global South (Wollenberg et al., 2012, p. 4) where wider economic deprivations are also prevalent. By way of an example, the CTA (Technical Centre for Agricultural and Rural Cooperation) indicates that approximately 65 per cent of the working population in sub-Saharan Africa is involved in farming and that the agricultural labour force produces some 32 per cent of the area's GDP (Gross Domestic Product). Despite this, agricultural employment is highly vulnerable with substantial numbers living in what is defined by the ILO (International Labour Organization) as 'extreme poverty' (Pye-Smith, 2012).

4.1   Fairtrade's politics of care

Although instigated by Max Havelaar coffee sales in Dutch supermarkets, early Fairtrade sales in the UK initially took place via alternative distribution networks, such as local church groups (Clarke et al., 2007). This was, in part, a practical means of distributing goods, but it also, importantly, reflected the fair trade movement's political critique of conventional global trade. The commodity chains of mainstream production, distribution and consumption, seen as exploitative and therefore ethically untenable, were challenged with chains that linked primary producers in the global South with consumers in the affluent global North (Jaffee and Howard, 2010). Consumers are thus positioned by Fairtrade goods and the Fairtrade label as 'ethical consumers'. As Barnett et al. (2011) argue:

> Ethical consumption ... seeks to use everyday consumption as a surface of mobilisation for wider, explicitly political aims and agendas. Thus, it marks an innovation in modes of 'being political' ..., one in which people are encouraged to recognise themselves as bearing certain types of *global* obligation by virtue of their privileged position as consumers, obligations which in turn they

are encouraged to discharge in part by acting as consumers in 'responsible' ways.

(Barnett et al., 2011, p. 13)

This 'responsible' behaviour is, however, at odds with what we might assume is pragmatic consumer behaviour. Given a finite budget, we might ask, why would consumers actively choose to spend more on a product than is necessary or go out of their way to purchase Fairtrade goods?

4.2   Consumer responsibility

There is more than one answer to this question, but we might wish to start by reminding ourselves of Belasco's (2008) three food choice variables (Chapter 6, Section 2): convenience, identity and responsibility. For Fairtrade consumers, we might argue, identity and responsibility override convenience.

Similar to the high rates of food self-provisioning and sharing in the Czech Republic (Chapter 7), the steady growth in the market share for Fairtrade products demonstrates that people are not driven solely by economic value, but bring social, cultural and ethical values to bear on the food they produce and consume. Kneafsey et al.'s (2008) study of alternative food relationships revealed a strong tendency for consumers to feel 'disconnected' from the food they were able to purchase at supermarkets. Indeed, interviewees in the study chose to shop at farmers' markets where they 'reconnected' by getting to know the producers and gaining a stronger sense of the provenance of the produce they bought.

According to Kneafsey et al. (2008), it is possible to see consumer–producer relationships, even across great distances, as 'caring practices' – or, to put this in Belasco's terms, as demonstrating responsibility. Indeed, Kneafsey et al. suggest that there is 'potential for care to relate to people and places beyond the immediate locality or close community' (Kneafsey et al., 2008, p. 49). In a similar sense, then, Fairtrade consumers are also 'connecting', but primarily with producers in another part of the world.

Kneafsey et al.'s and Barnett et al.'s shoppers seem to understand the relationship between consumption and politics as a form of 'action-at-a-distance' (Barnett et al., 2005, p. 7). Both highlight how taking responsibility for injustices elsewhere is important, as it enables 'individual consumption to be articulated with campaigns which demand not only individual responsibility but broader forms of collective accountability' (Barnett et al., 2005, p. 16). In other words, for some consumers, purchasing goods that have been certified as fairly traded goes some way to addressing their concerns about the influence of a range of powerful actors, including 'states, international agencies, and multinational corporations' (Clarke et al., 2007, p. 592).

This politics of care – whether enacted at the farmers' market or via consumption of Fairtrade goods (or indeed goods that are organic, locally produced, or 'rainforest protective') – is expansive. What this means is that an individual who cares about the social and environmental consequences of how food is produced may expand the geographical spaces within which they can make a difference by exercising agency in line with their value-based beliefs. Where our values and agency are in accord, we demonstrate a politics of caring, whether this is in a local, geographically constrained place, or at some considerable distance.

Activity 8.4   The politics of caring

How is ethical consumption explained by Barnett et al.? How is it made possible and disseminated as an idea?

Comment

Barnett et al. describe ethical consumption as a new politics of care, with consumers discharging a sense of global obligation, born of a sense of good fortune and privilege. Ethical consumption 'seeks to embed altruistic, humanitarian, solidaristic and environmental commitments into the rhythms and routines of everyday life' (Barnett et al., 2011, p. 13). A key element in much ethical consumption is the labelling of goods, for example, the use of the Fairtrade label. This allows shoppers to know their selected product has been independently certified as delivering more stable prices and other benefits to the primary grower. The use of an easily identified icon helps to expand the market for these products through increasing familiarity with the brand and its distinct qualities, both through conventional advertising, but also more informally through the visible presence of these products in households and workplaces.

---

5 Can 'every little help'? Ethical consumption and the risk of co-option

For Barnett et al. and Kneafsey et al., caring at a distance is a novel form of doing politics. But a prominent challenge to this politics in the past has been that it does not have the power to change the system as a whole; some dismiss it, like FSP, as a niche activity. Certainly, for most of their history, Fairtrade products were mainly smaller, 'ethical' brands. However, all that has changed in recent years with the mainstreaming of Fairtrade brands. In 2000, the Co-operative supermarket developed the first supermarket 'own-brand' Fairtrade chocolate bar; this was followed in 2002 by a range of Fairtrade own-brand products at Sainsbury's, while all the other major UK supermarkets expanded their stocks of Fairtrade own- and other-label goods. The popularity of alternative food products on mainstream supermarket shelves has contributed significantly to the year-on-year growth of Fairtrade-labelled goods, as reported by the Fairtrade Foundation. The availability of Fairtrade and other eco-label products at supermarkets has vastly increased the sales of these goods. According to FLO, sales of certified Fairtrade goods were over $5 billion (approximately £3.3 billion) in 2010 (Jaffee, 2012), and UK sales alone were over £1.3 billion in 2011 (Lucas, 2012).

However, mainstreaming, or conventionalisation, is giving rise to a new kind of critique – that the endgame of ethical consumption is a form of co-option which distorts social or environmental values by forcing them into a framework constructed by narrow capitalist economic interests.

This contention rests on a number of assumptions – about ethical consumption, the role of supermarkets, and understandings of what is a realistic approach to making food systems more environmentally and socially sustainable. Some argue that the term 'ethical consumer' is a tautology. Anti-consumerism, which might include anti-globalisation campaigns or **voluntary simplicity** movements (Barnett et al., 2011), takes the position that engaging with the global capitalist system, for instance by buying food at supermarkets, simply encourages social, economic and environmental degradation, either locally or elsewhere.

Voluntary simplicity
Lowering environmental impacts by reducing consumption, particularly of industrially manufactured and processed goods.

Lipschutz, however, raises a wider issue about the ethics of certification:

> Politics through market-based methods, which is what private certification amounts to, rests primarily on attempts to alter the

preferences of large numbers of consumers in order to put pressure on producers. Because consumer preferences ... are strongly influenced, if not determined, by the very system of production and consumption that motivates the social disruption and externalities of concern, there is a certain tautological process at work here.

(Lipschutz, 2004, pp. 206–7)

In other words, Lipschutz suggests, the very act of being a consumer creates complicity with global, commercial production and distribution. It is simply part of the neoliberal process of turning every part of life into a commodity (also known as 'commodification').

Figure 8.11 Fairtrade products are increasingly available in supermarkets, including supermarket own-label Fairtrade products

Jaffee (2012) shares this disaffection with the mainstreaming of Fairtrade products into supermarket systems (Figure 8.11). By 2010, Jaffee reports, 'the majority of the 100-percent fair trade retailers in the United States had left the FLO ... system', preferring a new, organic certification system, 'Fair for Life' (Jaffee, 2012, p. 109). The decision to offer certification rights to 'own-label' supermarket goods has created an environment in which, critics argue, the early social justice and sustainability intentions have been diluted:

> By redefining 'new advantages' as merely an increase in sales …
> the fair trade system [has] … achieved dramatic success in terms
> of growth, but at the cost of rendering fair trade primarily an
> adjunct to the conventional market, rather than posing a
> fundamental challenge to the terms on which it operates.
>
> (Jaffee, 2012, p. 111)

Jaffee argues that even within the Fairtrade system, some farmers,
caught between the demands of certification and the commercial
interests of buyer-driven commodity chains, have found themselves
selling their products at a loss (Jaffee, 2012, p. 108). According to this
research, then, the farmers were not empowered through the behaviour
of consumers in the way that the Fairtrade pioneers intended.

The pioneers of farmers' markets or ethical certification initiatives
would likely argue, however, that there is currently no viable alternative
to market-based approaches. There is no practicable solution making it
easy for people who can't grow their own food to access food that is in
all senses 'good'. They would suggest that scaling up necessarily means
working in the current global economic context, and transforming the
political and economic landscape in which people find themselves.

Activity 8.5   The sweet smell of success?

Drawing on the chapter as a whole, try to summarise how the scaling up
of ethical certification and consumption may have both positive and
negative consequences. Also, try to summarise these consequences at
both the local and global levels.

Comment

Ethical consumption has given affluent consumers ways of expressing
their political values and commitments in new ways and allowed
consumers to feel connected to globally distant producers. New forms of
'doing politics' have spread very rapidly, with ethical labels appearing on
mainstream products, including supermarket own brands. There are
hazards in this successful mainstreaming, however, including the danger
of standards being diluted. It is also the case that some originators of
ethical certification systems hoped they would become alternatives to
capitalism rather than a revision of it, and mainstreaming threatens that.

---

6 Summary

This chapter has explored two main market-based forms of scaling up responses to the environmental and social problems that arise out of the way most food is currently produced and sold in the global North: farmers' markets and ethical certification schemes. In different ways each offers alternatives to what has become mainstream food production, distribution and consumption.

In a market economy, with powerful multinational corporations able to traverse the globe in search of preferred commodities and profits, the tendency towards increasing marketisation and co-option of successful new forms of certified products such as Fairtrade is hardly surprising. With a majority of people now urban dwellers with limited access to horticultural land, and time pressures driving a desire for convenience, the increasing reliance on supermarkets for food is also no surprise. At the same time, however, many people carry a sense of disembeddedness and a desire for relocalisation. Moreover, smaller food producers are under increasing environmental and economic pressures, injustices which consumers may feel some responsibility to redress.

Critics have noted that the economic, political and ideological power of for-profit institutions in food systems mean that ethical behaviours are subsumed by the goal of maximising profits. In the words of one writer on food systems, it is 'as if "doing good" is one more thing to be bought and sold' (Guthman, 2007, p. 473). However both social movements and the expression of individual producer–consumer values may be said to be making a positive difference to environmental outcomes. As the American naturalist Aldo Leopold (Figure 8.12) wrote:

> We shall never achieve harmony with land, any more than we shall achieve absolute justice or liberty for people. In these higher aspirations, the important thing is not to achieve but to strive.
>
> (Leopold, 1953 [1993], p. 55)

Figure 8.12   The influential American naturalist Aldo Leopold (1887–1948)

Over the course of this block, you may have felt some discomfort thinking about how eating – this most intimate of our environmental actions – acts on us, and is acted on, through the decisions we make as consumers, producers and distributors of food. You may have been troubled by the decisions made by others, sometimes regardless of the interests of producers and consumers. If you have felt disconcerted, then this book is doing its job: the role of social scientists – which has been highlighted here – is not simply to describe or confirm the social order nor to acquiesce to normative behaviours; it is to consider, challenge and disrupt our everyday notions, and to help society to evaluate its social, political, economic and, of course, environmental choices.

References

Anonymous (2012) Unpublished interview with Santa Monica Farmers' Market organiser, conducted by Wendy Maples, 22 February.

Barnett, C., Cloke, P., Clarke, N. and Malpass, A. (2005) 'Consuming ethics: articulating the subjects and spaces of ethical consumption', *Antipode*, vol. 37, no. 1, pp. 23–45.

Barnett, C., Cloke, P., Clarke, N. and Malpass, A. (2011) *Globalizing Responsibility: The Political Rationalities of Ethical Consumption*, Chichester and Malden, MA, Wiley-Blackwell.

Belasco, W. (2008) *Food: The Key Concepts*, Oxford and New York, Berg.

Brown, A. (2001) 'Counting farmers markets', *Geographical Review*, vol. 91, no. 4, pp. 655–74 [online], http://www.jstor.org/stable/3594724 (Accessed 18 November, 2012).

Clarke, N., Barnett, C., Cloke, P. and Malpass, A. (2007) 'The political rationality of fairtrade consumption in the United Kingdom', *Politics and Society*, vol. 35, no. 4, pp. 583–607.

Common Cause Co-operative (n.d.) 'Lewes Farmers Market' [online], http://www.commoncause.org.uk/index.php?option=com_content&view=category&layout=blog&id=37&Itemid=54 (Accessed 16 November 2012).

Compassion in World Farming (n.d.) 'Know your labels' [online], http://www.ciwf.org.uk/your_food/know_your_labels/default.aspx (Accessed 14 July 2012).

Connell, D., Smithers, J. and Joseph, A. (2008) 'Farmers' markets and the "good food" value chain: a preliminary study', *Local Environment*, vol. 13, no. 3, pp. 169–85 [online], DOI: 10.1080/13549830701669096 (Accessed 20 November 2012).

Davis, K., Nkonya, E., Kato, E., Mekonnen, D. A., Odendo, M., Miiro, R. and Nkuba, J. (2012) 'Impact of farmer field schools on agricultural productivity and poverty in East Africa', *World Development*, vol. 40, no. 2, pp. 402–13.

Fairtrade Foundation (2011a) 'Fairtrade labelling international history' [online], http://www.fairtrade.org.uk/what_is_fairtrade/history.aspx (Accessed 17 November 2012).

Fairtrade Foundation (2011b) 'What is Fairtrade?' [online], http://www.fairtrade.org.uk/what_is_fairtrade/default.aspx (Accessed 17 November 2012).

Fairtrade Towns (2012) 'About' [online], http://www.fairtradetowns.org/about/ (Accessed 17 November 2012).

Franks, J. (2011) 'The collective provision of environmental goods: a discussion of contractual issues', *Journal of Environmental Planning and Management*, vol. 54, no. 5, pp. 637–60.

Good (2010) 'A Farm in Every Window' [online], http://www.good.is/post/a-farm-in-every-window/, posted 24 May (Accessed 17 November 2012).

Granvik, M. (2012) 'The localization of food systems – an emerging issue for Swedish municipal authorities', *International Planning Studies*, vol. 17, no. 2, pp. 113–24.

Guthman, J. (2007) 'The Polanyian Way? Voluntary food labels as neoliberal governance', *Antipode*, vol. 39, no. 3, pp. 456–78 [online], DOI: 10.1111/j.1467-8330.2007.00535.x (Accessed 18 November 2012).

Jaffee, D. (2012) 'Weak coffee: certification and co-optation in the fair trade movement', *Social Problems*, vol. 59, no. 1, pp. 94–116 [online], http://www.jstor.org/stable/10.1525/sp.2012.59.1.94 (Accessed 18 November 2012).

Jaffee, D. and Howard, P. (2010) 'Corporate cooptation of organic and fair trade standards', *Agricultural Human Values*, vol. 27, pp. 387–99 [online], DOI: 10.1007/s10460-009-9231 8 (Accessed 18 November 2012).

Kirwan, J. (2004) 'Alternative strategies in the UK agro-food system: interrogating the alterity of farmers' markets', *Sociologia Ruralis*, vol. 44, no. 4, pp. 395–415 [online], DOI: 10.1111/j.1467-9523.2004.00283.x (Accessed 18 November 2012).

Kneafsey, M., Cox, R., Holloway, L., Dowler, E., Venn, L. and Tuomainen, H. (2008) *Reconnecting Consumers, Producers and Food: Exploring Alternatives*, Oxford, Berg.

Korthals, M. (2010) 'Global justice and genomics: toward global agro-genomics agency', *Genomics, Society and Policy*, vol. 6, no. 2, pp. 13–25.

Leopold, A. (1953 [1993]) *Round River*, New York, Oxford University Press.

Lipschutz, R. (2004) *Global Environmental Politics: Power, Perspectives, and Practice*, Washington DC, CQ Press.

Lucas, L. (2012) 'Fairtrade UK sales show 12 per cent increase', *Financial Times*, 27 February [online], http://www.ft.com/cms/s/0/9e8f7f74-6171-11e1-8a8e-00144feabdc0.html#axzz20hXcUQVS (Accessed 19 November 2012).

Nally, D. (2011) 'The biopolitics of food provisioning', *Transactions of the Institute of British Geographers*, vol. 36, no. 1, pp. 37–53 [online], DOI: 10.1111/j.1475-5661.2010.00413.x (Accessed 18 November 2012).

Nelson, V. and Pound, B. (2009) *The Last Ten Years: A Comprehensive Review of the Literature on the Impact of Fairtrade*, Natural Resources Institute, University of Greenwich.

Polanyi, K. (1994) *The Great Transformation*, New York, Holt, Rinehart & Winston.

Pye-Smith, C. (2012) 'Increasing rural employment in sub-Saharan Africa', *CTA Policy Brief*, no. 4, February, Wageningen, CTA.

Pyle, J. (1971) 'Farmers' markets in the United States: functional anachronisms?' *Geographical Review*, vol. 61, no. 2, pp. 167–97.

Raynolds, L., Murray, D. and Heller, A. (2007) 'Regulating sustainability in the coffee sector: a comparative analysis of third-party environmental and social certification initiatives', *Agriculture and Human Values*, vol. 24, no. 2, pp.147–63 [online], DOI: 10.1007/s10460-006-9047-8 (Accessed 18 November 2012).

Royal Society for the Prevention of Cruelty to Animals (RSPCA) (2010) 'About Freedom Food' [online], http://www.rspca.org.uk/freedomfood/aboutus/-/article/FF_AboutUs (Accessed 18 November 2012).

Seyfang, G., Haxeltine, A., Hargreaves, T. and Longhurst, N. (2010) 'Energy and communities in transition – towards a new research agenda on agency and civil society in sustainability transitions', *CSERGE* [online], http://www.cserge.ac.uk/sites/default/files/edm_2010_13_0.pdf (Accessed 19 November 2012).

Smith, R. K., Jennings, N. V., Robinson, A. and Harris, S. (2004) 'Conservation of European hares *Lepus europaeus* in Britain: is increasing habitat heterogeneity in farmland the answer?', *Journal of Applied Ecology*, vol. 41, no. 6, pp. 1092–102.

United Nations Commission on Sustainable Development (UNCSD) (2012) *The Future We Want*, UNCSD [online], http://www.uncsd2012.org/content/documents/727The%20Future%20We%20Want%2019%20June%201230pm.pdf (Accessed 2 April 2013).

United Nations Conference on Environment and Development (UNCED) (1992) *Agenda 21: Earth Summit – The United Nations Programme of Action from Rio*, New York, United Nations Department of Public Information.

United Nations Economic Commission for Europe (UNECE) (1998) *Convention on Access to Information, Public Participation in Decision-Making and Access to Justice in Environmental Matters* [online], http://www.unece.org/env/pp/introduction.html (Accessed 2 April 2013).

Viva Lewes (2012) 'My space: Topsy Jewel's allotment', Issue 70, July, p. 81.

Whatmore, S. and Clark, N. (2008) 'Good food: ethical consumption and global change', in Clark, N., Massey, D. and Sarre, P. (eds) *Material Geographies: A World in the Making*, London, Sage/Milton Keynes, The Open University.

Wilkinson, J. (2007) 'Fair trade: dynamic and dilemmas of a market oriented global social movement', *Journal of Consumer Policy*, vol. 30, no. 3, pp.219–39 [online], DOI: 10.1007/s10603-007-9036-3 (Accessed 19 November 2012).

Williams, A. (2007) 'Comparative study of cut roses for the British market produced in Kenya and the Netherlands', *Précis Report for World Flowers*, Cranfield University [online], http://www.fairflowers.de/fileadmin/flp.de/Redaktion/Dokumente/Studien/Comparative_Study_of_Cut_Roses_Feb_2007.pdf (Accessed 19 November 2012).

Wollenberg, E., Nihart, A., Tapio-Biström, M.-L. and Grieg-Gran, M. (eds) (2012) *Climate Change Mitigation and Agriculture*, London and New York, Earthscan.

Block 6　Consolidation

Chapter 9   Mangroves, entanglement and an environmental imagination

Nick Bingham

Contents

1   Introduction

What are the challenges of sharing a dynamic planet?

This was the question posed at the outset of this module. It is a vast question that encompasses the current and future state of the environment and the natural and social causes of environmental change. Throughout this module, the question has been broken down into five smaller and more manageable questions that you have considered over the previous five blocks. This concluding block will consolidate what you have learnt so far by directly engaging with the module question.

This work of consolidating involves two interrelated activities. The first is reviewing. In this block you will revisit key parts of the module, literally looking again at (re-viewing) some of the key ideas that you have worked with. Second, you will also integrate some of these ideas, bringing them together in order to produce something new: what you have learnt throughout the module adds up to more than the sum of its parts.

One way in which this is so concerns *what* you have learnt about specific environmental issues in the module, such as biodiversity loss, water management, climate change and agriculture. One of the arguments that will be developed in this block is that these issues do not exist in isolation. When they are aggregated they yield what we may call an environmental **crisis of inhabitation**. This phrase refers to a growing awareness that human actions routinely degrade the environment on which we depend. It is based on the recognition that our actions have increasing – and increasingly severe – environmental consequences, many of which we simply cannot control, with the result that there are no easy options for solving what has become a crisis. The phrase also refers to the challenge of how we humans should live our lives. How should we inhabit this dynamic planet that we share with each other, with other species and, in a temporal sense, with other generations?

Crisis of inhabitation
The problems created by increasing degradation of the Earth, the effects this has on its ability to sustain our lives and the difficulties of solving this crisis.

As well as learning about specific environmental issues, you have also learnt *how* to think about environmental issues. You have developed what we may call an **environmental imagination**. An environmental imagination is a particular way of conceiving and thinking about environmental issues. There are many different ways of imagining the environment. The particular environmental imagination you have developed on this module requires you to work across various

Environmental imagination
A particular way of conceiving and thinking about environmental issues.

disciplines which together have given you an interdisciplinary perspective on environmental change. You have also worked with a conceptual framework that comprises three sets of analytical concepts: time and space; risk and uncertainty; and values, power and agency. In short, the knowledge you have acquired, the skills you have practised and the ideas that you have traced throughout the module are all part of this environmental imagination. But what defines it is the particular way in which they all come together. In this block you will develop and extend this environmental imagination by considering what it means to talk of a crisis of inhabitation.

This chapter and the next two will both consolidate and further develop this environmental imagination by enabling you to understand and analyse some of the responses that people are making to the crisis of inhabitation. The first response works through place to add resilience, a theme developed in this chapter through a focus on ecological restoration. The second response works through movement, and is exemplified in Chapter 10 by a focus on climate-induced migration. The third and final response works through reaching out to other people, places and situations, which is illustrated in Chapter 11 through the example of the transition movement. By the end of the block you will have developed a way of thinking that you can take beyond the module and apply to any environmental issue that you encounter, whether in your future studies or wider life.

The remainder of this chapter is the first step towards this goal. The next section offers an expanded sense of the two key phrases introduced above – crisis of inhabitation and environmental imagination – and how they frame the block. You will learn how to put this environmental imagination to work as we explore, in Sections 3 to 5, one particular attempt to respond to the crisis of inhabitation. This is the attempt to both restore and add resilience to some of the key mangrove habitats of West Africa. What the environmental imagination offers here is a way of appreciating the entanglement both of the various causes of environmental change and of the many connections – biophysical and social – that are involved. Analysing this entanglement is essential to understanding both the current state of the mangroves of Senegal and the success of any attempts to conserve and restore them.

2 From a crisis of inhabitation to an environmental imagination

At the beginning of the module you were introduced to the idea that humans have always sought to shape, modify and respond to their environments. First by necessity and then out of choice, we have sought to make ourselves at home across the globe, in the process making ourselves the ultimate invasive species. For almost the full span of human existence, such home-making has been relatively unproblematic. Before the Industrial Revolution, while we changed our local environment we did not cause environmental change on a global scale. In summary, we might say that throughout most of human history people have more or less successfully managed the tension between the Earth as a lively place and the Earth as a place to live.

In many respects, managing this tension has become significantly easier in the modern period, during which a series of social and technological developments facilitated ways and qualities of life that are dramatically different from what had gone before. As a consequence, the human population has expanded rapidly at the same time as the per capita consumption of resources and production of waste products has also been increasing. What we are learning now is that those ways and qualities of life have depended – and continue to depend – on an expenditure of biophysical resources (especially fossil fuels) which is simply not sustainable. Modernity has literally been fuelled by the burning in a few hundred years of hydrocarbons which it took millions of years to form. This has generated enormous material benefits for many millions of people, but – as we now understand – it has also produced enormous unintended consequences for our atmosphere, land, sea and biodiversity.

It is the scale and extent of these consequences which are now being recognised scientifically in notions such as the Anthropocene (see Book 1, Chapter 8, Section 4). Put starkly, there are now serious questions about whether future generations will inherit the Earth in the habitable state that we and our ancestors did. At the very least, a combination of climate change, mass extinction and the depletion and degradation of terrestrial and water resources is forcing us to reconsider both where in the world and how in the world the humans of the future will live. It is this reconsideration that constitutes a crisis of inhabitation; a forced confrontation with the consequences of our actions.

How might we respond to this crisis with determination and realism but without resignation? Before any problem can be addressed and solved it must first be fully understood. To help us understand the problem of contemporary environmental degradation, it is proposed that we think in terms of an environmental imagination, a distinctive way of thinking about the world and the forces that constitute it, its human and non-human inhabitants, and – crucially – the interrelationships between them.

Over the remainder of this block, the idea of an environmental imagination will be developed and applied as a constructive way of identifying and thinking about environmental issues in three respects:

- as a way of describing and interpreting environmental issues in terms of connections (in Chapter 9)
- as a way of investigating and analysing environmental issues using key concepts (in Chapter 10)
- as a way of evaluating responses to environmental issues using the notion of sharing (in Chapter 11).

It should be emphasised that the word 'imagination' is deliberately chosen here to underline the creativity – academically, politically and personally – that will be required to get to grips with the crisis of inhabitation and meeting the challenge of sharing a dynamic planet.

3   The entanglement of mangroves

The crisis of inhabitation will play out in different ways in different places. How the crisis is imagined, and how people respond to it, will vary significantly around the globe depending on the ecological features of the local environment and the social and cultural attributes of the people that live there.

Figure 9.1   Responding to a crisis of inhabitation: mangrove planting in Senegal

Along parts of the Senegalese coast people are responding to a crisis of inhabitation by planting mangrove trees (Figure 9.1). The mangroves in Senegal, as in many parts of the world, are being destroyed. Some are dying because of increasing pollution in coastal belts, while others are being cut down for fuel or in order to reclaim land from the sea so that the increasing populations in coastal towns can build a home. Mangroves have long been an integral part of the landscape of western Senegal where this photograph was taken. More than that, they have been critical to making this part of the world a place to live for humans. In recent times, however, this landscape and the people who live there have been put at risk as a result of anthropogenic activities. Exactly how and why this is the case is the focus of Sections 3 and 4. Having established the causes of the problem, the rest of the chapter will explore how local people have mobilised to transform their environment. They are transforming it from a place at risk to a more resilient place, a place that has an improved chance of being habitable in an uncertain future.

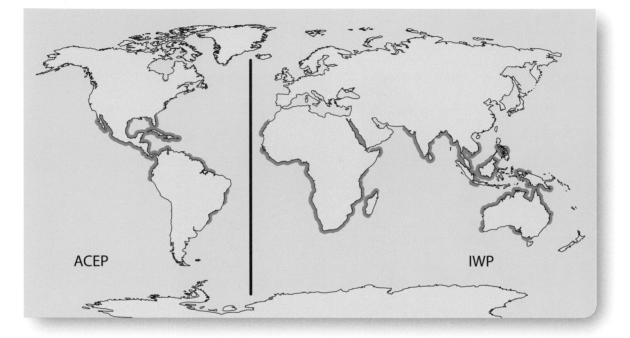

Figure 9.2   The global distribution of mangroves, showing the two main biogeographical regions: the Indo-West Pacific (IWP) is to the east and the Atlantic-Caribbean-East Pacific (ACEP) to the west

---

Activity 9.1   Mangroves: a coastal ecosystem

Figure 9.2 shows the distribution of mangroves along the world's coastlines. By considering an ecosystem such as mangroves we are returning to a place where land, sea and atmosphere meet. The module began in such a place on the coastline of East Anglia. Can you recall some of the challenges that people who live on coastlines must contend with?

Comment

The coast is an area of the planet where some of the most dramatic effects of environmental change are felt. Rising sea levels, more frequent and more extreme weather events and loss of land to erosion are profoundly altering these landscapes and providing challenges to local communities. The coast offers a useful location for exploring place-based issues of habitability that will affect more of the world's population over coming decades. Mangroves dramatise this particularly effectively, as one of the many services they provide for local communities is as a buffer to, and a shelter from, the worst effects of the strong winds and waves that are increasingly characteristic of the regions where they are located. The loss or degradation of mangroves will thus place at risk the communities that rely on mangroves as a coastal defence. This reminds us of our collective exposure to the elements and focuses our attention on the tension that we have encountered throughout the module: between the Earth as a lively planet – constituted and animated by the dynamic forces of air, water, earth and life – and the Earth as a place to live.

In order to develop an interdisciplinary understanding of mangroves, Sections 3.1 provides a scientific perspective on the ecology of mangroves. Section 3.2 then considers the role of the people who live within, and who seek to manage, mangrove ecosystems.

3.1   The ecology of mangroves

Often the most interesting ecosystems to study are those which appear to offer the most difficult environments for plants and animals to live in. They are usually inhabited by unique organisms with specialised adaptations to that environment. These ecosystems also tend to be the most vulnerable. Mangrove swamps are one such ecosystem.

Mangrove swamps form a wetland ecosystem that exists in coastal areas of tropical and subtropical regions and which is dominated by mangrove trees, mainly of the genera *Rhizophora* and *Avicennia*. Their global distribution can be divided into two main biogeographical regions (Figure 9.2). The Indo-West Pacific (IWP) region includes Asia, Australia, Oceania and the eastern coast of Africa. The Atlantic-Caribbean-East Pacific (ACEP) region includes the west coast of Africa, South and Central America, and the Caribbean. The geographical features that separate the two regions are the width of the Pacific Ocean and the cold water at the tip of South Africa. The IWP region is biologically more diverse than the ACEP region.

Since mangroves grow along the coastal fringe on the boundary between the sea and the land, they are subjected to a complex and changing environment. The seaward side of a mangrove swamp is essentially a marine environment. The environment of the landward side may be terrestrial, brackish water or fresh water, depending on whether the mangroves are adjacent to an estuary or land. There is a gradual reduction in salinity from the seaward side to the landward side. However, tidal movements change the salinity levels each day. At high tides, mangroves are inundated by salt water, leading to an increase in salinity. At low tides, in an estuarine environment, the influx of fresh water decreases salinity.

Mangrove trees create a sheltered environment where mud can accumulate around their roots. This mud contains a lot of plant remains which use up oxygen as they decompose, making it anoxic. Anoxic environments, lacking oxygen, can only support life forms such as bacteria that have adapted to those conditions. However, although their roots are in an anoxic environment, mangrove trees have access to oxygen from the atmosphere.

Although mangrove trees are capable of growing in fresh water, their specialist adaptations to the difficult conditions between the sea and land give them an advantage over more competitive species, since other tree species cannot survive in these conditions. To cope with high salinity, mangrove trees reduce the absorption of salt through their roots by the use of special filters that prevent high concentrations of salt entering. Another adaptation is the use of salt-secreting glands that extract salt from the plant tissues and secrete it onto the surface of leaves, where it crystallises and is then blown away or washed off by rain. Some species remove excess salt by shedding leaves.

The aerial roots, characteristic of mangrove trees (Figure 9.3), are an adaptation to the low oxygen levels in the soil. The upper parts of the aerial roots absorb oxygen from the atmosphere through pores on their surface and transport it, via a spongy tissue, to the lower parts embedded in the anoxic mud. The upper parts of the roots also help stabilise the plants and reduce the effects of wave action. The leaves and branches of mangrove trees also have normal access to oxygen from the atmosphere.

The seeds of mangrove trees germinate while they are still attached to the plant. When the seedlings are released they are able to embed themselves in the mud immediately, using their well-developed roots.

Figure 9.3 Establishing mangrove plants. The vertical aerial roots of the mangrove plants are clearly visible

3.2 Humans and mangroves

Humans derive many benefits from mangroves. As we have already noted, mangroves play an important role in coastline protection. Their extensive network of aerial roots reduces wave and tidal current velocities and creates sheltered areas along coastlines. This encourages sediment to settle and reduces the risk of soil erosion on adjacent habitats. Mangroves also absorb the impacts of wind, tidal waves and floods resulting from tropical storms.

By trapping sediments, mangroves protect other coastal ecosystems such as coral reefs and oyster beds from sediment inundation. The removal of sediment from the water column also reduces the concentrations of the associated nitrates, phosphorus and organic nutrients in the water and so helps reduce water pollution. Mangroves provide many goods and services for people (Figure 9.4). The sheltered areas that mangroves provide are important nursery grounds for commercial fisheries. Shrimps, crabs and shellfish such as oysters are abundant around mangroves, creating a valuable human food source. The mangrove trees themselves are a useful source of wood for fuel as firewood and charcoal, as well as for timber and wood products. Some mangrove plants have medicinal uses.

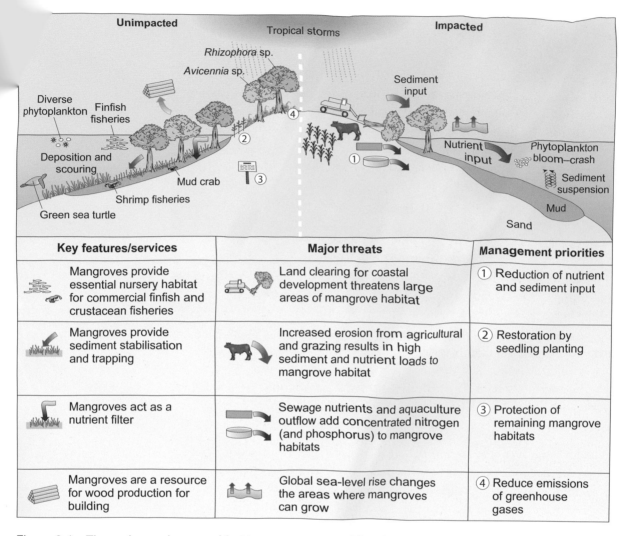

Figure 9.4   The main services provided by mangroves and the threats to those services

As we shall see, many of the threats to mangroves are the result of human activity, such as clearance of mangrove trees for coastline developments, or as a result of over-exploitation of the food resources. Although mangroves help to clean polluted water, excessive pollution is harmful to them. Pollution can arise from run-off of fertilisers and pesticides from agricultural land, or industrial and sewage pollution from urban areas. Sea level rise can lead to continuous sea inundation of mangroves above root level, causing them to die. Sustainable management of mangroves is thus necessary in order to maintain their important ecosystem services. We now look in more detail at the risks facing mangrove swamps and at some possible responses.

4 Mangroves at risk

Now that we have learnt something about the science of mangroves and human interaction with them, we can begin exploring the pressures on mangroves at the beginning of the twenty-first century. In order to understand these pressures, their origins and their implications, it is necessary to draw from our learning in previous blocks about the contemporary environmental challenges of life, water, carbon and food.

4.1 Mangroves and the challenge of life

In Book 1, Chapters 5–8 we explored biological life in its various dimensions, especially the contemporary challenge of how human lifestyles can place life at risk. Using the Deepwater Horizon oil spill as an example, Chapters 5–8 highlighted the relationship between biodiversity and human economic development. This relationship has come under increased scrutiny in recent years as the role of human activities in driving a sixth mass extinction has led to the view within the scientific community that a new geological epoch – the Anthropocene – has arrived. Because ecosystems are interconnected at a variety of scales, the anthropogenic drivers of ecological change can generate often irreversible species loss through both immediate and catastrophic impacts, and longer-term, cumulative stresses which can tip ecosystems (and thus the species that populate them) over thresholds of survivability. The tension between maintaining biodiversity, on the one hand, and human economic development, on the other, may be seen as one dimension of the broader crisis of inhabitation. In that context, it should be asked whether the planet's biodiversity can continue to coexist with current human lifestyles.

Examining the current state of mangrove ecosystems worldwide suggests that the prospects are not very promising (Figure 9.5). Mangroves are enormously rich in biodiversity. The unique way in which they colonise the land–sea interface makes them ecological spaces that are habitable for species ranging from algae and so-called 'fouling organisms' (such as barnacles, oysters, molluscs and sponges), through an enormous range of invertebrates and fish species (many of which use the mangroves as nursery habitats), to amphibians, reptiles, birds and mammals (including humans). However, mangroves' importance as a habitat has not always been valued. Mangrove deforestation has taken place around the world for several decades, from the Florida Everglades in the USA to the mangrove forests of East Asia (Warne, 2011). This has led to the loss, not only of the mangrove plants themselves, but also of the critical habitat that mangroves provide for many other species. One driver of this deforestation has been unsustainable economic development. Forests have been cleared for firewood and timber harvesting, land reclamation for urban expansion, agriculture, pasture, salt production and aquaculture (see Section 4.2 below). This development has been prompted by the availability of undervalued and often under-regulated land in areas of coastline with growing population pressures. The result has been the loss of an estimated half of the world's original mangrove forest area, with half of that loss estimated as taking place over the last five decades (Walters et al., 2008).

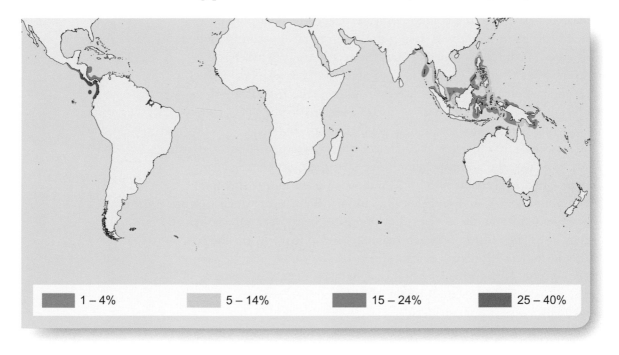

Figure 9.5   Map of global mangrove loss (Source: based on Polidoro et al., 2010, Figure 2)

4.2   Mangroves and the challenge of food

To discover the main reasons for this loss we now review some of the key messages from Chapters 5–8 of this book. There you learnt why and how agricultural production has become a key driver of environmental change and in particular how different modes of food provisioning have different environmental consequences. Through exploring the food chain you gained some insights into how the intensity of modern industrialised food production methods, the transformations of food during processing, the distances that food travels during distribution, and the shifting patterns of food consumption all combine to shape the environmental impacts of food. These four stages – production, transformation, distribution and consumption – are also points of intervention for those trying to make a difference by shifting food production and consumption towards a more sustainable basis.

The insights you gained in Chapters 5–8 illustrate how a particular model of agriculture – specifically shrimp aquaculture – is responsible for a significant proportion of the loss of the mangrove ecosystem over the past few decades, as we now see (Figure 9.6).

Figure 9.6   Shrimp ponds in Belize, Central America

Activity 9.2   Aquaculture and mangroves

Read the following short extract from an interview with Kennedy Warne, the author of a book on the disappearance of what he calls the 'rainforests of the sea' (Warne, 2011). He offers a concise but dense explanation of how shrimp aquaculture impacts on mangroves. Thinking back to what you learnt in Chapters 5–8 of this book, note down all the different factors that explain 'the connection between cheap shrimp and disappearing mangrove forests'. Pay particular attention to both biophysical and social issues.

> The problem with shrimp aquaculture is that in the industry's pioneering years, during the 1970s and 1980s, the ideal site for a shrimp pond happened to be at about the same position on the shore that mangroves flourish: low enough to get occasional tidal flow, but high enough not to be affected by tides all the time. Because mangrove forests tended to be public lands occupied by subsistence communities, they were readily appropriated by a combination of commercial aggression and governmental compliance.
>
> Governments in developing countries became keen backers of shrimp farming because shrimp fetched a high price in the West, and was therefore a reliable source of foreign exchange. It was relatively easy for aquaculture corporations to clear mangroves and build shrimp ponds, the land was cheap to rent and there was plenty of it, so the cost of farming shrimp was low. Probably the most odious part of the early years of shrimp farming was that when one pond was nutritionally exhausted, the company would abandon it and bulldoze some more mangroves to build a new one. So the forests gave way to ever-expanding swathes of ponds. And all the while, consumers in the West couldn't believe their luck that such tasty seafood was flooding into supermarket freezers and on to restaurant menus for such a cheap price. They never made the connection between cheap shrimp and disappearing mangrove forests.
>
> (*The Ecologist*, 2012)

Comment

Warne's short account touches on hydrology (tidal flows), land ownership in different parts of the world, business practice, economic factors (prices and foreign exchange earnings), regulatory regimes, consumer trends, and so on. If your notes picked up on just some of these aspects, you are well on the way to appreciating a key point of the module: that understanding environmental issues require an interdisciplinary analysis. Biophysical and social factors interact to produce environmental issues.

As a result, insights from both the sciences and social sciences are required to address these issues.

4.3   Mangroves and the challenge of water

The importance of interdisciplinary analysis was also evident in Book 1, Chapters 9–12, where we considered the current challenge of water security. This was defined as the aim of ensuring that 'every person has access to enough safe water at affordable cost to lead to a clean, healthy and productive life, while ensuring that the environment is protected and enhanced' (GWP, 2000, p. 12; see Book 1, Chapter 9, Section 3). As we discovered, what initially appears as a reasonable and reasonably achievable goal is enormously complicated in practice, often leading to controversy and conflict. One reason for this is the difficulties inherent in managing a flow resource such as water, which is always on the move and often changing state. Competition between different users for the different ecosystem services that water provides further intensifies this controversy. For example, there are many ways in which watercourses can be polluted during abstraction and usage. Making the right amount of water available at the right quality in the right place at the right time is a considerable challenge. And even if this can be achieved, it may be at the cost of other species and habitats that, like us, depend on water.

Mangroves exemplify the difficulties posed by the challenge of water, defined as water security. Located at the margins of land and sea and at the interface between fresh water and ocean water, mangroves have flourished because they have evolved highly specialised mechanisms for managing and adapting to the unique aquatic environment in which they live. Because they face towards the ocean, mangrove plants are characterised by their remarkable salt tolerance. But because they also face towards the land, mangroves are able to retain, remove, and rapidly cycle many kinds of nutrients, pollutants, and other particulate matter from terrestrial sources, acting as uniquely adapted filters. The entangled root system of the mangroves slows sediments as they pass through, encouraging the sediments to settle along with the many toxins and nutrients that can be attached to sedimentary particles (Figure 9.7). In addition, the root system of mangroves is highly efficient at removing various organic and inorganic nutrients from the water column, lowering nitrate and phosphorous concentrations in particular (NOAA, 2012).

Figure 9.7   The exposed roots of mangrove trees in Queensland, Australia

These mechanisms and the water quality improvements they facilitate are of enormous benefit, not only to the mangrove ecosystems themselves but also to the populations of neighbouring aquatic habitats, such as sea grasses and coral reefs. In certain parts of the world, the highly developed water filtration capacity of mangroves has been used to treat wastewater from the landward side, including sewage and the by-products of aquaculture (Yang, 2008). An increase in human-generated pollution around the coastlines where mangroves are situated often places those ecosystems under immense stress. This is because, although mangroves are resilient with regard to some aspects of water quality, such as nutrient concentration, they are also highly sensitive to other water quality changes beyond certain thresholds, such as salinity, as their ability to filter is highly specialised. The growth of agricultural and urban development in areas populated by mangroves has led to a massive increase in the prevalence of pesticides, fertilisers, waste materials, toxic chemicals and oil in those ecosystems. As a result, the future existence of mangroves in such areas will depend on our ability to address the challenge of water, not only for the benefit of humans but for other species too.

4.4   Mangroves and the challenge of carbon

Understanding the likelihood of action to protect mangroves requires us to review some of the lessons of Chapters 1–4 of this book. Our focus there was on how carbon changes form and location over a variety of timescales, from the geological to the everyday. Much of the carbon that formed coal or oil millions of years ago is now being consumed as fossil fuels as a result of our hydrocarbon-fuelled lifestyle. This is leading to the release into the atmosphere of vast amounts of carbon in the form of carbon dioxide. Modern agriculture is also leading to emissions into the atmosphere of methane, a gas that contains carbon. Increased emissions of carbon dioxide, methane and other greenhouse gases are contributing significantly to the risk of climate change, with uncertain but possibly catastrophic results. This, in turn, is prompting both the introduction of low carbon technologies and increasing research into planetary technical fixes, such as geoengineering. The story of carbon and its cycling and recycling draws attention to how the challenge of climate change is also a relationship between past and future. Our actions in the past have consequences for the future. The burning of fossil fuels in the present and geologically recent past has irreversibly committed the planet to future temperature changes, the extent of which is unclear and the impacts of which are uncertain. This uncertainty will persist, leaving it unclear what sort of legacy we are bequeathing to future human and non-human generations.

Understanding the challenge of managing carbon as one that requires managing the relationship between the past and the future helps us to view the problem of mangrove depletion in a new light. It has long been obvious that burning mangroves to clear them would release carbon dioxide into the atmosphere and thus contribute to anthropogenic climate change. But scientists have recently discovered that the problem caused by deforestation may be far more severe than previously estimated. In fact, according to one study (Donato et al., 2011), mangroves account for 10 per cent of the world's carbon emissions resulting from deforestation, even though they make up less than 1 per cent of the world's forests. This is because mangroves are extremely productive ecosystems that cycle carbon quickly. Mangrove forests store up to four times as much carbon as other tropical forests, including rainforests. The reason is that much of the carbon is trapped in the soil. Mangroves grow in soils that are on average five times deeper than other forest soils in the tropics and in the temperate and boreal regions (Figure 9.8). Tidal water buries organic and inorganic material in this soil, causing anoxic conditions which can store carbon over longer timescales than other forest soils. The implications are profound. Not only do such findings suggest that it is imperative to prevent any further losses of mangrove ecosystems, and to find ways of properly valuing the mangrove soils that currently survive; they also suggest that establishing more mangroves would be an efficient way of sequestering carbon efficiently and effectively. It is to this possibility that we will turn in Section 6.

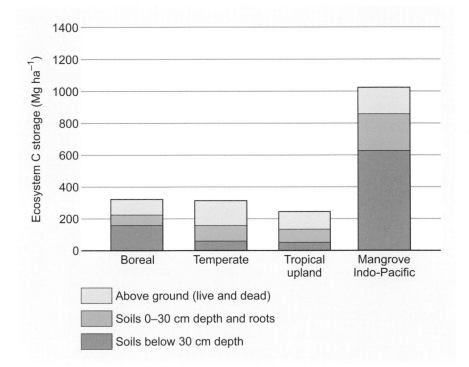

Figure 9.8   Diagram of mangrove soil depth (Source: based on Donato, 2011, p. 294, Figure 2)

Before we do that, however, we first reflect on how our exploration of the plight of the mangroves consolidates both what you have learnt about specific environmental issues (and how that adds up to thinking in terms of a crisis of inhabitation) and how to think about environmental issues (and how that adds up to an environmental imagination).

5   Towards an environmental imagination of connections

Reviewing the headline messages from Book 1, Chapters 5–12 and Book 2, Chapters 1–8 reminds us that the challenges posed by matters of life, water, carbon and food are not only highly significant issues in their own right, they are also of central importance to explaining our current crisis of inhabitation. These four issues are identified in contemporary environmental policy, planning, and politics literatures as the key areas that need to be addressed collectively and promptly if catastrophic environmental change is to be avoided. For example, Connie Hedegaard, the European Commissioner for Climate Action, stated in 2012 that: 'As the century progresses, the interrelated crises of water, food, energy, biodiversity and climate will only get more urgent and more entangled' (Hedegaard, 2012).

You have seen throughout the module that environmental challenges are a result of the interaction of biophysical and social factors, and that understanding them requires insights from both the natural sciences and the social sciences. Thus, the challenge of life connects biodiversity with economic development, the challenge of water connects the working of the water cycle with water management and ownership, the challenge of carbon connects the composition of the atmosphere with hydrocarbon-fuelled ways of life, and the challenge of food connects the state of the world's ecosystems and soils with changing diets.

Making sense of our current crisis of inhabitation requires an environmental imagination that recognises that environments and environmental issues entangle various ecological, social, political and economic processes (Figure 9.9). Thinking in this way – in terms of connections and interconnections – is one of the things you have been learning to do throughout this module. You have seen that thinking through all the different connections that make environmental issues is an interdisciplinary endeavour. Our logic has been that because environmental issues connect so many different entities and processes, then our ways of understanding those environmental issues must be capable of connecting all those different processes too.

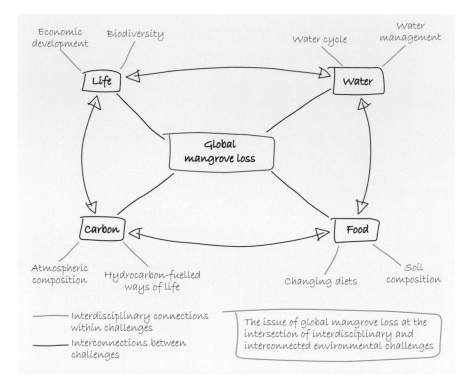

Figure 9.9   Diagram of connections within and between core issues

However, it is necessary to go one step further in order to understand the crisis of inhabitation, because, as our example of the current state of mangrove ecosystems illustrates, connections are not only important for single environmental issues but also for the relation *between* issues. The loss and degradation of mangrove ecosystems cannot be adequately explained by looking solely at life, water, carbon or food. The problem of mangrove destruction, rather, lies at the intersection of all those challenges. Agricultural and urban development along the coastlines where mangroves have historically been located has led to deforestation, expansion in intensive shrimp farming, and intensified pollution. These issues, which are intimately connected with food webs, the water cycle, carbon budgets and social practices, have all contributed to the decline in mangroves. This environmental imagination of connections also needs to be applied at the global level, as the above quote from Connie Hedegaard illustrates.

As you will see in the next section, it is when the entanglement of environmental issues is both recognised and taken seriously that responses can be most effective.

6   Restoration as discovery

Mangroves are entangled, not just in terms of their root system as we saw in Section 2, but in other senses as well. They are caught up in some of the key challenges of sharing a dynamic planet, challenges that are themselves the outcome of connections between many different processes, both biophysical and social in kind, and both near and far in origin. As such, the plight of mangroves provides an unwelcome reminder of the difficulty that we face as a species in managing the tension between Earth as a lively place, and Earth as a place to live. They have suffered from being considered expendable during a period of rapid coastal development. They have been cleared for short-term gain just at the moment when scientific research was revealing the critical role they play in making those areas habitable through ecosystem services such as nutrient filtration and soil stabilisation. If conserved, mangroves would help keep those areas habitable for future generations by sequestering some of the carbon that might otherwise accelerate further climatic change.

Figure 9.10   Mangrove planting in Joal-Fadiouth, Senegal

Many of the local people who depend on mangrove ecosystems are attempting to ensure the long-term habitability of those areas for human and non-human populations (Figure 9.10). The loss of mangrove ecosystems has also prompted a range of local and global actors to publicly engage with each other on mangrove conservation, so that the plight of mangroves is now an environmental issue in the sense that you were introduced to in Book 1, Chapters 5 to 8. That is, a public has formed around the issue of mangrove conservation, and that public seeks to raise the visibility of the issue before policy makers and other actors. Mangroves now have an official presence as endangered in United Nations and International Union for Conservation of Nature (IUCN) reports (e.g. Mangroves for the Future, 2012); and an online pressure group, Mangrove Action Project (MAP), is dedicated to mangrove protection (Mangrove Action Project, 2012) (Figure 9.11). Boosted by the recognition of the carbon sequestration potential of mangroves, activities designed to restore mangrove ecosystems have become a major conservation concern worldwide (Warne, 2011).

Figure 9.11   The Mangrove Action Project's website

It is too early to judge the success of many of these initiatives as it takes time for the health and sustainability of a newly planted mangrove forest to become evident and measurable. However, experience and research offer some insights into what characterises the most effective responses to mangrove loss. In order to illustrate this, we now focus on the attempts to restore mangroves in Joal-Fadiouth in Senegal (Figure 9.12).

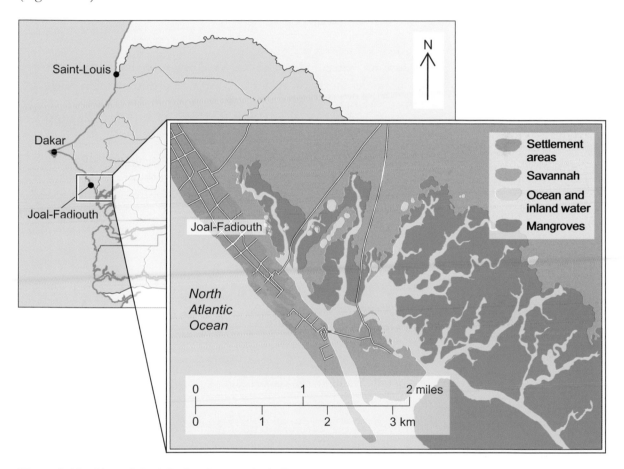

Figure 9.12   Map of Joal-Fadiouth area, including mangroves

The loss of mangroves in and around Joal-Fadiouth since the early 1980s can be traced to many of the factors introduced earlier in this chapter, such as urbanisation, infrastructure building and aquaculture. Regional droughts have also contributed. Around 82 hectares of mangrove ecosystem have been lost over that period (The Open University, 2012). Since 2002, local residents have been involved in initiatives to reverse this trend and establish new mangroves in order to build up future resilience of the area. Four lessons may be distilled from their experience.

First, an appreciation of the specificity of the locality in general, and of the reasons for the loss of mangroves in that locality, is critical to the success of restoration schemes. All too often, such an appreciation is absent, as geographer Bradley Walters and colleagues describe in their review of the 'Ethnobiology, socio-economics and management of mangrove forests' (Walters et al., 2008):

> Failure to better understand the local environmental and socio-economic contexts of mangrove restoration dooms many such efforts. Mangrove restoration projects often have moved immediately into planting of mangroves without determining the cause of previous degradation or why natural recovery has failed. Even where environmental conditions permit, natural or assisted restoration of a site, ongoing or future disturbance of an area by local people may prevent it. Ideally mangrove restoration success should be measured ... by the level of support and involvement of local communities and local governments. Mangrove rehabilitation programs that only utilize coastal communities as sources of replanting labour and do not involve them in the long-run management of the various uses of the restored ecosystem are less likely to be successful.
>
> (Walters et al., 2008, p. 229)

In conclusion, Walters and his colleagues propose that:

> Studies that pay careful attention to the actual *ecology* of resource use are especially critical in light of the widespread influence of people on mangrove ecosystems ... yet such information is almost always absent in planning and policy discussions.
>
> (Walters et al., 2008, p. 231)

This has certainly been the case in Joal-Fadiouth, where it was essential that the pressures of immigration and the centrality of oyster harvesting to the local economy were both recognised and addressed in the restoration efforts.

Second, successful restoration requires the involvement and investment of local communities. Having toured the world's mangrove ecosystems while researching his book, Kennedy Warne concluded that good 'Mangrove management must include the participation of the people who rely on it' (Warne, 2011, pp. 134–5). He worries about a trend towards what he calls 'restoration-lite':

> Planting mangroves has even become an official Guinness World Records activity. The current world record of 541,176 mangrove propagules [seedlings] planted by a team of 300 people within a twenty-four hour period was set in July 2009 by the Pakistan Ministry of the Environment. That plantathon, on mudflats near the mouth of the Indus River, surpassed the previous record of 447,874, set a month earlier by an Indian army regiment in Assam. What next – the Mangrove World Series?

> (Warne, 2011, p. 111)

Warne objects in particular to the assumption that one size fits all: 'What could be easier than jabbing a mangrove propagule into the mud? … What tends to be overlooked is whether such plantings succeed in producing viable forests. Many fail, and fail dismally' (Warne, 2011, p. 111). Those involved in the Joal-Fadiouth project seem to have learnt some of these lessons, with local leadership, public education and community involvement key to the replanting and – crucially – maintenance of the area's mangroves.

Third, if restoration is to be successful in a particular locality, lessons must be learnt from best practice elsewhere and adapted to the specific ecological and social context in which the project is taking place. Thus, even though the mangrove planting project in Joal-Fadiouth was initiated locally, it was inspired by similar efforts elsewhere in Senegal, and one of the reasons for its success was a partnership with these mangrove restoration projects. The partnerships were organised by the NGO Oceanium, which received a US$1m donation from the French food company Danone, and operationalised by 78,000 volunteers from 323 villages nationwide. Up to 100 million mangrove trees were planted between 2006 and 2012 (Africa The Good News, 2009; Rio Plus Business, 2012). The work is connected to the UN's Livelihoods programme. Oceanium – led by a charismatic ecologist named Haidar El Ali (who became Senegal's environment minister in 2012) – puts great stock on its easy-to-reproduce methods which, it suggests, can be scaled up effectively.

Finally, it has become clear that if it is to succeed – in Joal-Fadiouth and elsewhere – mangrove restoration must involve a commitment to something new. The process of establishing new mangrove forests has become less about a nostalgic attachment to the past and more about moving towards emergent futures that involve more entanglement between humans and their environments. In this sense, mangrove restoration projects reflect a broader shift in conservation work from thinking in terms of recovery to discovery (Lorimer, 2012). This discovery of emergent futures and new entanglements is being undertaken by 'communities of practice' (Wenger, 1998) that are locally based and led but globally connected and aware. One important feature of such communities of practice is the role they play, not only in developing the knowledge of their members but in ensuring that such expertise is widely shared and disseminated. It is in this sense that we might talk about working in place in search for resilience in the face of a crisis of inhabitation. Perhaps, as the writer Anne Dillard suggests, the form of the mangroves themselves could be a model for us: 'the planet is less like an enclosed spaceship – spaceship earth – than it is like an exposed mangrove island, beautiful and loose' (Dillard, 1988, p. 150).

Activity 9.3   Responding in place

Before you finish the chapter, pick another example of a successful, place-based initiative designed to respond to environmental change. The example you choose may be from this module, or it may be one with which you are familiar from outside the module. To what extent do the lessons from the Joal-Fadiouth mangrove planting project describe the characteristics of the project you have chosen?

These four lessons are:

- appreciation of local specificity
- community involvement
- adaptation of best practice from elsewhere to local realities
- an orientation towards the future.

---

7   Summary

The chapter began by reintroducing the module question *What are the challenges of sharing a dynamic planet?* Noting the scale of the question, it was suggested that only through consolidating the different elements of the module together into an overall way of thinking – termed an environmental imagination – would we truly be able to grasp the complexity of environmental issues and how we should respond to them in the future. This environmental imagination has three components: describing and interpreting environmental issues in terms of connections, investigating and analysing using the module concepts, and the notion of sharing. This chapter focused on the first of these to explore how places might be (re)made to become more resilient in the face of the threats of environmental change. Environmental change, we noted, always touches down in a particular place at a particular moment. All places are constituted by a particular set of connections, and it has been argued that a full awareness of these connections is necessary before action can be taken. The environmental imagination you have developed on this module is a means to helping you comprehend the myriad connections that make and transform places.

We have also worked with the idea that humans face a wider crisis of inhabitation. Through the example of mangrove ecosystems we reviewed key elements of Book 1, Chapter 5–12 and Book 2, Chapters 1–8 and showed how the challenges of life, water, carbon and food are interconnected. As a species, humans can no longer be confident that either the places we live in or our ways of living will necessarily be available or adequate in the future. Thinking about the entanglement and interdependence of environmental issues in this way helped us in the last section of the chapter to draw some speculative conclusions about how communities can respond to produce more sustainable ways of life. This section also showed us the importance of local environmental involvement and knowledge in discovering new ways of inhabiting the planet.

References

Africa The Good News (2009) 'Senegalese NGO plants 34 million mangroves to offset carbon emissions', 9 November [online], http://africagoodnews.com/content/senegalese-ngo-plants-34-million-mangroves-to-offset-carbon-emissions (Accessed 29 November 2012).

Dillard, A (1988) *Teaching a Stone to Talk: Expeditions and Encounters*, New York, Harper Perennial.

Donato, D. C., Kauffman, J. B., Murdiyarso, D., Kurnianto, S., Stidham, M. and Kanninen, M. (2011) 'Mangroves among the most carbon-rich forests in the tropics', *Nature Geoscience*, vol. 4, no. 5, pp. 293–7 [online], DOI: 10.1038/ngeo1123 (Accessed 28 November 2012).

Global Water Partnership (GWP) (2000) *Towards Water Security: A Framework for Action*, GWP, Stockholm and London [online], http://www.gwptoolbox.org/index2.php?option=com_reference&reference_id=75&pop=1 (Accessed 7 August 2012).

Hedegaard, C. (2012) 'Science is crucial in supporting the low carbon transition' [online], http://ec.europa.eu/commission_2010-2014/hedegaard/headlines/news/2012-03-06_01_en.htm (Accessed 1 December 2012).

Lorimer, J. (2012) 'Multinatural geographies for the Anthropocene', *Progress in Human Geography*, vol. 36, no. 5, pp. 593–612.

Mangrove Action Project (2012) [online], http://mangroveactionproject.org/ (Accessed 29 November 2012).

Mangroves for the Future (2012) [online], http://www.mangrovesforthefuture.org/ (Accessed 29 November 2012).

National Oceanic and Atmospheric Administration (NOAA) (2012) 'Mangrove ecology' in *Encycopedia of Earth* [online], http://www.eoearth.org/article/Mangrove_ecology?topic=49514 (Accessed 1 December 2012).

Polidoro, B. A., Carpenter, K. E., Collins, L., Duke, N. C., Ellison, A. M., Ellison, J. C., Farnsworth, E. J., Fernando, E. S., Kathiresan, K., Koedam, N. E., Livingstone, S. R., Miyagi, T., Moore, G. E., Nam, V. N., Ong, J. E., Primavera, J. H., Salmo, S. G. III, Sanciangco, J. C., Sukardjo, S., Wang, Y. and Yong, J. W. H. (2010) 'The loss of species: mangrove extinction risk and geographic areas of global concern', *PLoS ONE*, vol. 5, no. 4, April [online], http://sci.odu.edu/gmsa/files/Polidoro%20et%20al.%202010a.pdf (Accessed 2 January 2013).

Rio Plus Business (2012) 'Rio + 20 business focus: a new approach to carbon compensation', 1 June [online], http://rioplus.org/rio20-business-focus-a-new-approach-to-carbon-compensation/ (Accessed 29 November 2012).

The Ecologist (2012) 'Shrimp: luxury food with a hidden environmental price tag', 17 February [online], http://www.theecologist.org/how_to_make_a_difference/food_and_gardening/1248977/

shrimp_luxury_food_with_a_hidden_environmental_price_tag.html (Accessed 28 November 2012).

The Open University (2013) 'Improvisation in Senegal' [Video], *DST206 Environment: sharing a dynamic planet* [online], http://learn2.open.ac.uk/course/view.php?id=201601 (Accessed 1 November 2012).

Walters, B. B., Ronnback, P., Kovacs, J. M., Crona, B., Hussain, S. A., Badola, R., Primavera, J. H., Barbier, E. and Farid Dahdouh-Guebas, F. (2008) 'Ethnobiology, socio-economics and management of mangrove forests: a review', *Aquatic Botany*, vol. 89, no. 2, pp. 220–36.

Warne, K. (2011) *Let Them Eat Shrimp: The Tragic Disappearance of the Rainforests of the Sea*, Washington, DC, Island Press.

Wenger, E. (1998) *Communities of Practice: Learning, Meaning, and Identity*, Cambridge, Cambridge University Press.

Yang, Q., Tam, N. F. Y., Wong, Y. S., Luan, T. G., Su, W. S., Lan, C. Y., Shin, P. K. S. and Cheung, S. G. (2008) 'Potential use of mangroves as constructed wetland for municipal sewage treatment in Futian, Shenzhen, China', *Marine Pollution Bulletin*, vol. 57, nos 6–12, pp. 735–43.

Chapter 10   Migration, complexity and an environmental imagination

Nick Bingham

Contents

1 Introduction

Chapter 9 introduced the idea that we are living through a crisis of inhabitation and that understanding and responding to this state of affairs requires an environmental imagination. The chapter argued that one component of this environmental imagination is the ability to think in terms of connections. The term connections is used in two ways. The first describes how individual challenges – such as life, water, carbon and food – involve complex entanglements of biophysical and social processes. The second is that the individual challenges are themselves interrelated and interdependent. Action to address one challenge may thus have consequences for the others. Chapter 9 concluded by suggesting that understanding these connections in policy and practice is critical for the formulation and implementation of appropriate responses.

You should by now have a strong sense of the complexity that characterises environmental issues and of why an interdisciplinary approach that is capable of tracing such entanglements is necessary for studying them. This chapter adds a second layer to the environmental imagination that is being developed throughout this block. The chapter seeks to answer a question that you might have already been asking yourself: if everything is so interdependent, how do we – personally, politically and academically – establish which of the multiplicity of connections matter most? If we do not have a robust way of approaching this question, the risk is that we become paralysed by the overwhelming complexity of environmental issues rather than empowered by understanding them.

This is where the second component of the environmental imagination comes in: the role that key concepts can play in understanding issues. In this module you have been working with three sets of key concepts:

- time and space
- risk and uncertainty
- values, power and agency.

This chapter employs these concepts as a toolkit for grasping the complexity of environmental issues. It does this by demonstrating how these concepts help us focus on key aspects of entanglement, thereby allowing us to deepen our analysis without getting lost in the myriad of connections. As you work through the chapter, you will consolidate your understanding in the sense of both reviewing your earlier learning and integrating this learning by further developing an environmental imagination.

Whereas in Chapter 9 we explored how particular places may be kept habitable by mobilising local knowledge and action, in this chapter we examine what happens when, as a result of climate change, particular places are rendered uninhabitable by those who call them home, prompting them to leave and move elsewhere. This is a response which has been receiving increasing academic, policy and public attention in recent years under the name **climate-induced migration** (CIM). Climate change and CIM each illustrate the constantly shifting character of the dynamic planet on which we live, and how what we consider to be habitable may change over time. It is to this world on the move and its implications for making places home that we now turn.

Climate-induced migration (CIM)
The movement of people triggered by environmental deterioration resulting from climatic change.

2   World on the move

Throughout the module we have explored the different ways in which the Earth as a dynamic planet changes over time.

Activity 10.1   Long-term biophysical changes

Can you name some of the long-term biophysical processes that illustrate the Earth as a dynamic planet? Which of these occur naturally without the intervention of humans, which are solely human-induced, and which can be both natural and human?

Comment

Some of the major long-term biophysical processes you may have thought of are:

- earthquakes
- volcanic eruptions
- tectonic plate movements
- climate change
- flooding
- sea level change
- species change (including adaptation, changes in species distribution and extinction).

You may also have listed other processes not examined in the module, such as asteroid impacts.

All of these processes can occur naturally. However, humans can have an impact on some of these processes, such as climate change, flooding, sea level changes and species extinction. Earthquakes are caused naturally, although some minor and limited quakes have resulted from human activities such as mining. However, humans have yet to cause volcanic eruptions or tectonic plate movements.

All these changes have been happening throughout the history of the Earth. Plants and animals have often adapted to change (Figure 10.1). When they cannot adapt (or cannot adapt fast enough) they have become extinct; dinosaurs are the most obvious example. But long-term changes to the Earth can also provide the conditions for new species to evolve. For example, although volcanic eruptions can threaten species with a distribution that is highly localised in the vicinity of the eruption, some plant species may actually benefit, particularly those able to colonise bare rock. Species may evolve on isolated islands such as Madagascar in the Indian Ocean and the Galapagos Islands in the Pacific Ocean. However, these species may be unable to migrate if affected by climate change (Figure 10.2).

Figure 10.1   A hoopoe (*Upupa epops*), a bird of southern Europe, Asia and North Africa. Owing to a changing climate, it is now breeding in southern Britain

Figure 10.2   A Galapagos tortoise (*Chelonoidis nigra*) from the Galapagos island of Isabella. Isabella has five active volcanoes, so volcanic eruptions could potentially kill all the Isabella subspecies of Galapagos tortoise

Can humans adapt to the changes caused by a dynamic Earth in similar ways to other animals? Like other animals, we cannot, as a species, control the incidence or severity of earthquakes, volcanoes or other plate tectonics-related activity. We could opt to live away from areas of geological risk, but evidence shows that humans often inhabit earthquake-prone areas and have even built cities such as San Francisco and Tokyo in high-risk zones. Flooding and sea level change are natural processes, although they are increasingly related to anthropogenic climate change. Remember, we are living during the Quaternary Ice Age, which has periodic colder glacial and warmer interglacial stages, and accompanying changes and adaptations. During the last 11,500 years, we have been in a warmer interglacial stage. However, anthropogenic carbon dioxide emissions since the Industrial Revolution have produced a rate of change of the global temperature that exceeds the glacial/interglacial changes (see Chapter 1, Figure 1 7).

As you saw in the last chapter, there are some opportunities to adapt to such changes by adding resilience to places. However, there are limited ways in which humans can prevent or moderate other climate-induced changes in the most-affected areas of the planet. In such circumstances, people may be forced to migrate. The anthropologist Anthony Oliver-Smith summarises three ways in which global climate change will contribute to the displacement of people (Oliver-Smith, 2009):

- *Loss of ecosystem services.* As you saw in Book 1, Chapters 2 and 4 and Book 2, Chapter 1, global climate change can profoundly reduce the capability of local environments to support human and other life through the provision of ecosystem services such as water, food and energy. Beyond a certain point, such change can push people to migrate in search of sufficient resources.

- *Loss of land.* The combined effect of the reduction in habitable land that the loss of ecosystem services will generate, and the actual disappearance of terrain owing to global climate change-induced sea level rise, will over time displace human populations, especially from the world's coasts.

- *Increased intensity and frequency of climate-based natural disasters.* Climate change will, via increased ocean surface temperatures, lead to an increase in extreme weather events, including more severe tropical storms with higher storm surges that will probably interact with rising sea levels to devastating effect. Migration will be one response for people faced with such forces.

Oliver-Smith also suggests that each of these factors will interact with the others to compound and intensify their effects. Again, the entanglement of different interconnected causes and effects becomes apparent.

These movements, adjustments and realignments of our dynamic planet have many implications for where and how human beings (and other species) live, and how they make the Earth a place to live.

Activity 10.2   Tuvalu: a country at risk

Tuvalu is a small island state in the South Pacific (Figure 10.3a). With a maximum height of 4 metres above sea level, this group of nine atolls is likely to be the first country to be submerged because of climate change-induced sea level rise (Figure 10.3b).

Think for a minute about some of the questions that this raises.

What will happen to the people on the island as a consequence of sea level rise? What will happen when circumstances change (especially slowly) and existing support networks are stretched?

Comment

Some of the people on these islands are already seeking to move elsewhere, although for many this option is simply unaffordable. Conceptually, the very idea of permanence is questioned by the submergence of an entire nation. The legal responsibility for the people remains with the state of Tuvalu, but it is unclear how the state can discharge its responsibilities to its citizens without a territory. Tuvalu has asked Australia to accept its migrants, but many people may choose not to go to Australia. Ethical responsibility for climate change is unclear, so it is not obvious which actors should pay for the losses suffered by the people of Tuvalu and the costs of resettling them.

Climate change is likely to leave certain parts of the world much less habitable than before, either because they have disappeared or because they have become uninhabitable – for example, as a result of flooding, drought or extreme weather. As climate change takes hold, it will become increasingly impossible in many places to manage the tension between the Earth as a lively place and the Earth as a place to live.

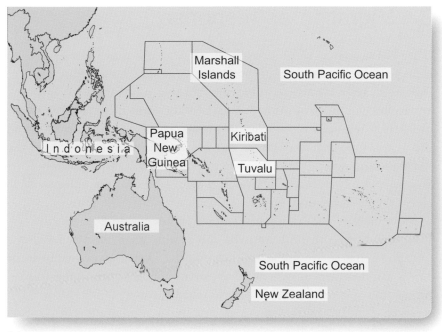

(a)

(b)

Figure 10.3   (a) Map of the South Pacific Ocean showing the position of Tuvalu; (b) Aerial view of Tuvalu

3   Migration as response

It should not really surprise us that people might move in response to changing environmental conditions. First, humans have a long history of moving in response to environmental change. Adaptation to environmental fluctuations – fluctuations that are often called 'natural' disasters – has been a necessity throughout history for societies round the world. One adaptive option that has enabled people to survive these fluctuations is migration, either temporary or permanent (Oliver-Smith, 2009). Historically, it has been suggested that the collapse of the classic Maya civilisation around the eighth century AD, the abandonment of the Viking settlements in Greenland between the twelfth and fifteenth centuries, and the exodus from the US state of Oklahoma and surrounding areas during the Dust Bowl drought in the 1930s are all linked to climatic fluctuations that threatened the food production systems on which people relied (Orlove, 2005). More recently, there has been well-documented cyclical migration in the Sahel region of Africa that has been linked to environmental changes among other factors (White, 2012).

Second, and as we have already noted, some species have already begun to shift their patterns of inhabitation in response to contemporary climate change. Species migration, of course, has always taken place, but in a major review of changes in the distribution of animals and plants, published in the journal *Science*, scientists found what they were confident was unequivocal evidence that climate change is the cause of a mass movement of plant and animals (Chen et al., 2011). According to one of the authors, Professor Chris Thomas, although there are wide variations between individual species, overall animal and plant species are retreating away from the equator and moving towards the poles at a rate of about 16 to 17 kilometres per decade: 'These changes are equivalent to animals and plants shifting away from the equator at around 20 cm per hour, for every hour of the day, for every day of the year. This has been going on for the last 40 years and is set to continue for at least the rest of the century' (Thomas, quoted in Connor, 2011). This rapid rate of movement away from both lower altitudes to higher elevations and from lower latitudes towards the poles may be caused by many factors. However, it is clear that climate change is one of the primary drivers because the rate of movement is most rapid in those areas that have undergone the greatest warming.

Human beings have always coped with environmental change and climatic variability by migrating (Adger et al., 2003), and we are now facing many of the same pressures as those non-human species that have already begun to move. Many parts of the tropical countries of the global South are likely to be affected, to differing degrees, by more frequent extreme weather events in the future. Where local populations are unable to mitigate those problems, they are likely to migrate. **Displacement migration** takes place when people feel they have no other option but to move. People may be displaced owing to a number of reasons, such as war and civil unrest. Displacement migration due to environmental change is 'typically undertaken as a last resort when other coping strategies are exhausted' (Adger et al., 2003, p. 189).

Climate-induced migration, or CIM, is an example of displacement migration. During the twenty-first century, the planned migrations of the past are likely to become dwarfed in number and extent by CIM. Since the 1980s, the degree to which climate change is forcing people to migrate has been receiving more attention in academic and policy circles and in the media. One commonly quoted estimate is that by 2050 there will be 200 million climate refugees (Myers, 2002).

If other causes of environmental change are taken into account, predictions for the displaced population become even higher. A 2007 report from the charity Christian Aid, based on United Nations population and climate change data, estimates that over the next 50 years as many as one billion people, or one in seven of the people on the Earth today, could be forced to leave their homes as environmental refuges (Christian Aid, 2007). According to these accounts, in addition to climate change, the causes of displacement will include conflict, large-scale development projects and widespread environmental degradation, so that places that previously supported human life, for example in the Sahara, the Middle East and south Asia, will be unable to continue doing so. 'Forced migration is now the most urgent threat facing poor nations,' said John Davison, the report's lead author. 'Climate change is the great, frightening unknown in this equation' (quoted in Vidal, 2007, p. 16).

Figure 10.4 maps the suggested global distribution and predicted direction of climate-induced migration, while Figure 10.5 uses classifications from the work of Gregory White, a political scientist and author of the book *Climate Change and Migration* (2012), to usefully summarise some of the features of new and future climate-induced migrants.

Displacement migration
Migration which is undertaken when other coping strategies are exhausted.

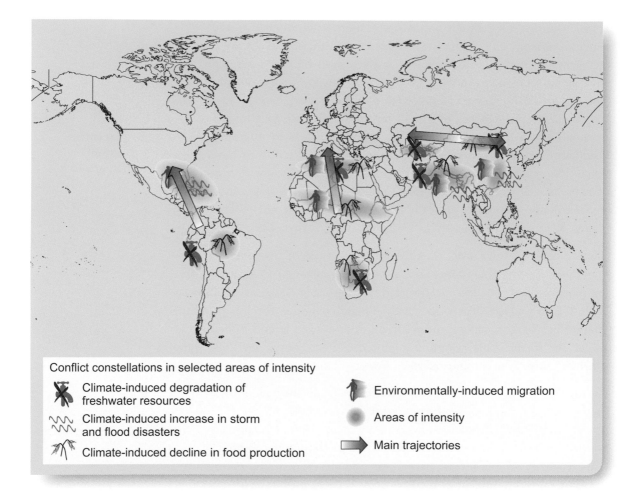

Figure 10.4   Map of potential climate-induced population displacements (Source: German Advisory Council on Global Change, 2007, Figure 1)

White notes that the typology of environmental refugees (Figure 10.5a) presents conceptual challenges. For example, Type I events, such as hurricanes, may have connections to climate change in that their frequency and intensity are predicted to increase with a warming planet. Furthermore, the Type III category may not always present as gradually as the table might suggest; rather, climate change may manifest itself in extreme ways if thresholds or tipping points are reached.

The matrix of cause and volition (Figure 10.5b) is White's provisional attempt to present some of the dynamics of agency. He notes that for Type III refugees (Figure 10.5a) the migrations that result are often less obviously 'forced' than the Type I and II categories, but nonetheless are not simply 'voluntary' (hence his 'compelled' category).

TYPOLOGY OF ENVIRONMENTAL REFUGEES					
	I Disaster **Unintended,** **catastrophic event**		**II Expropriation** **Wilful, purposeful** **destruction**		**III Deterioration** **Incremental**
Sub-category	Natural	Technological	Development	Ecocide	Greenhouse gases Depletion
General example	Hurricane	Nuclear disaster	Dam building	Defoliation	Climate change and island inundation Deforestation
Empirical example	Hurricane Katrina, 2005	Three Mile Island, 1979	Three Gorges Dam, China	Agent Orange, Vietnam, 1963–1969	Carteret Islands Amazonia

(a)

MATRIX OF CAUSE AND VOLITION			
	VOLITION		
CAUSE	**Voluntary**	**Compelled**	**Involuntary**
Economic	Migrant		Trafficked individual
Environmental		Climate-induced migrant – person displaced by climate change (Type III)	Person displaced by cataclysm or state policy (Types I or II)
Political			Traditional refugees (according to the 1951 Convention Relating to the Status of Refugees)

(b)

PERSON DISPLACED BY CLIMATE CHANGE (TYPE III)			
Volition	**Voluntary**	**Compelled**	**Forced**
Category	Environmentally–motivated migrant	Environmentally–forced migrant	Environmental refugee

(c)

Figure 10.5   White's tables showing: (a) Typology of environmental refugees; (b) Matrix of cause and volition; (c) Person displaced by climate change (Source: based on White, 2012, pp. 26–8, Tables 1.1–1.3)

The classification of Type III migrants (Figure 10.5c) is White's attempt to unpack the variety of possible Type III migrants to take into account that it does not make sense to consider them all as acutely dislocated.

The estimates of climate-induced migration offered by Myers and Christian Aid, then, make huge claims and speak of massive complexity. Although White's analysis (Figure 10.5) complicates some of these claims, the prevalence and scale of the problem and the multiple connections involved in its creation can leave us feeling rather paralysed. How can we further investigate these claims and analyse this issue such that we are better able to get to grips with it?

4   Investigating and analysing the complexity of climate-induced migration

By now you will have a sense that climate-induced migration (CIM) – like the mangrove ecosystems explored in the previous chapter – is enormously complex. Both its causes and consequences are diverse and far-reaching, encompassing biophysical, social and technical processes. This chapter has suggested that an environmental imagination that describes and interprets environmental issues in terms of connections and interdependencies is essential for understanding CIM. But tracing connections will only take us so far. If everything is connected, at least in theory, then how do we know what really matters in practice? If the issue of CIM takes us from the most global of planetary forces shaping the planet's habitability to the micro level of personal decisions about if and when to migrate, then how do we work out which connections we should pay more or less attention to?

This is where the three groups of analytical concepts introduced and developed in this module are useful: time and space; risk and uncertainty; values, power and agency. These concepts allow us to delve a little deeper into the entanglements that characterise environmental issues. They enable us to understand the various types of connections introduced in the last chapter. Each group of concepts may be considered as a tool that will help us recognise and comprehend particular features of the world in general and environmental issues in particular.

Used in this way, the concepts comprise a toolkit which you can bring to bear in a flexible way to make sense not only of the environmental issues covered in this module but of other issues that you will encounter, including those that are new and emerging. On a 'dynamic planet', new situations will constantly arise. That is the case with environmental problems triggered by human agency. Moreover, because of the way that Earth and life processes interact, this dynamism would continue even if human interventions in ecosystems were infinitely cautious and careful.

How, then, might we bring to bear the investigative and analytical insights that the key concepts offer to the question of CIM? In what follows you will take your lead from the largest study of migration ever undertaken, the UK Foresight study of *Migration and Global Environmental Change* (Foresight, 2011). What you will learn is how a collection of researchers used similar conceptual devices to unpack some of the assumptions on which the claims about the scale and implications of CIM that we have encountered have been based. By doing so they respected and took seriously the enormously complicated character of this issue, but they were also to demystify it by identifying and defining some clear patterns from the complexity.

4.1 Using risk and uncertainty

We have used the concepts of risk and uncertainty to draw attention to the fact that decisions are almost always taken in the light of imperfect, incomplete or unclear information. As an old saying indicates, apart from death and taxes there is not much that we can be truly certain about. Environmental issues involve some significant risks and uncertainties, in particular because of the extended timescales involved. Since the late 1960s, there has been a marked shift in how the world's industrial nations have approached environmental management and protection; increasingly, there has been a recognition that if environmental policy is to be effective it has to concern itself more with preventing future harm and avoiding potential problems, rather than dealing with harm after it has occurred. On this view, environmental policy should be proactive rather than merely reactive. The result of this shift in thinking on environmental policy can be seen in many arenas: from policy documents and party manifestos, through regulations and laws, to government action plans and international treaties, as well as in the practices of both private and public sector organisations. Environmental thinking has become much more future oriented.

Although there is now some degree of consensus among politicians, environmental activists and other actors that risk and uncertainty are central to environmental issues and responses to them, there is much less agreement on precisely what those concepts mean and how they should be applied. As you have seen, when people talk about risk, uncertainty and environmental issues, they can be talking about some related but very different things, including hazards, threats, probability and unknowns (Book 1, Chapter 2).

Activity 10.3   Hazards, risks and the precautionary principle

From your learning earlier in the module can you:

- distinguish between a hazard and a risk

- define the precautionary principle?

Comment

From Book 1, Chapter 2 you may have recalled that a *hazard* may be defined as an event or a happening that poses a threat to humans or to the environment. A *risk* may be defined as the product of the probability (or likelihood) that a particular hazard will occur and the severity of the potential harm. Risk may be expressed numerically:

Risk = Probability that a hazard will occur × severity of the hazard.

The *precautionary principle* holds that where there is a risk of environmental damage, scientific uncertainty should not be used as a reason for postponing measures to prevent such damage.

What aspects of climate-induced migration might employing the concepts of risk and uncertainty as investigative and analytical tools draw our attention to? We might start with some of the claims that have been made about CIM, and in particular the numbers of migrants involved. Inevitably, such claims are made on the basis of predictions that are generated with imperfect, incomplete or unclear information. We are therefore dealing with uncertainties by definition. We have already explored in the module how difficult it is to make precise calculations about the working of dynamic systems such as the Earth's climate and the behaviour of people, either as individuals or as groups. Forecasts of CIM (such as those in Section 3 above) have to take account of both climate change and human behaviour, thus exacerbating the problem. In this context how reliable can forecasts of future CIM be?

It was with precisely these sorts of questions in mind that the team behind the Foresight migration study reviewed some of the key quantitative claims about CIM and the methodologies by which they were generated. They noted first that many of the figures which currently circulate in policy circles worldwide are based on only a few key early studies (in particular, Myers, 2002), with new estimates built on top of old ones without the robustness of the original data ever really being interrogated. Such lack of investigation and analysis has had a significant impact in this field of study. Second, they proposed (following other critiques) that the concept of risk which Myers employed to generate the very influential figure of 200 million refugees was problematic, given the kind of issue that migration is. In short, the suggestion was that the model Myers used to generate the 200 million figure did not do justice to the multiplicity and subtleties of the social and natural processes that cause CIM. As a result, his study ended up painting a very simplistic picture of the relationship between the people who might be considered 'at risk' of environmental change and those who would actually move as a response to that situation. Myers ignored the possibility that some of those who might find themselves and their homes exposed to an increased risk as a result of climate change might choose to stay and try to add resilience to their communities and environments (as we saw in the previous chapter; see also Gemenne, 2011).

While Myers' approach and the large and dramatic figures that it generated may well have been instrumental in placing the question of climate-induced migration onto national and international policy and political agendas, the argument of the Foresight team is that there are risks in continuing to promote the idea that a complex and multifaceted issue such as how and why people might change their place of habitation can be reduced to dramatic headline figures. The Foresight team suggest that it is far better to proceed on the basis that an appropriate treatment of the risk of complex environmental issues, which involve many uncertainties, is not one that generates estimates of global totals. Instead, it is better to treat, analyse and present the uncertainties of the future by producing scenarios such as the one shown in Figure 10.6. What it summarises is a synthesis of the headline human mobility outcomes across the three key global ecological regions that the report focused on – drylands, low-elevation coastal zones and mountain regions – according to four future scenarios that the research team developed to help understand how migration may be influenced by future global environmental change and other factors. The vertical axis in Figure 10.6 signals different scenarios of the economic drivers of migration, ranging from low to high global economic growth. The horizontal axis signals different scenarios of the political drivers of migration, ranging from exclusive/fragmented governance to inclusive/connected governance. Thus, the four scenarios generated by the Foresight team can be summarised as:

- *Scenario A:* high global [economic] growth, and exclusive local social, political and economic governance

- *Scenario B:* high global [economic] growth, and inclusive local social, political and economic governance

- *Scenario C:* low global [economic] growth, and exclusive local social, political and economic governance

- *Scenario D:* low global [economic] growth, and inclusive local social, political and economic governance.

(Foresight, 2011, p. 64)

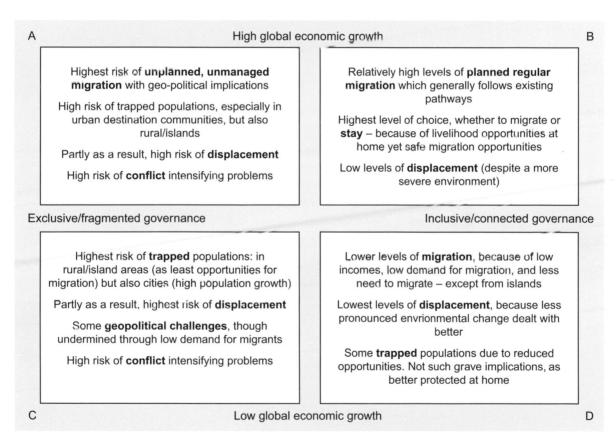

Figure 10.6 Four possible scenarios for climate-induced migration (CIM) (Source: Foresight, 2011, p. 16, Figure ES.4)

For the team, the headline here is that 'this synthesis reveals that "no migration" is not an option in the context of future environmental change: migration will continue to occur in the future and can either be well managed and regular, or, if efforts are made to prevent it, unmanaged, unplanned and forced' (Foresight, 2011, p. 16).

4.2   Using values, power and agency

You have seen how we may use the concepts of risk and uncertainty to orient ourselves to different ways of analysing environmental futures. We now explore how the concepts of values, power and agency can help us to understand how we have reached the current crisis of inhabitation and what the implications of that are for the future.

The concept of power, we have seen, is helpful in understanding what happens when there are various actors, each seeking to promote their own interests. The concept encourages us to consider how different actors might have access to different sources of power, such as economic resources, political leverage, influence over the media, and so on. Actors' power can vary over time and between places, depending on the extent to which the actors can establish the language, ideas and values that are used to set agendas and to define and debate environmental issues. So, in our analysis of power we have looked, first, at the resources that make actors powerful and, second, at the extent to which actors can shape the discourses that are used to communicate understandings about environmental change and how it should be addressed. These two approaches have been termed power as resources and power as discourse, respectively (Book 1, Chapter 3, Box 3.1).

Like the concept of power, the concept of value is a complex one. To give you a simple way of navigating this complexity, we distinguished between two broad kinds of value (Book 1, Chapter 7). The first was instrumental value. Instrumental value reflects the value of an environment for an individual or an actor, or in relation to the collective needs of humanity. Instrumental values are often expressed in monetary terms, as in the case of ecosystem services. The second kind of value is the intrinsic value that an environment has in and of itself, and is based on the idea that, irrespective of its use to humans, the environment is something that has value in its own right. The idea of intrinsic value reflects a moral sense of duty or care towards living or non-living things and it strongly shapes what individuals or groups believe to be right or proper behaviour towards the environment.

Finally, agency was defined as the difference that a social actor makes to the world (Book 1, Chapter 3, Section 2). Agency is itself shaped by power (what actors can achieve) and by values (what actors want to achieve). However, agency is not reducible to either power or values because agency is not always deployed intentionally or knowingly. The agency of actors may be shaped by infrastructures and by a lack of knowledge of the consequences of their actions (Book 2, Chapters 2 and 3). An actor may carry out a particular action that may have unintended consequences over time and space.

How might using the concepts of values, power and agency help us delve a little deeper into the entangled issue of CIM? What aspects of complexity does employing these concepts as investigative and analytical tools draw our attention to? We focus here on power, especially power in terms of resources. Power works when an actor is able to build up and link together various resources in order to influence other actors. Those resources include people, animals, plants, technologies, infrastructures and skills, as well as political, economic and military resources. You have seen that control of resources can enable actors to exert influence at a distance, and how the absence of resources can leave actors in a powerless position.

This insight resonates with one of the findings of the Foresight report. While migration is an adaptive strategy for many people faced with the consequences of future climate change, the Foresight team also concluded that climate change is likely to make migration less possible as well as more necessary. This is because migration requires a lot of resources, such as money, friends who can help you, knowledge of how to move, and so on, yet populations who experience the impacts of climate change are likely to experience a squeeze on the availability of these resources. As a result, many people will simply be unable to move. People may also be stopped from moving because some countries have responded to the 'threat' of migrants entering their countries by strengthening and policing, even militarising, their borders. Their agency is thus curtailed. However, 'to the international community, this "trapped" population is likely to represent just as important a policy concern as those who do migrate' (Foresight, 2011, p. 9; Figure 10.7). In other words, if migration is considered (as the Foresight report suggests it should be) as part of an appropriate adaptation to global environmental change, how might state, regional and global bodies mobilise in the present and future to facilitate movement for those significant groups of people without the (power as) resources to leave their homes (and thereby to prevent them becoming trapped)?

EU told to prepare for flood of climate change migrants

Global warming threatens to severely destabilise the planet, rendering a fifth of its population homeless, top officials say

Ian Traynor in Brussels
The Guardian, Monday 10 March 2008

Ice boulders left behind after a flood caused by the overflowing of a lake in Greenland. Photograph: Uriel Sinai/Getty images

In its half-century history, the EU has absorbed wave upon wave of immigrants. There were the millions of political migrants fleeing Russian-imposed communism to western Europe throughout the cold war, the post-colonial and "guest worker" migrants who poured into western Europe in the boom years of the 1950s and 60s, the hundreds of thousands who escaped the Balkan wars of the 90s and the millions of economic migrants of the past decade seeking a better life.

Now, according to the EU's two senior foreign policy officials, Europe needs to brace itself for a new wave of migration with a very different cause - global warming. The ravages already being inflicted on parts of the developing world by climate change are engendering a new type of refugee, the "environmental migrant".

Figure 10.7   Online newspaper article illustrating 'security' rhetoric around CIM

As with the concepts of risk and uncertainty, using the concept of power reveals a particular, if under-explored, dimension of CIM and yields a deeper insight into the particular ways that different social and natural processes come together in practice. How actors respond to climate change will depend on the power capabilities they have at their disposal and how, if at all, they are able to deploy these capabilities under conditions of uncertainty and change. Without understanding the concept of power, it is difficult to analyse how populations may become trapped, now and in the future, owing to climate change. This analysis of the power of some people to migrate from environmentally risky places while others remain trapped is one of the key findings of the Foresight research, and is likely to influence policy substantially in coming years. The power of others to (directly or indirectly) limit such migrations and to entrap populations is another. For example, the report highlights the case of Somalia where armed conflict hinders the movement of pastoralists, who would otherwise relocate when confronted with drought (Foresight, 2011).

Activity 10.4   Using the key concepts

Here we have explored one way in which the concepts of values, power and agency can be used to investigate and analyse CIM, thus bringing some focus and clarity to a complex issue. To consolidate your understanding, can you think of other examples of how these concepts can be employed to further analyse CIM?

Comment

CIM is a very complex subject, as you are learning, and so there are many examples you could have chosen. When considering this question, you may have thought about the extent to which debates around CIM have been shaped by the power of discourse. As you will recall from Book 1, Chapter 3, discourses frame how people talk about environmental issues. They are shaped by accepted understandings, practices and social values. Once established, we noted, a discourse can enable people to make sense of issues, but it can also form an established way of thinking about issues, thus limiting the extent to which consideration is given to new or alternative approaches. An actor who shapes the discourses that other use can thus wield power, helping to determine not only what is discussed, but how it is discussed.

In the case of CIM, the displacement of people has sometimes been framed in global media outlets in terms of the 'security threat' it poses to the economies of the global North, such as European countries facing CIM from Africa. Some media in Europe focus not so much on the problems faced by the populations who may be displaced, nor even on the broader risks of global climate change, but on the costs that will borne by the economies of the countries to which displaced people are likely to seek to migrate. Framing CIM as a threat to European countries presents just one particular dimension of the issue, one that is based on the perceived interests of European political and economic elites. However, this viewpoint tends to receive a disproportionate share of media space, as many of the world's most powerful print and broadcast media are owned by European and North American corporations.

Thinking of power as discourse leads us to reflect on how and why the formulation of CIM as a security threat to the global North has become so influential, and it suggests that other understandings and dimensions of CIM have been marginalised, both in the media and in political conversations in the global North. The problems faced by people who cannot migrate and the uncertainties that they face are less frequently discussed.

4.3   Using time and space

We have used risk and uncertainty to think about the futures of environmental issues, and values, power and agency to think about how those issues are shaped in the past and present and the consequences this has for the future. This brings us to the final set of key concepts: time and space. These concepts attune us to the fact that, while environmental change always touches down in particular places and at particular moments, to understand the full impact of these changes we often need to look further afield.

An awareness of the different temporalities of environmental change is important for understanding the Earth as a dynamic planet. Concepts of time matter when we seek to explain environmental processes and to make predictions about the future. We have encountered time in the linear sense of moving along from a starting point to a finishing point; for example, when thinking about the duration of human impacts on the planet in relation to the vast expanse of geological time. We have also seen how time works to shape environmental issues in terms of cycles and rhythms, some of which are repetitive, such as tides, day and night and the seasons, others of which are less predictable and play out over millions of years, such as ice ages. Finally, we have looked at how environmental change may accelerate during particular moments of time; for example, when a tipping point is reached.

Activity 10.5 Tipping points

Can you recall the definition of tipping point from earlier in the module, and the context in which this term was introduced? See if you can introduce the concept of positive feedbacks in your answer.

Comment

In Book 1, Chapter 3 you were introduced to the idea of a tipping point as a threshold which, if crossed, causes a system to change from one state to another. The example of climate change was used to illustrate this. So far, climate change owing to anthropogenic greenhouse gas emissions has been relatively small scale, but climate scientists predict that the climate system will cross a threshold after which climate change will accelerate. This is because positive feedbacks will take place within the climate system as a result of climate change (Book 2, Chapter 1). For example, planetary warming will lead to the melting of the Earth's ice sheets, thus reducing the planet's albedo which in turn will lead to further warming, and so on.

Like time, space is a multifaceted concept. We have considered space in terms of scale (local to global, for example), as bounded (in terms of biophysical and political/administrative boundaries, for example), as distance between places (connected and separated by spatial relationships such as migration, transport and trade, for example), and as locations (which may last, but which may also shift physically through the process of place tectonics or disappear completely, as in the case of sea level rise).

Again, we can ask how using the concepts of time and space might help us probe a little deeper into the entangled issue of CIM? What aspects of environmental issues does the use of these investigative and analytical concepts draw our attention to? Using the example of CIM, one thing that becomes clear is that a framing of CIM within a security-based discourse of CIM is problematic. According to this version of events, climate-related environmental change will lead to a new and unprecedented wave of human migration as millions of people flee from the effects of sea level rise, flooding, drought and extreme weather events. The discussion focuses on migrants moving to the states of the North Atlantic and Australasia (White, 2012).

However, according to the social scientists contributing to the Foresight study, this security threat has so far had little basis in empirical reality. By paying attention to the empirical spatialities and temporalities of migration related to environmental change, the Foresight study has concluded that, while there is evidence that people do indeed move in relation to climate events, such movement tends to be short-distance and short-term and is often cyclical. In part, this is because international migration requires access to resources that most displaced people simply do not have (see Section 4.2 above). However, the main reason is that people are using migration as a temporary adaptation strategy and want to return home when conditions improve, which is easier if they move only short distances, such as to the nearest urban centres. Even in countries such as Senegal, where there has been a long history of international migration, evidence suggests that those who are moving due to changes in rainfall patterns move largely within the country (White, 2012). So for many people migration is temporary and may be cyclically based around seasons, especially in agricultural communities. However, it is worth bearing in mind that there may be thresholds of change beyond which such temporary adaptations are simply not adequate to sustain life. The conditions at home may never improve enough to make returning a viable option. Such thresholds are likely to be crossed with increasing frequency over coming decades.

Once again, using the module concepts to focus and deepen our attention yields a better understanding of a complex and entangled issue.

Activity 10.6   Working with the concepts of time and space

Here you have seen just one way in which the concepts of time and space can be used to investigate and analyse the issue of climate-induced migration, providing some depth, focus and relevance to a complex issue. As a way of consolidating your understanding of the concepts, can you analyse other ways we could put time and space to work in the context of explaining CIM?

Comment

You could, for instance, choose to focus on space, and specifically on how space is bounded. Most of the current concerns over CIM relate to whether environmental change will lead to migration where people cross national borders. The emphasis is thus largely on international climate-induced migration. However, people in countries such as Senegal were moving across West Africa long before CIM became an issue. These movements, some of them established over many centuries, followed pastoral practices, community social relations and trade. National boundaries were established much more recently and were drawn up by colonial powers with little reference to these kinds of migration or existing patterns of settlement. In some cases, people from the same ethnic group found that they belonged to two different countries, and their regular movements between neighbouring villages were considered to be international migration since they crossed the new boundaries. Partly as a result, Senegal does not control migration between itself and many of the countries that surround it. Instead, it is part of the Economic Community of West African States where there is free movement between the states involved. National political space is bounded but migration spaces are not. There are many other examples of such areas of free movement, including the European Union, which stretch across political boundaries.

The analysis of a spatial category – boundedness – can also usefully draw on time. Given the ongoing and continuous nature of migration and the persistent but slow pace of climate change, how do we know when, and to what extent, migration is actually climate-induced? As stated above, people have always migrated from one part of Senegal to another, and from Senegal to other countries. At what point does ongoing migration become recognised and classified as CIM? These examples show that using space and time, both individually and together, as investigative and analytical tools can lead to new ways of thinking through such questions and understanding CIM.

4.4   Synthesising concepts to investigate and analyse climate-induced migration

We have explored how employing the module concepts as investigative and analytical tools can help us unpack the typically entangled character of environmental issues, offering a sense of depth to the unavoidable complexity of these issues.

Before we move on, it is important to emphasise that we can go one step further than this and combine these groups of concepts. The module concepts you have been learning to work with – space and time; risk and uncertainty; power, values and agency – are all adaptable enough to be assembled in new ways in response to new and emerging environmental challenges. The concepts form a toolkit that you can use in a synthetic and flexible way. For example, and continuing to think about migration, it is possible to see how thinking about power and risk together could help us to understand the vulnerability of those communities affected by environmental change. Similarly, an analysis that encompasses time, space, values, power and agency could help open up new understandings of resilience. One such example is how communities may cooperate to enhance the resilience of their ecosystems, as in the case of mangroves in the previous chapter. You should feel encouraged to keep experimenting with different combinations of these concepts.

The Foresight team drew on several concepts when designing the conceptual framework for their research. Space and time were central to this framework. Other concepts were also introduced to guide the research and help the researchers grapple with the complexity of environmental issues in general and CIM in particular.

The approach of the Foresight team, like that of the interdisciplinary team that collaborated to produce this module, has been to begin from an assumption of complexity before working to untangle it, in the process working through complexity to make sense of the many connections that shape environmental issues. Using the conceptual tools you have worked with on the module will help you to understand and work with complexity, preventing it from becoming overwhelming.

5   Summary

This chapter has developed another component of the environmental imagination that you are consolidating in this block. In the previous chapter you developed the ability to describe and interpret environmental issues in terms of their entanglement and connections. This chapter has added another component – the ability to use the analytical concepts of time and space; risk and uncertainty; and values, power and agency – to investigate and analyse the complexity of environmental issues.

After reviewing some key points about each of those sets of concepts, you saw how – both separately and together – these concepts add depth and focus to the imagination of connections. They offer a mobile toolkit that may be used to help you unpack and interrogate the complexity of other environmental issues: both those covered in the module and those further afield; both now and in the future. This was illustrated through the example of climate-induced migration, which is a response to the crisis of inhabitation that global environmental change is generating.

Finally, the chapter has added a second type of response to what we have called a crisis of inhabitation. While Chapter 9 focused on adaptation in place, this chapter has examined movement. You might think of such movement as one possible reaction to the failure of place-based responses that were explored in the last chapter. In the next chapter we explore a final response – reaching out – which relies on the movement of other things, not just people.

References

Adger, W. N., Huq, S., Brown, K., Conwaya, D. and Hulme, M. (2003) 'Adaptation to climate change in the developing world', *Progress in Development Studies*, vol. 3, no. 3, pp. 179–95.

Chen, I-C., Hill, J. K., Ohlemüller, R., Roy, D. B. and Thomas, C. D. (2011) 'Rapid range shifts of species associated with high levels of climate warming', *Science*, vol. 333, no. 6045, pp. 1024–6.

Christian Aid (2007) *Human Tide: The Real Migration Crisis*, London, Christian Aid.

Connor, S. (2011) 'Climate change drives animals to high ground', *The Independent*, 19 August [online], http://www.independent.co.uk/environment/climate-change/climate-change-drives-animals-to-high-ground-2340152.html (Accessed 7 December 2012).

Foresight (2011) *Migration and Global Environmental Change: Final Project Report*, London, Government Office for Science [online], http://www.bis.gov.uk/assets/foresight/docs/migration/11-1116-migration-and-global-environmental-change.pdf (Accessed 7 December 2012).

Gemenne, F. (2011) 'Why the numbers don't add up: a review of estimates and predictions of people displaced by environmental changes', *Global Environmental Change*, vol. 21, Supplement 1, pp S41–S49.

German Advisory Council on Global Change (WBGU) (2007) *World in Transition: Climate Change as a Security Risk*, WBGU [online], available at http://www.wbgu.de/fileadmin/templates/dateien/veroeffentlichungen/hauptgutachten/jg2007/wbgu_jg2007_kurz_engl.pdf, p. 4, figure.

Myers, N. (2002) 'Environmental refugees: a growing phenomenon of the 21st century', *Philosophical Transactions: Biological Sciences*, vol. 357, no. 1420, pp. 609–13.

Oliver-Smith, A. (2009) 'Disasters and diasporas: global climate change and population displacement in the 21st century', in Crate, S. A. and Nuttall, M. (eds) *Anthropology and Climate Change: From Encounters to Actions*, Walnut Creek, CA, Left Coast Press.

Orlove, B. (2005) 'Human adaptation to climate change: a review of three historical cases and some general perspectives', *Environmental Science & Policy*, vol. 8, no. 6, pp. 589–600.

Vidal, J. (2007) 'Climate change to cause mass migration', *The Guardian*, 14 May [online], http://www.guardian.co.uk/environment/2007/may/14/climatechange.climatechangeenvironment (Accessed 7 December 2012).

White, G. (2012) *Climate Change and Migration: Security and Borders in a Warming World*, Oxford and New York, Oxford University Press.

Chapter 11   Transition, sharing and an environmental imagination

Nick Bingham and Nigel Clark

Contents

1 Introduction

In Chapter 9 you explored some of the ways that people in different places are mobilising to respond to the challenges of living on a dynamic planet and to the crisis of inhabitation in which we now find ourselves. You have explored ecosystems as entities that are mobile and changing over time and you have considered the difficulties that people may have remaining in one place under conditions of change (see also Book 1, Chapter 1). Chapter 9 also introduced you to the idea that an environmental imagination based on describing and interpreting environmental issues in terms of connections will enable us to better understand the challenges posed by those issues.

In Chapter 10 you saw how humans and other forms of life move across the surface of the Earth in response to the challenges posed by changing environmental conditions. This chapter developed a second component of an environmental imagination by deepening your understanding of the three sets of module concepts to probe further into the entanglement of environmental issues and to identify some of the key features that define these issues.

In Chapter 11 – the final one of this block and of the module – we examine a third set of responses that bring together aspects of the first two. We look at the ways in which people reach out and connect with those in other places in order to share ideas, strategies and resources on how to respond to local and global environmental issues. We also consider how we can evaluate the options available to us when faced with so many large, complex and interconnected environmental issues. This chapter will complete the process of building an environmental imagination that can do justice to our understanding of environmental change and our responses to it. It will do so by developing the notion of sharing, something which has been threaded throughout much of the module as a possible guide to action.

The idea of sharing is important as people cannot solve environmental issues in isolation from each other. As you have seen throughout the module, local communities frequently find themselves affected by environmental changes or conditions whose causes extend through space and time far beyond the places in question. This means that many environmental challenges, by definition, cannot be addressed effectively at the local scale. With the prospect of major changes in Earth systems, it is clear that people in localised places cannot meet environmental challenges alone. In this chapter we will explore two main ways of responding through sharing. The first is by circulating different ideas, plans and types of experimentation. The second is by forging relationships of care and responsibility between more or less distant places: connections that are in many cases 'thickening' into new transnational or even global relations of solidarity. Taken together, these responses suggest sharing as a key approach for addressing environmental issues.

2   Planetary boundaries and inhabiting a safe operating space

In this block we have used terms such as the Anthropocene and a crisis of inhabitation to capture the scale and consequences of contemporary environmental change as involving the interaction between human activities and Earth system processes. But how might we quantify the Anthropocene and measure the extent of the crisis? This is the question that motivated a group of renowned Earth system and environmental scientists to propose a new framework for understanding how humanity is stressing the planet. The group, led by Johan Rockström from the Stockholm Resilience Centre and Will Steffen from the Australian National University, identified nine earth system processes which have thresholds which, if crossed, risk 'irreversible and abrupt environmental change' (Rockström et al., 2009, p. 472). These Earth systems are: climate change, ozone depletion, ocean acidification, biodiversity, freshwater use, the global nitrogen and phosphorous cycles, change in land use, chemical pollution, and atmospheric aerosol loading. Rockström and his colleagues attempted to quantify the thresholds, called 'planetary boundaries', for the first seven of these, in order to establish how far we have already collectively pushed those systems. Their aim was to offer the international community a well-defined sense of a 'safe operating space' within which humans can freely pursue 'long-term social and economic development' (Rockström et al., 2009, p. 475) (Figure 11.1).

However, there is some debate among scientists on the feasibility and desirability of measuring all the planetary boundaries (Nordhaus et al., 2012). One critical point is that of scale. The idea of boundaries does not distinguish between boundaries that apply at a genuinely planetary scale and those that matter primarily at a local or regional level. For example, and as you have seen earlier, there is a global threshold for climate change, namely the so-called tipping point which, if reached, would lead to a fundamentally different global climate. It also makes sense to talk in planetary terms about some of the other boundaries, such as ocean acidification, ozone layer depletion and biodiversity loss. But for others it may be more meaningful to conceive of the boundaries in local terms, with global effects simply being the aggregate of the local ones. Take, for example, the case of the nitrogen and phosphorous cycles. Many artificial fertilisers contain nitrogen and phosphorous. Setting a global limit for the application of nitrate- or phosphorous-based fertilisers could lead to people forgoing the benefits that fertilisers provide for the poor soils of Africa, on account of the harm caused by fertiliser over-application elsewhere. Reducing fertiliser application in some areas could significantly set back human welfare, given that more than half of the people on the planet are fed by food grown with synthetic fertiliser. Similarly, managing individual watersheds for freshwater use may make more sense than managing global freshwater consumption to keep it below a somewhat arbitrary global limit. It could, therefore, be more useful to define planetary boundaries at multiple scales: local, regional and global.

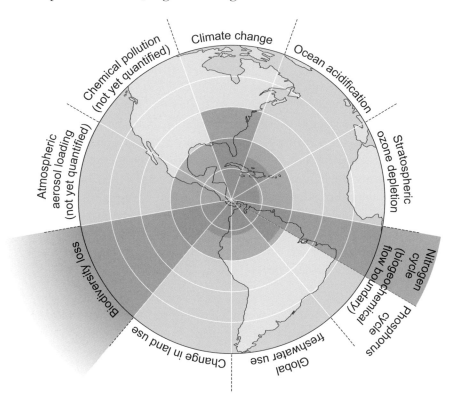

Figure 11.1   Beyond the boundary. The figure depicts the idea of planetary boundaries superimposed on a map. The inner blue shading represents the proposed safe operating space for nine planetary systems. The orange wedges represent an estimate of the current position for each variable. The boundaries in three systems (rate of biodiversity loss, climate change and human interference with the nitrogen cycle) have already been exceeded (Source: based on Rockström et al., 2009, Figure 6)

A second point of criticism is that the research by Rockström and colleagues derives most of its limits by looking at the geologically recent past, at conditions during the Holocene, the present interglacial stage that began around 11,500 years ago. This is only a very short part of the Earth's history; climatic changes on longer timescales, for example, have been far more extreme than they have been during the Holocene.

These arguments suggest that we should be cautious about adopting the idea of planetary boundaries wholesale and uncritically. Despite this, the idea that boundaries exist, even if they are difficult to define and quantify, can be useful in drawing attention to the need for humans to limit those activities that cause environmental changes; for example, by reducing chemical pollution and seeking to use the world's land more sustainably. As the editors of the journal *Nature* commented, 'even if the science is preliminary, this is a creditable attempt to quantify the limitations of our existence on Earth, and provides a good basis for discussion and future refinement' (*Nature*, 2009, p. 448).

As a result, the language of planetary boundaries has gained significant purchase at a policy level. It was invoked by the UN Secretary-General Ban Ki-moon in his presentation of the report of the High-Level Panel on Global Sustainability (United Nations Secretary-General's High-Level Panel on Global Sustainability, 2012), and formed the basis of a discussion paper from Oxfam (Raworth, 2012).

As we shall see in the next section, one of the ways in which the idea of planetary boundaries is useful is in thinking about the crisis of inhabitation around which Chapters 9 to 11 are framed.

3   Innovating towards a safe operating space

Whatever the controversies surrounding the precise status and measurement of the various planetary boundaries, the idea of a safe operating space provides a clear sense of the conditions under which the planet will continue to be sustainably habitable for humans and other species. If we as a species are going to solve what we have called a crisis of habitation, then the idea that there are boundaries which place limits on our activities offers us targets to work to.

But how are we going to reach these targets? As noted in the Introduction, one of the challenges of sharing a dynamic planet is determining what to do in the face of profound risks to our ways of life, to other species, and to the environments which we share. How, in other words, should we respond? One option is to work to add resilience to the places where we live (Chapter 9). A second option is to move away from places that environmental change has rendered uninhabitable (Chapter 10). A third response, discussed later in this chapter, is to become involved in actions to ameliorate the effects of environmental change. This response may be particularly apt for those who are not directly engaged in either of the first two efforts but who nonetheless feel an urgent sense of responsibility and a willingness to act.

Collaboration between some of the scientists involved with the planetary boundaries approach and a group of social scientists based in the UK at the University of Sussex's Social, Technological and Environmental Pathways to Sustainability (STEPS) Centre has resulted in some guidance on this issue (see STEPS Centre, 2011). In a paper published in 2012, the STEPS Centre proposed that transgressing global thresholds would lead to ecological turbulence and to uncertain futures and that doing nothing was no longer an option (Leach et al., 2012). More than that, they argued that even making severe and sustained adjustments to existing policies may be an insufficient response. Instead, the researchers proposed that radical changes are needed so that not only can climatic, ecological and other tipping points be avoided but sustainable development goals can be set to address the basic needs of the global population while creating an environmental safety zone, or 'safe operating space'. According to Melissa Leach and her co-authors at the STEPS Centre, such radical change means fundamental shifts, not just in policies and technologies, but in how we innovate. **Innovation** is defined here as 'new ways of doing things, in science and technology, but also associated institutions and social practices. The question then becomes what types of innovation might be able to bring about such radical change?' (Leach et al., 2012, p. 2).

According to Leach and her colleagues, the 'top-down' policy proposals from governments and international organisations for addressing environmental change of the last 20 years are not enough to return humanity to the safe operating space of a habitable planet. They criticise such proposals for being difficult to implement and for being wedded to technological responses advanced by science and engineering, such as geoengineering to address climate change and biotechnology in order to increase agricultural production (see Chapters 4 and 7). They argue that, since the 1992 United Nations Conference on Environment and Development in Rio de Janeiro, the political momentum for radical change has been lost. Governments, governmental bodies, international legal conventions and international organisations have lost touch with the many grassroots initiatives in small rural and urban communities around the world where local-scale innovations and ideas have emerged. Although local knowledge, solutions and initiatives for solving global environmental challenges abound, they have remained marginal in national and international policy, and their importance to global environmental issues has been neglected. The task of connecting (or reconnecting) the local with the global is now urgent according to Leach et al., with bottom-up approaches from local communities being the most effective way of establishing a safe operating space for humanity. In sum, innovation must not just be top-down and technologically driven. It must include local efforts and knowledge and will be social as much as technological. Towards this end, they suggest that the best responses to meeting the challenge of living within planetary boundaries will be based on **multi-scale approaches** which recognise and connect the multiple actors involved and match the scale of the problem.

Leach and her colleagues suggest that if multi-scale approaches are to work, attention needs to be paid to three dimensions of innovation:

- *Direction*: It is important to be both clear and transparent about the goals and principles which drive policy and innovation. These should be based not on the perceived need for economic growth, or on ideas of progress, but instead should have the prime objective of securing transformations towards an environmentally safe operating space. In particular, innovations should be promoted that 'can

Innovation
New ways of doing things in science and technology and in associated institutions and social practices.

Multi-scale approaches
Approaches to solving environmental issues that connect actors working at different spatial scales, from individuals, communities and groups to those working on global decision making and policy.

improve the capacity to learn from, respond to, and manage environmental feedback from dynamic social-ecological systems. In these, grassroots innovations that draw from local knowledge and experience, and social and organizational innovations … are at least as crucial as advanced science and technology' (Leach et al., 2012; see also Book 2, Chapter 9).

- *Diversity*: Nurturing diverse approaches and forms of innovation, both social and technological, allows us to respond to uncertainty and surprise arising from the complex, interacting biophysical and socio-economic nature of global environmental change. Diversity may take many forms: biodiversity, different approaches to sustainability, diverse institutional practices and innovations. Fostering diversity is important because the needs and resources available in different parts of the world will vary.

- *Distribution*: The distribution of resources and the relative size of ecological footprints within the safe operating space are at the heart of the concept of sharing a dynamic planet. As radical changes towards the creation of an environmentally safe operating space are planned and implemented, different stakeholders will be affected in different ways by the necessary transformations and innovations. Trade-offs will need to be negotiated and the distributional impacts of these are a central issue. These distributional impacts will include both changes to the relative share of natural and economic resources among actors, and changes to the environmental risks that they face. Some actors will gain while others will lose. To illustrate this last point, the authors use a case that touches on several issues from the module, noting that while large-scale irrigation projects in East Africa may, on the one hand, be celebrated as contributing to sustainability via their facilitation of increased agricultural productivity and thus national food security, they may, on the other hand, be experienced as land grabs by those directly affected (see Book 1 Chapter 4, and below). For such reasons, Leach et al. propose that a variety of actors should be involved in designing policy responses so that local-level communities are engaged in, rather than excluded from, ecosystem stewardship, with best use made of local knowledge and innovative ideas. This approach would also enable marginalised groups to secure fairer access to locally produced resources.

The rest of the chapter focuses on this last dimension of distribution in order to consider how humans should respond to environmental change.

4   Distribution as securing

With their focus on distribution Leach and her colleagues bring to our attention the question of who gains and who loses from the ways in which different policies and activities shape environments in the search for a safe operating space for humanity. One broad way in which environments are being shaped in this sense is securing. **Securing** refers to efforts to control resources or territory either by acquisition or by other means. We have given some attention in the module (for example, in the discussion of bird sanctuaries in Book 1, Chapter 2) to securing resources and territory in order to safeguard them from the risk of degradation or loss due to environmental change. In some instances this is so that they can be passed on in a good state for the benefit of future generations. However, and as you have also seen, some actors may seek to secure an environment or a feature of an environment not because they wish to protect, conserve or otherwise add resilience to it, but because they wish to use it for economic reasons. The land acquisitions for agriculture that we explored in Book 1, Chapter 4 are an obvious example of this version of security, where the economic needs of local communities in the global South have been jeopardised to secure the needs and desires of those in the global North. As we have seen throughout the module, securing environments for economic benefit has emerged as a major priority in many states, urban centres and corporations. Each of them has been busy generating ambitious initiatives to secure material resources – and their own physical environments – in order to reduce the risks posed by an increasingly unstable future. For example, in the UK, major infrastructural investments have been made in constructing and maintaining the Thames Barrier to protect London from storm surges and high tides (Figure 11.2) (and also from rising sea levels in the future, as the result of climate change). However, there are distributional consequences to the decision to protect London: namely, fewer resources are available to protect other places. Securing London has been considered more important than securing towns on the East Anglia coast, for example, even though these towns are arguably in more immediate danger of flooding (see Book 1, Chapter 1).

Securing
Gaining control of territory and resources in order to guard them from the risk of loss or degradation.

Figure 11.2   The Thames Barrier

Activity 11.1   Solar sunshields: who benefits?

In Book 2, Chapter 4 you were introduced to the concept of geoengineering. One geoengineering strategy that you learnt about was the proposal to deflect incoming solar radiation by placing solar sunshields in outer space. A study by Lunt et al. (2008), using climate modelling, found that such reflectors could theoretically prevent the average global temperature from increasing. They also found, however, that there would be significant regional differences in the effects on climate. While the tropical latitudes would be cooler, the higher latitudes near the poles would be warmer. The results, they concluded, would include reduced global rainfall and a decrease in the extent of Arctic ice.

Imagine a situation where Canada was proposing to deploy a set of these shields. What would be the advantages and disadvantages of such a project to that country? And what would be the advantages and disadvantages to a tropical country such as Senegal?

Comment

For Canada, the advantages would be temperature stabilisation and the increased shipping and resource extraction possibilities that would result from a smaller Arctic ice sheet. The disadvantages include the impacts of continuing climate change on land, owing to decreased rainfall.

For a tropical country such as Senegal, temperatures would also stabilise, but the climate would be cooler than previously. Combined with lower rainfall, this would mean significant impacts on agriculture, on which its people are much more dependent than are those of the industrialised nations of the global North.

Of course, a much more detailed assessment would be needed of the advantages and disadvantages of the project for each country, and this would need to take into account the uncertainties and risks involved. However, this example serves to underline the importance of considering the distribution of costs and benefits from interventions designed to take us to a safe operating space.

Securing, therefore, can take place for different reasons to promote different values. Land and resources may be secured to promote environmental values, but it may also take place to promote the interests of privileged centres. Foreign interests may appropriate communal lands (Book 1, Chapter 4), water may be privatised (Book 1, Chapter 12) and states and corporations may contest the control of oilfields (Book 2, Chapter 2). Here environmental securing takes advantage of the mobility of capital (which stands in marked contrast to the immobility of the majority of the planet's people, as we saw in the previous chapter), seeking to gain access to ecological goods and services for certain groups of people at the expense of others.

Securing for economic gain is likely to expand in breadth and scale if current trends continue. One of the world's leading financial investors and hedge fund managers, Jeremy Grantham, warns that as the world runs out of resources – energy, metals and food – commodity prices will escalate rapidly. As such, the 'market mechanism is reflecting what our leaders ignore' (Grantham, 2012). He suggests that massive increases in the consumption of hydrocarbons and some metals over the last 200 years (accelerating dramatically in the past 50) are simply unsustainable in both economic and environmental terms. The response to this will be painful, as resources will become too expensive for those people and countries that cannot absorb the price hikes. In sum, there will be a 'rationing through price' (Grantham, 2012).

The irony is that it will be from many of the poorer countries that the richer countries will be acquiring the resources which allow them to survive more comfortably under conditions of environmental change and resource depletion. According to the economist Dambisa Moyo

(2012), the Chinese government is busy making deals for access to economic resources with what she calls the 'axis of the unloved': developing countries that are rich in resources but poor in economic and political capital (Moyo, 2012). Moyo argues that wealthy countries are increasingly using their political and economic power to gain access to scarce resources, which poorer countries are prepared to give up in return for investment, employment and infrastructure. Sooner rather than later, resources will run out given the world's massive and growing need for them. Civil conflicts have been triggered in countries over resource wealth, including, for example, Angola (oil and diamonds), Burma and Cambodia (timber and gems), Indonesia (natural gas), Sierra Leone (diamonds) and Sudan (oil) (Moyo, 2012; Ross, 2004). Moyo suggests that civil wars will escalate into full-scale commodity wars if current patterns continue. However, not everyone agrees with Moyo's analysis, either in its focus on China or in its assumption that resource scarcity will necessarily lead to conflict. For instance, even countries with long-running territorial disputes, such as India and Pakistan, may cooperate over water because they realise that long-term water security is only assured through cooperation (Alam, 2002; also see Dinar, 2011).

The increasing trend towards the securing of the environment, together with Grantham's financial analysis, suggest that the channelling of resources for the benefit of certain privileged centres, and the exclusion of other people and places from access to these resources, can have serious consequences. Planner Aiden While observes of efforts to adapt to post-peak oil that 'One might ... warn of the dangers of a new protectionism and increased socio-spatial polarisation as some places and some communities find it easier to adjust to a post-carbon future than others' (While, 2008, p. xii). This observation applies no less to strategies to secure other resources and places against environmental change and economic uncertainties.

We now turn to a second mode of distribution, one based more on sharing than securing. Initiatives such as the Transition Network, the fair trade movement and the movement La Via Campesina which campaigns against land grabs offer alternatives to the more exclusive forms of ecological securing (Massey, 2006; Whatmore and Clark, 2006). Concerned about environmental risks and ambitious and strategic in their outlook, these alternative approaches put a premium on justice and equity as well as security.

5   Distribution as sharing

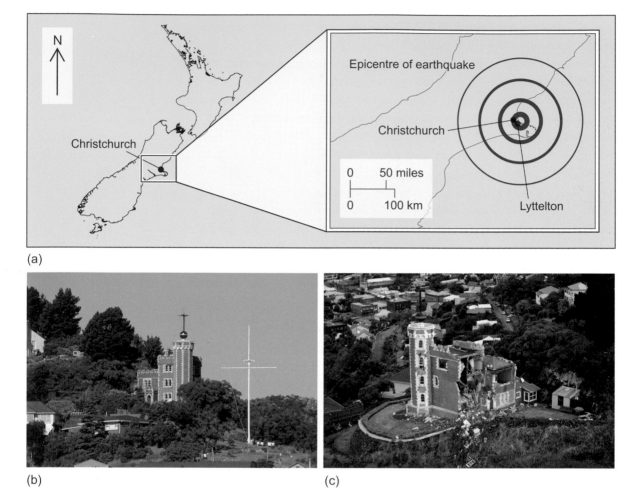

(a)

(b)   (c)

Figure 11.3   (a) The location of Lyttelton, New Zealand, epicentre of the 2011 earthquake; (b) the Lyttelton Timeball Station prior to the earthquake. It was at that time a tourist attraction but historically had been an important part of the port, by providing a visual signal which enabled sailors to accurately set their ships' clocks; (c) The Lyttelton Timeball station after the earthquake

Lyttelton, the port of Christchurch in New Zealand's South Island, lies nestled in the valley of an extinct volcanic cone now flooded by the sea (Figure 11.3a). On 22 February 2011, the town began to shudder and crumble (Figures 11.3b and 11.3c). An earthquake of magnitude 6.3 was taking place, with its epicentre at a relatively shallow 5 kilometres below the Earth's surface. The resulting destruction caused extensive loss of life and damage to the built environment in the nearby city of

Christchurch and structural damage to at least half the houses and buildings in Lyttelton.

PROJECT LYTTELTON
the soul of a sustainable community

Figure 11.4   Cover of *PL: Our Story*, a publication documenting the history and vision of Project Lyttelton (Source: Project Lyttelton, 2012)

The town of Lyttelton has a community-based organisation, Project Lyttelton, which grew out of an earlier project to regenerate the town's main street in 1994. Project Lyttelton is a focal point of the local community. Its activities involve a time banking scheme (a monetary system in which value is based on units of time rather than on commodities or cash), composting and waste minimisation, energy initiatives, seasonal festivals, community gardens and a farmers' market (Figure 11.4). This is a town that, long before the earthquake, was trying to transform itself – moving away from a reliance on fossil fuels, preparing itself for climate change, seeking to strengthen its local cultural and economic life and attempting to make itself more sustainable in a changing world. It was a transition town initiative long before the idea of 'transition town' had crystallised. It was one of the early international members to join the Transition Network (Project Lyttelton, 2012).

In the aftermath of this earthquake and the devastation that it wrought, the strong community bonds nurtured by Project Lyttelton have been critical in shaping the town's response to the disaster. New ways of relating, new social practices and new material infrastructures have played a significant role in the recovery of the town in the face of an enormous literal and figurative shock. The concept of resilience is useful to understanding how the people of the town have coped with the aftermath of the earthquake. Resilience, you may recall, is the capacity of a system to recover from a disturbance (Book 1, Chapter 3; Book 2, Chapter 9). It is one of the key measures of the sustainability of a system. The response of the people of Lyttelton has aimed to enhance the community's resilience and its capacity to recover from a catastrophic natural disturbance. The case of Lyttelton may, therefore, offer lessons on how other communities might respond to undesired environmental change. Indeed, it was with a view to sharing the lessons they had learnt that the people of Lyttelton contributed to a short film about their experiences. Activities to enhance the resilience of the community have, if anything, intensified in the aftermath of the earthquake (Jefferies, 2012).

Crucial to supporting Lyttelton's efforts at moving forward has been the Transition Network. The Transition Town movement began in the UK in the small town of Totnes during the early years of the twenty-first century. Its aim is to find new ways to respond to peak oil and climate change which draw on local knowledge and resources and strengthen the local culture and economy. The idea was quickly taken up by other place-based communities, including villages, towns, cities, islands, districts and suburbs, both in the UK and across the world, leading to the formation of the transnational Transition Network.

In many ways the partial destruction of Lyttelton was a new challenge to the Transition Network, a different kind of predicament from those to which it had been set up to respond. It was a reminder that, alongside human-induced environmental changes, the Earth itself remains capable of delivering shocks and surprises of its own. But, in significant ways, the earthquake of 22 February 2011, and the seismic activity that both preceded and followed it in the region, are indicative of the kinds of challenge that many places could face as major Earth systems transform. As we have seen, changing climate resulting in rising sea levels and the increasing intensity of extreme weather events – a combination of both gradual and more rapid environmental changes – could see many more local communities facing challenges that exceed their own experience and knowledge. These will overstretch their resources and capacities for resilience and thus cannot be dealt with effectively at the local scale alone. The Transition Network (Figure 11.5) is one example of the new networks that have emerged precisely in order to address such problems. They can be seen as an example of the proposal from Melissa Leach and colleagues for innovative multi-scale responses that connect a range of local activities under the umbrella of a global movement. The global Transition Network is a result of the linking-up activities of movements in many different locations around the world.

Figure 11.5   The Transition Network logo

Activity 11.2   Connecting people and places

Can you think of other examples from the module where people, places or communities have linked up with others in order to respond to environmental challenges that extend beyond individual places in time and space?

Comment

Just from Book 1, Chapters 1–4, you might have thought of the following responses:

- how activists in Happisburgh linked up with communities in other places also concerned with coastal change
- the international alliances to protect and manage multi-species flyways
- transnational cooperation over climate change

- the Mali Declaration over land grabs.

You may have thought of other examples from other chapters.

The Transition Network provided a ready-made audience – a public, we might say, using the language of Book 1, Chapter 6 – to share the town of Lyttelton's experience of the earthquake and the reconstruction activities that followed it. In doing so it also became a kind of mediated community through which support of many kinds could be offered. The network illustrates how the safe operating space of habitability is shared between different people and places across time and space. The Transition Network seeks to work towards the transformation required to achieve the goal of living equitably within that space.

There are two aspects of the Transition Network that are worth noting. First, the Network enables different places to share ideas, plans, strategies and experiences of responding to change. That is, it offers a set of connections and mediations through which ideas and resources are able to circulate widely. Second, the Network facilitates the development and expression of caring relationships across distances. Before we explore these two aspects in more detail, in Sections 5.2 and 5.3 respectively, we first investigate, in Section 5.1, the idea of sharing on which they are premised.

5.1   The basis of sharing

The Transition Network and the organisations that it connects seek to promote inclusive, as opposed to exclusive, ways of engaging with environmental change, because they recognise that the capacity of actors to respond is unevenly distributed both socially and geographically. In recognition of the historical disparities in the contributions of different populations to climate change, in particular those from the global North, there is a strong sense of commitment from many environmental and social groups to assisting less powerful and less privileged communities to respond to these changes. These communities have contributed less to environmental changes but tend to feel the effects equally, if not more. Such concerns with environmental justice on a global scale are often combined with a resolve towards intergenerational justice (Adger et al., 2005).

The very idea of justice hinges on calculating, or at least speculating about, who owes what to whom. This brings to the fore the question of how we value the environment. There are different ways that the environment can be valued, with economists arguing that different instrumental and intrinsic valuations can be combined to yield the concept of total economic value (Book 1, Chapter 7). But as you may recall, we also considered the possibility of another, more emergent, form of value, in which people find themselves being touched or moved by the plight of other people or other things, prior to any calculation or deliberation. This capacity to be affected by what others are going through can be a source of novel forms of valuation and attachment, as well as being the motivation behind the swelling of public support for environmental issues and the communities that may suffer from environmental change (Book 1, Chapters 6 and 7).

In times of rapid and sometimes disastrous environmental change – such as the catastrophe that struck Lyttelton and the crisis of the Deepwater Horizon oil spill – many people find themselves drawn to take responsive action in advance of any consideration of who or what is deserving of assistance. For such people, caring for others who have been laid low – whether by a human-made environmental disaster or an upheaval of the Earth itself – may actually exceed a commitment to justice. Many people simply recognise that we are all dependent on others, in ways that are more profound and more pervasive than we could ever put a price on. Such generous dispositions are often found in environmental thought and practice, all the way from the most local and personal levels through to the global scale. As radical environment and development theorist Wolfgang Sachs expressed it some years ago, humans must 'search for civilizations that are capable of extending hospitality to twice as many people on the planet as today without ruining the biosphere for successive generations' (Sachs, 1999, p. xi).

A careful and thoughtful orientation towards environmental change is a vital part of any effective response. However, we should not underestimate the importance of a basic kind of caring, generous and responsive attitude towards the needs of others (both human and non-human), or what we might call an imagination of sharing. Indeed, far from detracting from a more scientific, legal or policy-oriented approach to environmental problems, it might be argued that it is precisely such a generous opening to affected others that inspires and drives forward the more objective pursuit of environmental solutions (Clark, 2011). In other words, it is from a starting point of caring and being affected that many researchers, activists and policy makers set out to address environmental challenges.

Figure 11.6   Are sharing, hospitality and generosity more central to human social life than we usually recognise?

It is also worth keeping in mind that generous dispositions do not wait for major environmental problems or catastrophes to occur. As you saw in Book 2, Chapter 2, many people display attitudes of hospitality and sharing when it comes to such everyday activities as eating together, or giving away surplus crops or other provisions to friends and neighbours (Figure 11.6). In many cultures it is quite normal to offer sustenance to complete strangers. In fact, some social theorists and philosophers argue that generosity of some kind or another is at the core of human social life, though often in unrecognised ways (Diprose, 2002; Vaughan, 2002). Even in the most apparently competitive capitalist societies, ordinary relations of caring and gifting provide a foundation without which market-based social and economic relations would not endure for long. What this means is that instituting more generously responsive attitudes towards others, both proximate and distant, who have been harmfully affected by environmental change, does not really require a radical overturning and reinvention of existing values. It merely depends on greater acknowledgement of values which already pervade daily life, although often in invisible or under-recognised ways.

However, acknowledging that these social impulses permeate human life leaves unanswered the thorny question of how we can make more of them. In particular, how can we extend generosity and hospitality to reach out to help others who may be geographically – or (in the case of future generations) temporally – distant? It is to this question that we now turn.

5.2   Circulating ideas and models

Having explored the importance of sharing to social life, let us now return to the two aspects of the Transition Network that can help humans operate better within the safe operating space of habitation. The first way – in which what Darling (2010, p. 126) calls 'outward-looking, yet place-based, moments of political responsibility' reaching out to assist other people in other places – is through the sharing of advantageous plans, techniques or strategies. The desire both to share ideas with, and receive ideas from, others communities explains why the community initiative at Lyttelton joined the Transition Network.

The practice of circulating desirable models for change is now widespread in international policy circles, and extends far beyond the realms of responding to environmental change. Particularly in the field of urban policy, it is common practice for cities to seek to emulate proven models of transition and development in the hope of reproducing success stories. There is now considerable expertise with regard to the promotion, transfer and operationalising of urban policies. However, many of these initiatives prioritise economic growth; those with explicit environmental agendas are often more concerned with securing environmental spaces for urban elites than they are with generous or hospitable responses to the needs of other places.

The Transition Network is an exception as it is oriented towards more just and positive environmental futures. It is marked by:

- a high degree of sensitivity to local social, cultural and ecological conditions, with protection and enhancement of place an explicit aim of the network

- recognition that the circulation of ideas and models is a matter of translation as much as transfer, because lifting strategies from one context and inserting them unchanged into another can lead to uncertain and unforeseen consequences

- a related recognition that one of the values of smaller-scale, niche-based experiments is that they may allow for failure to be accommodated as part of the broader learning process (Seyfang and Smith, 2007).

The Transition Network thus circulates a particular model of sharing of ideas and practices.

5.3   Making solidarities

The second way in which the Transition Network helps humans operate more effectively and equitably in the face of environmental change is that it provides a way for people in different places to develop and express relations of care and responsibility for those in other places. Or to put it another way, the Transition Network has, over a relatively short span of time, established an extensive system of communication through which people come to be affected by the environmental predicament of those in other places. Through this interconnective architecture, people in more or less distant places are not only exposed to what others are enduring; they also have opportunities to make contact and to offer support, information, advice or resources.

The fair trade movement explored in Book 2, Chapter 8 operates along similar lines with regard to food. It works along commodity chains in order to recast both producers and consumers as more than faceless and placeless figures. Through their purchasing behaviour consumers express solidarity to producers in distant places, thus exercising agency from a distance along the supply chain.

Activity 11.3   Making connections

Spend a few minutes thinking about your own community. Consider its formal organisations such as councils, schools, churches and mosques, as well as its less formal voluntary and social groups. Can you think of examples where these organisations and groups are making links with other places in ways that build resilience and promote sharing? If no ideas occur immediately, it may be helpful to do some web searching, perhaps starting with your local paper's news site.

Comment

One of the authors of this chapter (Nick Bingham) considered his own community of Kings Heath, Birmingham. He thought of the Fairtrade group based at the local church, the local Transition group, the active links to communities in many other parts of the world sustained through the local mosques, temples and churches, particular charity shops on the high street which support activities in specific parts of the world, and the local secondary school's connections with India, South Korea and South Africa.

For privileged individuals and groups in the global North, the feeling that one should do something about climate change can be felt keenly, but often without a practical sense of how to make a significant difference. By building, maintaining and deepening connections to specific communities in other parts of the world who may be, or may become, vulnerable as a consequence of climate change, the Transition Network and other initiatives like it offer a tangible way of providing material assistance during episodes of crisis, but also an opportunity for mutual learning for the benefit of all. As such, they stand in marked contrast to the more exclusionary versions of securing that we reviewed earlier (Section 4).

These kinds of connections and solidarities are not substitutes for either the profound structural and lifestyle changes that are needed to mitigate climate change or the extensive transnational trade-offs in the distribution of resources that the pursuit of climate justice calls for. The future looks increasingly likely to see some place-based responses to environmental change and a decline in available energy resources. This will leave many places and their communities extremely vulnerable.

However, connections such as those made by the Transition Network offer immediate care and support to vulnerable people. The intimate exchanges fostered through the Network also help build bridges towards larger-scale solutions to the current global environmental predicament. These hopeful and innovative experiments in solidarity between more or less distant places will be just as important as innovations in socio-technical infrastructure and practice. They will be an important component of the diversity of responses that Leach et al. (2012) consider vital for treading pathways to a safe operating space.

5.4   The prospects for global transition and the making of a global environmental public

In many respects the future is uncertain, but one thing is clear: we can now expect global environmental change. Even if atmospheric carbon levels are halted at their current level – an increasingly unlikely prospect – thermal inertia will ensure that the oceans continue to expand and sea levels rise. This, in turn, will have numerous ecological consequences for the future. Even if habitat loss could be stalled, the degradation that has already taken place will continue to cascade through ecosystems in the future, with uncertain consequences for populations and species. Under changing environmental conditions, communities and peoples will have to respond. We should recognise that there will be times when place-based responses may struggle to keep up with the pace of change. Inevitably, there will be occasions when experiments will fail; indeed, the possibility of failure is part of what defines experimentation. And added to that there is the growing likelihood of the increasingly self-interested securing of resources and territories by powerful actors.

All this points to the need to find new modes of sharing across time and space in the search for a safe and habitable operating space. Initiatives such as the Transition Network seek to take this necessity seriously. They utilise existing global communication, media and transport infrastructures in order to generate alternative engagements with environmental challenges. Those involved in such networks share not only the plight of those who suffer from environmental degradation; they also share and build the possibilities for innovation, resilience building and positive future change.

At its best, this is an effort in constructing a transnational, multi-scale, global environmental public, a public that does not pre-exist but needs to be built up by sharing information and experience, shaping agendas, and organising political action. As Sheila Jasanoff, an expert in science and technology studies argues, people need to be more than recipients of evidence and information: they need to care about what is happening at the planetary scales and to feel 'affected', moved and energised into activity (Jasanoff, 2010). The planet needs this too, and the Transition Network shows us that such visions are neither impossible nor idealistic. In many regards, scientists and environmental activists who commit themselves to publicising (in other words, making public) global environmental predicaments are themselves already a community of affected interests operating at transnational or even fully global scales.

And there is growing evidence that many other people are quite capable of learning to be affected by information about major Earth systems; they expand their imaginative horizons to take in the planet as a whole. In this regard, ideas such as the Earth imagined as the organism-like Gaia, global climate tipping points or the favoured species at risk of extinction can play a catalysing role by helping turn complex evidence into a more intuitively graspable image. Such images may be an opening to collective political action (Marres, 2012). If we are to move towards a safe operating space, let alone distribute it fairly, it is going to be via the multi-scale approach propounded by Leach et al., through a gradual weaving together of situated issues and publics into larger networks of communication and action. In doing so, sharing becomes an important criterion for guiding our actions, a hopeful sign in a crisis.

6   Summary

In this final chapter of the block and of the module we have reflected on the notion of a safe operating space for humanity and other species. We have explored how we might journey towards such a space from our current crisis of inhabitation, a crisis generated by environmental change and the transgressing of planetary boundaries. Drawing on the work of Melissa Leach and others at the STEPS Centre and their engagement with the work of the Stockholm Resilience Centre on planetary boundaries, the chapter suggested that considering how environmental and economic resources are distributed within this safe operating space is critical for generating just responses to our current and prospective environmental challenges. These responses will be multi-scale because global issues demand it, and they will need to be ecologically sustainable and ethically justifiable. One way of responding is through securing. Securing reaches out across the planet, but may lead to inequitable results if environments are secured for a minority rather than for the collective good of present and future generations. A second way of reaching out is through sharing. Through the example of the Transition Network, we noted how sharing can take place both by circulating ideas and models of how to respond to environmental change at different scales, and by making direct connections with people in other places so that solidarities are generated across national and other boundaries. Such movements alone will not take us to a safe operating space, but the core of their idea – sharing – may be crucial if the global environmental public necessary to experiment with and put into practice new and more sustainable ways of managing the tension between the Earth as both a lively place and a place to live is to be found.

References

Adger, N., Arnell, N. W. and Tompkins, E. L. (2005) 'Successful adaptation to climate change across scales', *Global Environmental Change*, vol. 15, no. 2, pp. 77–86.

Alam, U. (2002) 'Questioning the water wars rationale: a case study of the Indus Waters Treaty', *The Geographical Journal*, vol. 168, no. 4, pp. 341–53.

Clark, N. (2011) *Inhuman Nature*, London, Sage.

Darling J., (2010) 'A city of sanctuary: the relational re-imagining of Sheffield's asylum politics', *Transactions of the Institute of British Geographers*, vol. 35, no. 1, pp. 125–40.

Dinar, S. (ed.) (2011) *Beyond Resource Wars: Scarcity, Environmental Degradation, and International Cooperation*, Cambridge, MA, MIT Press.

Diprose, R. (2002) *Corporeal Generosity: On Giving with Nietzsche, Merleau-Ponty, and Levinas*, Albany, NY, State University of New York Press.

Grantham, J. (2012) 'The big crunch', *New Statesman*, 11 July [online], http://www.newstatesman.com/sci-tech/sci-tech/2012/07/big-crunch (Accessed 10 December 2012).

Jasanoff, S. (2010) 'A new climate for society', *Theory, Culture & Society*, vol. 27, nos 2–3, pp. 233–53.

Jefferies, M. (2012) 'Lyttelton: rising through the aftershocks', 28 February [online], http://www.resilience.org/stories/2012-02-28/lyttelton-rising-through-aftershocks (Accessed 3 January 2013).

Leach, M., Rockström, J., Raskin, P., Scoones, I., Stirling, A. C., Smith, A., Thompson, J., Millstone, E., Ely, A., Arond, E., Folke, C. and Olsson, P. (2012) 'Transforming innovation for sustainability', *Ecology and Society*, vol. 17, no. 2 [online], http://www.ecologyandsociety.org/vol17/iss2/art11/ (Accessed 10 December 2012).

Lunt, D. J., Ridgwell, A., Valdes, P. J. and Seale, A. (2008) '"Sunshade World": a fully coupled GCM evaluation of the climatic impacts of geoengineering', *Geophysical Research Letters*, vol. 35, L12710.

Marres, N. (2012) *Material Participation: Technology, the Environment and Everyday Publics*, London, Palgrave Macmillan.

Massey, D. (2006) 'Geographies of solidarities', in Clark, N., Massey, D. and Sarre, P. (eds) *A World in the Making*, Milton Keynes, The Open University.

Moyo, D. (2012) *Winner Take All: China's Race for Resources and What It Means For Us*, London, Allen Lane.

Nature (2009) 'Earth's boundaries', Editorial, vol. 461, no. 7263, pp. 447–8.

Nordhaus, T., Shellenberger, M. and Blomqvist, L. (2012) *The Planetary Boundaries Hypothesis: A Review of the Evidence*, Oakland, CA, Breakthrough

Institute [online], http://thebreakthrough.org/blog/2012/06/planetary_boundaries_a_mislead.shtml (Accessed 10 December 2012).

Project Lyttelton (2012) 'The soul of a sustainable community' (home page) [online], http://www.lyttelton.net.nz/ (Accessed 11 December 2012).

Raworth, K. (2012) *A Safe and Just Space for Humanity*, Oxfam Discussion Paper, February, Oxford, Oxfam.

Rockström, J., Steffen, W., Noone, K., Persson, Å., Chapin, F. S., III, Lambin, E., Lenton, T. M., Scheffer, M., Folke, C., Schellnhuber, H., Nykvist, B., De Wit, C. A., Hughes, T., van der Leeuw, S, Rodhe, H., Sörlin, S., Snyder, P. K., Costanza, R., Svedin, U., Falkenmark, M., Karlberg, L., Corell, R. W., Fabry, V. J., Hansen, J., Walker, B., Liverman, D., Richardson, K., Crutzen, P. and Foley, J. (2009) 'Planetary boundaries: exploring the safe operating space for humanity', *Ecology and Society*, vol. 1, no. 2 [online], http://www.ecologyandsociety.org/vol14/iss2/art32/ (Accessed 7 December 2012).

Ross, M. L. (2004) 'How do natural resources influence civil war: evidence from thirteen cases', *International Organization*, vol. 58, no. 1, pp. 35–67.

Sachs, W. (1999) *Planet Dialectics: Explorations in Environment and Development*, London, Zed Books.

Seyfang, G. and Smith, A. (2007) 'Grassroots innovations for sustainable development: towards a new research and policy agenda', *Environmental Politics*, vol. 16, no. 4, pp. 584–603.

STEPS Centre (2011) 'About' [online], http://steps-centre.org/about/ (Accessed 10 December 2012).

United Nations Secretary-General's High-Level Panel on Global Sustainability (2012) *Resilient People, Resilient Planet: A Future Worth Choosing*, New York, United Nations [online], http://www.un.org/gsp/sites/default/files/attachments/GSP_Report_web_final.pdf (Accessed 4 January 2013).

Vaughan, G. (2002) 'Mothering, co-muni-cation, and the gifts of language', in Wyschogrod, E., Goux, J.-J. and Boynton, E. (eds) *The Enigma of Gift and Sacrifice*, New York, Fordham University Press.

Whatmore, S. and Clark, N. (2006) 'Good food: ethical consumption and global change', in Clark, N., Massey, D. and Sarre, P. (eds) *A World in the Making*, Milton Keynes, The Open University.

While, A. (2008) 'Climate change and planning: carbon control and spatial regulation', *Town Planning Review*, vol. 79, no. 1, pp. vii–xiii.

Acknowledgements

Grateful acknowledgement is made to the following sources:

Book cover

Cover Image: Copyright © Tobias Helbig/iStockphoto

Chapter 1

Figures

Figure 1.1: Copyright © Purestock/Alamy; *Figure 1.4 and 1.15*: Marshak, S (2008) Earth: Portrait of a Planet, W. W. Norton; *Figure 1.5*: British Antarctic Survey; *Figure 1.9*: US Geological Survey; *Figure 1.10*: Copyright © David Hoskings/Getty Images; *Figure 1.12*: Copyright © Laguna Design/Science Photo Library; *Figure 1.14*: Copyright © Denny Rowland/Alamy.

Chapter 2

Figures

Figure 2.2: taken from www.hubbertpeak.com; *Figure 2.4a*: Copyright © AZP Worldwide/Alamy; *Figure 2.4b*: Copyright © Sameer Shah/Alamy; *Figure 2.4c*: Copyright © Mike Stone/Alamy; *Figure 2.5a*: Copyright © Peter Brogden/Alamy; *Figure 2.5b*: Copyright © Gary Whitton/Alamy; *Figure 2.5c*: Copyright © Craig Aurness/Alamy; *Figure 2.5d*: Copyright © Graham Jepson/Alamy; *Figure 2.7*: OPEC; *Figure 2.8*: Eagleamn; *Figure 2.10*: Copyright © Scott Darsney/Getty Images; *Figure 2.12*: Copyright © Yvonne Hemsey/Getty Images.

Chapter 3

Figures

Figure 3.2: IPCC (2011) 'Summary for policymakers', in Edenhofer, O. et al. (eds) IPCC Special Report on Renewable Energy Sources and Climate Change Mitigation, Cambridge, Cambridge University Press; *Figure 3.3*: Arvizu, D. P. et al. (2011) 'Direct solar energy', in Edenhofer, O. et al. (eds) IPCC Special Report on Renewable Energy Sources and Climate Change Mitigation, Cambridge, Cambridge University Press; *Figure 3.5a*: NASA/Science Photo Library; *Figure 3.5b*: Copyright ©

Aber/Alamy; *Figure 3.5c*: Copyright © Philippe Hays/Alamy; *Figure 3.9*: National Renewable Energy Laboratory (NREL); *Figure 3.15a*: Lewis, A. S. (2011) 'Ocean energy', in Edenhofer, O. et al. (eds) IPCC Special Report on Renewable Energy Sources and Climate Change Mitigation, Cambridge, Cambridge University Press; *Figure 3.15b*: Lewis, A. S. (2011) 'Ocean energy', in Edenhofer, O. et al. (eds) IPCC Special Report on Renewable Energy Sources and Climate Change Mitigation, Cambridge, Cambridge University Press.

Chapter 4

Figures

Figure 4.2: NASA; Figure 4.5a: Copyright © Angela Hampton Picture Library/Alamy; *Figure 4.5b*: taken from www.hangthebankers; *Figure 4.6*: NASA; *Figure 4.7*: Copyright © NDP/Alamy; *Figure 4.8*: Courtesy of Alfred Weneger Institute; *Figure 4.9*: Oelkers, E. (2008) 'Carbon dioxide sequestration: mineral carbonisation of CO2', Elements, vol. 4 no. 5, Mineralogical Society of America; *Figure 4.10*: Copyright © David Brabyn/Corbis; *Figure 4.11*: Copyright © BBC MMIX; *Figure 4.12*: Vidal, J. (2011) 'Geo-engineering: green versus greed in the race to cool the planet', The Observer, 10 July. Copyright Guardian News & Media Ltd 2011; *Figure 4.13*: The Scream, 1893 (oil, tempera & pastel on cardboard), Munch, E. (1863-1944)/Nasjonalgalleriet, Oslo, Norway/ The Bridgeman Art Library: Copyright © The Munch Museum/ The Munch – Ellingsen Group, BONO, Oslo/DACS, London 2013; *Figure 4.15*: Gilbert, S. G./Science Photo Library.

Chapter 5

Text

Vidal, J. (2011) 'Food speculation: "People die from hunger while banks make a killing on food"', Observer Food Monthly, 23 January. Copyright © Guardian News & Media 2011.

Figures

Figure 5.1a: Copyright © GFC Collection/Alamy; *Figure 5.1b*: Copyright © Fabrizio Ruggeri/Alamy; *Figure 5.2*: Copyright © AP/Press Association Images; *Figure 5.3*: Courtesy of Haileybury and Imperial Service College, Hertfordshire; *Figure 5.4*: Martin Godwin/The Guardian. Copyright © Guardian News & Media Ltd 2010.; *Figure 5.7*:

Simms, A. et al. (1996) The UK Interdependence Report, New Economics Foundation; *Figure 5.8 left*: Copyright © travelib prime/Alamy; *Figure 5.8 right*: Copyright © Lebazele/Getty Images.

Chapter 6

Figures

Figure 6.1: Belasco, W. (2008) Food: The Key Concepts, New York, Berg Publishers; *Figure 6.3*: Copyright © Pal Hansen/The Observer; *Figure 6.4*: Copyright © Yadid Levy/Alamy; *Figure 6.6*: Lang, T. and Heasman, M. (2005) Food Wars: the Global Battle for Mouths, Minds and Markets, London, Earthscan; *Figure 6.7*: Wilkinson, R. and Pickett, K. (2010) The Spirit Level: Why Equality is Better for Everyone, London, Penguin Books.

Chapter 7

Figures

Figure 7.1: Copyright © Joerg Boethling/Alamy; *Figure 7.2*: Alber, J. and Kohler, U. (2008) 'Informal food production in the enlarged European Union', Social Indicators Research, vol. 89, no. 1, Springer; *Figure 7.3a*: Copyright © AFP/Getty Images; *Figure 7.3b*: Copyright © Murdo MacLeod; *Figure 7.4*: Spaargaren, G. (2003) 'Sustainable consumption: A theoretical and environmental policy perspective', Society and Natural Resources, vol. 16, no. 8, Routledge, Taylor & Francis Journals; *Figure 7.5*: Copyright © blickwinkel/Alamy; *Figure 7.6*: Copyright © Tereza Cerna; *Figure 7.8*: Copyright © TheOtherOne/Alamy.

Chapter 8

Figures

Figure 8.1a and 8.3: Copyright © Wendy Maples; *Figure 8.1b and 8.4*: Copyright © Joe Smith; *Figure 8.2*: Brown, A. (2001) 'Counting farmers markets', Geographical Review, vol. 91, no. 4; *Figure 8.5*: Copyright © The Francis Frith Collection; *Figure 8.6*: Copyright © AFP/Getty Images; *Figure 8.7*: Copyright © Andre Penner/AP/Press Association Images; *Figure 8.8*: Copyright © Andrew Darrington/Alamy; *Figure 8.10*: Copyright © Sue Atkinson/Fairtrade; *Figure 8.11*: Copyright © Marcus Lyon/Fairtrade; *Figure 8.12*: Copyright © Everett Collection Historical/Alamy.

Chapter 9

Figures

Chapter 10

Figures

Chapter 11

Figures

Index

and Pareto optimality 55
interdisciplinary approach to environmental issues
  300, 317
  and mangrove ecosystems 312–13
intergenerational equity
  and geoengineering 132, 134, 143
intergenerational justice
  and sharing 382
Intergovernmental Panel on Climate Change (IPCC)
  on geoengineering 130
intermittency problems
  of low-carbon energy technologies 101–3, 104
International Energy Agency
  on peak oil production 45–6
International Labour Organization (ILO) 282
international law
  and GMOs 226
International Maritime Organization 136
International Union for Conservation of Nature
  (IUCN) 320
internet
  and global technological transformation 98
intrinsic values 350
ions 17
  dissociation 29–30
Iron Age 46
isolated systems
  and energy 81–2
Israel
  and oil politics 61–2, 65
IUCN (International Union for Conservation of
  Nature) 320
Jaffee, D. 286–7
Jasanoff, Sheila 389
Jehlička, P. 247
justice
  and distribution as sharing 382–3
  and food cooperation
    environmental justice 272
    the politics of care 282–4
    social justice 281

kinetic energy
  and tidal energy 93, 95
  and wind turbines 91
Kirwan, James 269, 270
Kneafsey, M. 266, 283, 285
Kuwaiti oilfield fires 7, 33

Kyoto Protocol (1997) 136

La Via Campesina 158, 162, 377
labelling of food 276–9
  and ethical consumption 284, 286–7
Lackner, Klaus 125–6, 127
land
  acquisitions 372, 374
  global climate change and loss of 337
Langrange orbits 118–19, 131–2
Latin America
  growth in agricultural production 161
Leach, Melissa 370–2, 388, 389, 390
Leopold, Aldo 288–9
Lipschutz, R. 285–6
livestock 173–4
  greenhouse gas emissions from 25
living standards
  and food self-provisioning 248
local communities
  and distribution
    as securing 374
    as sharing 381–2, 386–8
  establishing a safe operating space 371
  and geoengineering 132, 134, 142, 144
  and mangrove ecosystems 305, 323
local food production
  La Via Campesina 158, 162, 377
local planetary boundaries 367–8
localism/localisation
  and farmers' markets 263, 266, 267–8, 271
  and the food supply chain 235, 262
  scaling up local food initiatives 272–5
London
  Thames Barrier 374, 375
Lovelock, James 123
low-carbon energy technologies 77–107, 315
  and climate change 96–7, 106–7
  defining 80
  and environmental risk 106–7
  and fossil fuel energy 79, 98, 102, 105, 106, 107
  and geoengineering 115, 129, 134–5, 144
  and infrastructure change 77, 78–9, 104
  and the laws of thermodynamics 80–1, 103
  scaling up 77, 98–105
    and EROEI 98–101
    intermittency problems 101–3, 104
    investment problems 104–5, 106